JUST ONE OF THE PIONEERS

MY DAYS WITH SCOTTISH AVIATION AND DE HAVILLAND'S

BY

WILLIAM T. NEILL O.B.E.

CIRRUS ASSOCIATES

PUBLISHED BY:
Cirrus Associates (S.W.),
Kington Magna,
Gillingham,
Dorset,
SP8 5EW UK.

ISBN 1 902807 13 8

PRINTED IN ENGLAND BY:
Bookcraft Ltd.,
First Avenue,
Westfield Trading Estate,
Radstock,
BATH,
BA3 4BS.

PHOTO SCANNING BY:
International Graphics Services Ltd.,
24-31 Fourth Avenue,
Westfield Trading Estate,
Radstock,
BATH,
BA3 4XE.

DISTRIBUTORS:
Cirrus Associates (S.W.),
Kington Magna,
Gillingham,
Dorset,
SP8 5EW UK.

COVER: The prototype Prestwick Pioneer demonstrates its STOL characteristics at Prestwick. From an original painting by Professor Dugald Cameron, to whom we express grateful thanks for permitting it to be reproduced here.

ACKNOWLEDGEMENTS

Originally this book was never intended for publication, and the only reason that it has been published is that I was fortunate enough to find an editor and publisher who was interested enough to read my manuscript. I found him quite by accident when I was reading an article in the British Aerospace Systems quarterly Pension Review when it was running an article about pensioners who had already written their memoirs, or who had already done so but could not find a publisher.

This led to correspondence with Peter Campbell of Cirrus Associates. I have never met Peter but we have communicated at length by letter and telephone and I have the highest regard for his professionalism. He has edited my manuscripts with patience, dedication, perseverance and skill. He has kept every promise and met every deadline. As a result he has distilled a lengthy life story which would have run to well over 600 pages into a concise and enthralling book which I hope will be bought by many and enjoyed by all. I give him my heartfelt thanks for his tremendous help, which makes me feel that my efforts have not been wasted.

I give thanks also to my son-in-law and daughter, Dave and Fran Hadden, for their help in sorting out all my word processor disks and copying them onto disks compatible with the Microsoft system.

I also thank my wife Joy for putting up with the many hours that I have spent glued to my word processor.

CONTENTS

PART III: SCOTTISH AVIATION LTD POST-WAR (1945–1949)

PART IV: THE DE HAVILLAND GROUP (1949-1958)

FOREWORD

From a century and a half further on, we may tend to ascribe to the profession of an engineer of earlier times some sort of glamorous *cachet,* in the sense that we still recognise, long after their passing, the greatness of many of their names. The main reason this should be so is that much of their outstanding work lives on into this new century with its reputation (if not its metalwork) untarnished. After all, these people were the movers and shakers of their time, and to them we owe most of the major industrial developments of the past 150 years which, although they have transformed the way of life of modern man, we now tend to take so very much for granted.

I was fortunate to live and work as an engineer at a time when the traditional values of inventiveness, hard work, honesty and morality still counted for a great deal. In recent decades I feel that our governments have made a real mess of things and the future looks less than rosy. In our once-great Britain, manufacturing and other wealth-creative industries are already dead or are in terminal decline. For the past 60 years engineering has been considered as 'unglamorous' and certainly has not been as remunerative as many other professions; today every professional engineering magazine is lamenting about this. Maybe this book will show just how wonderful and exciting a life an engineer can enjoy.

But a *caveat* is perhaps appropriate here: although I have recorded, over the years, all I can remember of my background, my varied career and my other interests, I recognise that much of it will probably be of little interest to anyone outside the circle of our family and friends. The book that follows has therefore been distilled by my publisher from a manuscript some three times as long, hopefully to appeal to a wider audience, such as those fascinated by the social history of the first part of the 20th century, and particularly those who have followed the ups and downs of British aviation history. I hope that you will enjoy my personal recollections of the years when I was privileged to be involved as both engineer and executive, a unique period in our aviation history.

However, I do increasingly wonder why so many people want to write their memoirs. For the famous, when the fame begins to fade there seems to be this urge to publish their life story: others presumably do it for money or egoism. In recent years I have read well over 50 autobiographies and most of them have been unbelievably boring. And I am only too well aware that autobiographies, even written by those very much in the public eye, can flop, many ending up in cut-price bookshops or in the 'pulp bin'; for example, William Hague's book, originally offered at £29.99, can now be purchased for just £3.99 – such is the discount price of fame.

Why so? Many of us who have been privileged to lead what we consider to be adventurous, powerful or otherwise unusual lives fall into the trap of assuming that, just because we have found our lives to be particularly fascinating, many others will feel the same.

I am not famous (or notorious) although I have had an adventurous and enjoyable life, so why should I not write my memoirs? But I am doing so, not for ego, fame or money, but primarily for my own satisfaction and, I hope, for the benefit of my children and grandchildren, as well as for others who read this account. I firmly believe that my experience may help them in their own lives and give them an insight into standards of behaviour; the advantages of a good education; the integrity to fight for what is right even if it means making sacrifices; the importance of integrity and discipline; the realisation that old ideas and standards may just be better than the new; and the remembering of the old adage that pursuit of the better can be the enemy of the good.

I dedicate my efforts to my wife Joy, the sweetest, most beautiful and kindest girl anyone could wish for: my children, Gill, Alastair, Peter & Fran, and my grandchildren, Annabel, Nell, James, Daniel, Thomas, Andy, Roddy, Neil, Beth, Katherine & William, in the hope that they will read them, enjoy them and, I hope, learn from them.

All that follows is true but, for obvious reasons, some of the names and places have been disguised – I hope.

William T. Neill
January 2002

PART I: MY EARLY DAYS IN SCOTLAND (1915-1939)

CHAPTER 1

FAMILY

I was born on 8th April 1915 in a terraced house in Kilmarnock, within shouting distance of Rugby Park football ground. I can still hear vividly the roars of the crowds there and the great congestion in roads nearby when there was an important football match. I can remember well how we boys would stand outside the main entrance until half-time when we were allowed free entry. Sometimes we would go to friends' houses in Dundonald Road where the gardens backed on to the ground, and we would jump over the wall and hope that we did not get caught. In those days the punishment was a good whack on the bottom if we were caught by a steward or policeman. Rugby Park was the sports ground for Kilmarnock Academy and other athletic clubs in the district. There was a superb running track and all the other amenities required for athletics. There were two rugby union pitches, and I learned to play rugby there.

I never knew Andrew Turnbull, my maternal grandfather; he was born on 5th August 1846 and died on 10th September 1909 aged 63. From what I can glean from existing records and stories he must have been quite a man. Between 1868 and 1886 he fathered ten children and maybe one or two more on the wrong side of the blanket. This I have never been able to prove, but I had my strong suspicions and indeed met them in later life. Only five of his legitimate children survived beyond the age of six: these, in order of age, were Lizzie, Robert, Edith, Effie and Austin.

Andrew was a joiner by trade, then a timber merchant, then an accountant and house factor *cum* estate agent, and he later became the Town Chamberlain of Kilmarnock. He was a Baillie and a Justice of the Peace and his obituary was a lengthy one; it was published as a 12-page booklet and makes fascinating reading. He was a man of many parts, highly thought of and very successful. I am told he liked his whisky and was very fond of the ladies. He travelled widely and my mother had many curios brought back from all over the world. He died of a heart attack, sitting in his chair reading a magazine. I would like to know what magazine it was – *Playboy* was not published in these days but maybe there was an equivalent or better!

I can only remember my grandmother vaguely; she was a shadowy figure with little personality and poor health – no wonder after giving birth to 10 children and losing five of them in infancy. There is no doubt that she was dominated by her husband, and was never taken on any of his holidays abroad.

I can remember being walked up to Wallacebank in Wellington Street when grandma was dying; it was a beautiful house with a large garden, all now demolished. I was always nervous there as my uncle Austin had two tricks. He would squirt a soda syphon down my neck, or he would put his teaspoon in his hot tea and then place it on my hand or leg. I was taken to see grandma's body lying in her big bed, and was so frightened that I burst into tears.

Andrew's oldest daughter, Lizzie, married Hugh Robertson, a metal turner by trade, and they had three children, Enid, Betty and Robert. His second child, Robert, married Hugh's sister Mary. His second daughter, Edith Hope, became my mother.

When my grandfather died, it was alleged that Lizzie took his keys, went to his office and took all the money, bonds, title deeds, share certificates, bank books etc. and hid them. This caused great bitterness, followed by a law suit which lasted for more than nine years. Grandfather had set up a family trust; he had collected a portfolio of properties worth about £50,000, which was a lot of money at that time. One of the trustees was a builder & plumber and another was a lawyer; both had a closer relationship with Grandad than anyone realised at the time. He gifted a nice house and furnished it for each of his children when they married.

When my grandmother died Effie had a joint deposit account with her mother worth £13,577. She drew out the money and went off with most of her mother's valuable possessions, such as jewellery, paintings, silver and furniture. This resulted in another law suit which was not settled for over 12 years. A lot of the property had to be mortgaged to pay the legal fees, so instead of receiving a valuable legacy the children were left with debts, which were a great worry to them. A large proportion of the repairs to the properties were carried out by the trustee who was a builder, thus increasing the debts.

(A close friend of mine is a lawyer, now retired to the Isle of Man. His father, also a lawyer, had a picture above his desk of a dairy cow: at one end was a farmer tugging the horns and at the other was the farmer's brother pulling the tail, while sitting on a stool in the middle was the lawyer milking the cow – very appropriate!)

Latterly we became very friendly with my aunt Mary and her sons Andrew and Jim; they had a good influence on my life and regularly visited our home at 23 Charles Street. Andrew and Jim were my boyhood heroes; Andrew was an electrical engineer and Jim was a motor mechanic, and they taught me a lot of their skills, which stood me in good stead later. When the depression arrived in 1926 they became unemployed and emigrated to America. Andrew joined the Cleveland Light & Power Company in Ohio, and eventually became their chief engineer. Jim got a job in New York but soon became homesick and returned home. After six months he was still without work, so he went back to America again and got another job as a motor mechanic in New York. Then he met a girl, got married and settled down happily. The last time I saw him was when I was in New York in 1953.

Andrew married an American girl called Nacelle. She had gone to America as a baby and her parents were from a mining family in Armadale near Bathgate; they had a son called Drew. On their first visit home Andrew hired a Buick Saloon car, and although I was only 14 he taught me to drive. Nacelle wrote to us every Christmas and when I was in America on business during 1953 I spent several days with them in Cleveland, Ohio, where they had a lovely house on the shores of Lake Erie. Andrew had a power-boat and a fine Buick Sedan, and I had a great time sailing, fishing, and sight-seeing. Andrew retired in 1963 and with Nacelle visited us in Arran; years later he died of a heart attack. Nacelle continued to write to us every Christmas. Drew got married and had two children, but when Nacelle died we never heard from them again.

Robert (Bertie), Robert and Mary's youngest son, worked all his life in the Town Chamberlain's office, thanks to his grandfather's connections. He had bright red hair, an unusual Turnbull trait. Aunt Mary remained a close friend and came with us often to Arran and stayed with us in our holiday home. Because of her husband's fondness for drink she was a strict teetotaller, but she became an accomplished maker of all kinds of wine, bramble, loganberry, nettle, crab apple, rowan and others. At that time winemaking was not as popular as it is now and the methods were less sophisticated. Nevertheless with yeast, sugar and a simple fermentation process the wine was very potent indeed. Aunt Mary always claimed that it was non-alcoholic: she loved to invite her friends to her wine tasting, which became a family joke, as everyone became very happy and more than a little inebriated.

Bertie was six years older than I was, but we were quite friendly. He was attractive and quite the ladies' man, and he used to take me to the dances at the Palais in Ayr on Saturday nights, one of the most popular places in Ayrshire. Neither of us had a car, but there were regular coaches from Kilmarnock to Ayr returning at 1 am: the return fare was a shilling (5p). We also bought season tickets for Clyde Ferries' evening cruises, from Troon, Ayr and Ardrossan. These were absolutely marvellous on the old Clyde paddle steamers, like the *Juno*, *Glen Sannox*, *Caledonia*, and the *Marchioness of Graham*. One of them, the *Waverley*, is still plying and is very popular. There was always a band on board with dancing and community singing and, of course, girls. The scenery around Arran and the Kyles of Bute was fabulous and returning in the moonlight was very romantic; the present generation does not know what it has missed. Bertie suffered from very smelly feet and the first time I shared a room with him the 'hum' was dreadful. Bertie's ideal holiday was a week in Blackpool, but he never persuaded me to go with him for the obvious reason. It is remarkable how many Scottish lads married Lancashire lasses as a result of their holidays and the Golden Mile.

And now to the paternal side of my family. My father's parentage was always something of a mystery. He never spoke of his early years and, apart from knowing that he lived in Loudon Kirk, a tiny hamlet near Galston, the rest was shrouded in secrecy.

After his death we found his birth certificate. He was born on 13th September 1869 at 30 minutes past midnight at 106 West Street, Gorbals, Glasgow. His father was registered as William Bowman, a journeyman flesher, who lived at 80 Main Street, Gorbals. His mother was Mary Docherty, a dried fish saleswoman who lived at 134 Main Street, Gorbals. I always wanted to go and visit these addresses but so far have not been able to do so. Maybe some of my grandchildren will search them out – provided that they have not been demolished.

All my early questions about this side of the family were parried with the reply: "you are too young to know about these things." I discovered that Dad had three half-brothers, James Neill – a lawyer – and Robert and Thomas Neill, who ran a knitwear business in Rutherglen Road, Glasgow. There was also a Barr connection as Dad had a number of tools and measuring equipment stamped *James Barr*. James Barr was the founder of an engineering company, which eventually became Glenfield & Kennedy, one of the world leaders in water and hydraulic engineering. James Barr was the inventor of the first water meter and hydraulic valve. Later he founded Barr Thomson whose works were opposite Kilmarnock Academy's new playing fields, and Dad received his early engineering training there.

We never found out the whole truth, but piecing together all of the few facts and a lot of rumour we think the story is as follows: the Neill family had a prosperous butcher's business in Galston including a butcher's shop. James Neill, the elder son, was in charge and was reputed to be a bit of a lad, especially with the ladies. He got Mary Docherty pregnant. Now Mary sold fish to the shop in Galston and William Bowman supplied it with meat and was friendly with Mary. It is believed that the Neill family persuaded or paid Mary and William to register the baby as their own. James Neill lived at Loudon Kirk with his wife Margaret Howie and they brought up my father and changed his name to William Bowman Neill. Margaret Howie's sister, Agnes, married James Barr's son John and they lived in a nice house in Howard Park Drive, Kilmarnock; they had two children, Nana and Barbara. Nana married James Livesey, who came from Lancashire and was works manager at Glenfield & Kennedy; they had one son. Barbara married William Wilson, who was a draughtsman at Glenfield & Kennedy, but they had no children. We were friendly with the Barrs and visited frequently. They all had shares in Glenfield & Kennedy and Barr Thomson's and were comfortably off.

In those days children born out of wedlock and the parents were ostracised. Scandals were hushed up whenever possible and people went to great lengths to cover up. It says a great deal for the Barrs and the Neills that Dad was brought up with loving care and accepted into the families without prejudice. James Neill was a very successful lawyer in Glasgow and was married with two children, Phoebe and Andrew. He and Dad were on the best of terms, and he was best man at Dad's wedding. Tragically Andrew died during an operation to have his tonsils removed. Phoebe was a beautiful girl and married Hugh Gemmil, whose family had a building and joinery business in West Kilbride. Hugh and Phoebe had two sons, tragically both born blind. I sold machinery to the Gemmil business and did some repairs and overhauls, but never knew that one of the sons was married to my cousin Phoebe. It's a strange world. When her parents died we lost touch.

I knew Robert and Thomas well but never met their families. I sold them knitting machines and other equipment, and of course they knew Dad's family background, but when I tried to talk about Galston and Loudon Kirk they clammed up and I learned nothing. Their business went bankrupt in 1938 and I lost touch.

Dad was one of the nicest, kindest men one could ever wish to meet. Unfortunately he had no business sense and was exploited by his friends, customers and relations. He was a marvellous craftsman; his training at Barr Thomson was excellent both as an engineer and cabinet maker. He was first-class with his hands, was a competent locksmith and there was little he could not make or mend. There was no lock he could not open and he was much in demand, particularly when people locked themselves out or lost their keys. He built one of the first wireless sets; the body was in a jam jar mounted on an old gramophone record with a crystal and a 'cat's whisker.' I remember to this day our amazement when we heard voices and music emerging from this strange contraption. He progressed to building a more sophisticated set with valves, oscillators, amplifiers, tuning knobs and a loudspeaker, all mounted in a beautiful mahogany case. We listened with rapture as Dad tuned in to many stations in Europe, and one night we even received a programme from New York. He was able to listen in to police radios and messages between ships. We had a lot of fun with that; to me it was magic. He was a very caring father and taught me many of his skills, so that even before I left school I was a competent engineer and craftsman.

I never found out how and why he left Barr Thomson, but he started his own business in his early fifties. He called himself an Engineering & Machinery Merchant. I could never understand why he went into the selling business and did not concentrate on his many skills, but I later learned that he was not in good health and had glaucoma. He ran the business from 23 Charles Street and the middle bedroom on the half-landing became his office and storeroom. As the upstairs spare bedroom was used for lodgers my sister and I slept in little single beds in the same room as Mum and Dad. Dad had a part-time helper called Miss Patrick who kept the books and typed letters. Our next door neighbour at 21 Charles Street was a lawyer, who seemed very prosperous. He always had new cars and sometimes took me fishing. He had no children but he and his wife were always taking expensive holidays.

High tea was the main meal of our day. Mum was a marvellous cook, and a very frugal one as we had little money, but we never went hungry. One day Dad broke down in tears. He had had a bankruptcy notice served on him and said he was ruined. The year was 1926 and I was barely 11 years old. The whole country was in deep depression and there was also the miners' strike. Dad had a host of bad debts amounting to over £2,000 and had asked our next-door neighbour to try to collect them. It turned out that the lawyer did collect most of them but Dad never saw the money. Eventually the lawyer was arrested for embezzlement of many of his clients' money, but he never went to jail as he asphyxiated himself in his nice Rover car.

Because of this Dad was able to come to some arrangement with his creditors and the bankruptcy notice was withdrawn. He then had to find new premises as there was a danger that, although the house was in Mum's name, if he continued to run a business there the creditors might have a claim on part of the house. So he moved to 32 John Finnie Street. When I became a little older, I used to go round with Dad on my holidays. He never had a car and had to use public transport carrying his big bag of samples. He was not a good salesman and could usually be persuaded to reduce his prices. It was a shame really as he worked so hard and had some very good ideas. He imported knitting machines from Chemnitz in Germany and was the first person in Britain to sell electric shavers from Austria.

TOP: My father in the horsedrawn buggy he used for his work, c.1880. The Half Way Hotel was a pub mid-way between Kilmarnock and Prestwick.
BOTTOM: A family group at 23 Charles Street, Kilmarnock (1922). My father is 2nd from L. in the back row, my mother is immediately in front of him.
Photos: author's collection.

LEFT: I have an opportunity to drive cousin Andrew Turnbull's Buick (1931).
RIGHT: Our 1932 summer camp on Arran – Andrew Ferguson, Guy Scoular, George Black and myself (below). Photos: author's collection.

CHAPTER 2

SCHOOLDAYS

One of my earliest memories was the night that the Germans bombed the Nobel explosive factory at Ardeer near Stevenson. I was in my father's arms outside the house. The sky was fiery red and the noise of the explosions was terrifying. It was said afterwards that I could not possibly remember things like that at my age; nevertheless the memories are still vivid.

My early childhood was not a very happy one. I was never cold or hungry but I was always insecure and nervous. I remember at the age of four feeling rejected when all the others went off to Aunt Effie's wedding and I was left in the charge of one of my sister's school friends. I joined the infant class at Kilmarnock Academy just before my 5th birthday and in the first week was sent home because I had soiled my pants; I was ashamed and terrified. The infant teacher was Miss Rome; she was a very caring teacher and felt sorry for me, with the result that she took great care and patience to make me feel at home in spite of my nervousness and hatred of school. The class had 35 pupils but she was such a dedicated teacher that when we left her class we could all read, write, count and spell. Any backward children got special tuition for an hour after normal stopping time. She was patient but determined and any child not trying hard enough was threatened with the tawse [a leather strap], which worked wonders. No one was accepted for the junior school unless they were literate and numerate. It is astonishing that these methods which worked so well should have been abandoned.

Kilmarnock Academy had an infant school, a junior school and a senior school up to University Entrance. Infant and junior school required a residential qualification. Senior school required a pass at qualifying level, or an entrance exam for those who had not been admitted from the junior school. Competition for places was fierce as Kilmarnock Academy had an outstanding reputation. The only other school in the county which came anywhere near was Ayr Academy. There was great rivalry between these two schools, not only academically but in sporting activities including Literary and Debating Societies. Both schools were fee-paying, but a number of bursaries were available. A major catchment area for both schools was "the valley," a colloquial name for Darvel, Newmills and Galston. These towns were very prosperous because of the knitting and lace industries. Parents were very ambitious for their children and even the labouring classes were determined to have at least one of their children at University – usually Medicine, the Law, Accountancy, Teaching or the Church. The children therefore were high achievers and provided great competition for the natives of "Old Killie."

The school was co-educational and the senior division had a streaming system, A, B, and C streams which changed with abilities and subjects. Failure to meet the standard for any stream resulted in downgrading or *vice versa*.

No pupil, therefore, suffered from being in too high or too low a stream and moved around according to progress and ability.

Discipline was strict and corporal punishment was commonly applied, not only for bad behaviour but also for not trying hard enough. Punishment was given before the whole class or, for serious misdemeanours, before the whole school; this applied to girls as well as boys. Because of the public nature of the punishment there could not be allegations of cruelty or abuse. This provided a most effective deterrent as one's friends watched how the recipient behaved. Six of the best on both hands was a test of stoicism, not to be taken lightly. It was unheard of for any pupil to speak back to a teacher, let alone be rude to one. What terrible harm the do-gooders and social reformers have done to the discipline in schools and other places. As a result the educational system today is totally out of control and it is nearly impossible to teach even those who wish to learn.

Truancy was not unknown, but it was not common. Every morning started with Assembly for the whole school. The Head made a short speech followed by prayers. When the pupils returned to class, the register was called, so absences were immediately established. All absences had to be accounted for either by a letter from the parents or a sick note from a doctor. Kilmarnock had seven schools, covered by two full-time attendance officers who quickly visited the parents of errant children and who had the power to apply for a court order if the cases were repetitive. Successful court orders were followed by a fine on the parents. Children of school age were never seen in public during school hours. If any pupil played truant, it was called "plunking"; they would do so in places where they were unlikely to be seen, like country walks or billiard halls. The punishment for plunking was six of the best on each hand.

Nowadays truancy is rampant, compounded by minor crimes like shoplifting or break-ins. Solutions are discussed at length but nothing happens. Politicians have neither the common sense nor the will to tackle these growing problems and the old-fashioned methods which worked so well are shunned and the lack of any effective deterrent escalates the difficulties and encourages others.

It was well recognised that sport and physical exercise were an essential element in the school curriculum. Two periods per week were allocated to physical training, swimming and gymnasium activities. These together with games were compulsory, and a medical certificate was necessary to be excused. On one day each week lessons stopped at 3 pm and everyone had to take part in games at the sports ground. To prevent congestion groups were formed by age and by preferred choice of sport, and times and days were rotated accordingly. We had the choice of rugby union, soccer, hockey, athletics, cricket, tennis, basketball, netball and even golf. On Saturday mornings there were sporting events and competitions with other schools, all energetically and enthusiastically supervised by teachers who gave their time generously and without payment.

School started at nine, lunch break was at half past twelve and lessons recommenced at half past one, finishing at four o'clock. Backward pupils were given extra tuition from 16.00 to 17.00 hrs and this was mandatory, but parents were advised beforehand. The first year in infant class concentrated solely on reading, writing and simple arithmetic, and each pupil had to be proficient in these skills before they could join junior school. Subjects taught there were the three 'Rs,' plus history, geography, literature and essay writing, and branches of mathematics including geometry, trigonometry, algebra, fractions and decimals. Art, religious instruction, and physical education were also taught. Pupils did not progress to the next year until they reached the required standard.

Homework of at least 4 hours per week was assigned, always containing written exercises which were rigorously checked the next morning. Pupils who fell below the expected standards were paraded in front of the class, and repeated shortfalls were punished by the strap.

There were no school meals in those days and most pupils walked home for lunch or brought it with them. The last year in junior school was qualifying year, which was similar to the more recent "Eleven Plus." No pupils could pass on to senior school until they passed the qualifying exam.

Senior school was populated with junior school qualifiers plus an intake from other schools; in Ayrshire these were mainly from "the valley" (Darvel, Newmills and Galston), either fee-paying or by bursaries. There was a Roman Catholic school close to Kilmarnock Academy, *St Joseph's*; rivalry was strong, and abuse was not unknown, but there was never any violence or fighting, as discipline in both schools was very firm. There was also strong competition between the Academy pupils and the incomers from "the valley," both in academic and sporting fields, and some fights occasionally occurred in the playgrounds.

Bullying was quite common, and I can remember only too vividly one boy from Stewarton who committed suicide as a result: he jumped off the railway bridge at his home village. This caused a major sensation and discipline was tightened still further. At break times playgrounds were patrolled by at least two teachers, and any serious breaches were reported to the headmaster. Culprits were paraded before the whole school and received a good belting from the headmaster. Another deterrent was our janitor, Alex Keddie. He was an ex-Regimental Sergeant Major from the Royal Scottish Fusiliers. He taught boxing in the gym and bullies were matched in such a way that they got a good hiding from someone stronger and better. Kilmarnock Academy was co-educational throughout and although I cannot recall any bullying by girls of a serious nature, any who behaved in that way would have been belted too, just like the boys.

I was a very nervous insecure little boy at school. I was called "baby-face" and was bullied, but I never complained as I did not wish to be called a clipe [tell-tale]. My sister, who was three years older than me, realised that and spoke to the brother of one of her friends who was a good rugby player and who lived close to us. He took me under his wing and, although I was too young for rugby, I became the mascot of the first team. I went to all their school matches and trained with them, and as soon as I was old enough practised with them and became a useful flank forward in the junior team. All the sporting activities at that time took place at Rugby Park as the Academy did not have its own sports field. I also joined the Cadet Force and took up boxing. Alex Keddie, our janitor, was a Lieutenant in the Cadets, and he too took me under his wing and gave me special tuition.

One of the school bullies was a redheaded lad called Robert Bone, whose father was a baker and lived in a tenement in Titchfield Street. Kilmarnock Academy was on a hill, Tankerha' Brae, and there were long flights of steps leading down to Sturrock Street. His favourite ploy was to get behind me when I was at the top of the steps and kick my school case with all my books and homework out of my hand so that it burst open and all the contents cascaded down the steps. I never had new clothes and my mother used to stitch newspaper to the outside of my vest, called a "semmit" in these days. So that the newsprint did not soil my shirt it in turn was covered by a sheet of brown wrapping paper, which of course crackled. Bone used to poke me and laugh at the crackles. When I was about 14 mother bought me my first new suit from a mail order catalogue; it had short trousers and the cloth was not all that good but I was very proud of it and was allowed to wear it to school for examination day as Mum thought it would boost my confidence. Bully Bone drew everyone's attention to my new suit and then picked up a handful of mud and smeared it all over me. I saw red and tore into him, and gave him a good hammering. We were reported but due to the circumstances I did not get punished, indeed I became something of a hero. He never bullied me again.

As I explained earlier there were three streams in the senior school. The subjects taught were advances to those already mentioned for junior school plus languages (French, German, Greek or Latin), sciences, chemistry, physics, dynamics, engineering drawing, woodwork and metalwork, all leading to a Lower School Certificate or a Higher one taken in the fourth, fifth, or even sixth year depending on ability.

There was an active social life as well, and in addition to all sporting activities we had dramatic societies, debating societies, dancing classes embracing all forms, particularly Scottish, and musical activities of all kinds. The Cadet Force had a full-scale fully manned pipe band. The teaching staff participated enthusiastically and their unpaid free time was given generously.

The Academy did not have its own sports field, and it was decided that a fund should be started to buy land and erect a pavilion with changing rooms, showers and catering facilities. 1927 saw the start of energetic fund-raising. Parents and local firms gave generously, especially from "the valley" where there were many wealthy families.

Pupils were encouraged to organise *cafés chantants*, raffles, concerts, dramatic and musical evenings, and in spite of the terrible recession in the 1926–1936 period money began to roll in, so much so that the new sports ground and pavilion were in use by 1930.

My great friend at school was Guy Scoular, whose father had a prosperous grocer's in King Street. Guy had three brothers and a sister, and the Scoular family were rather 'superior,' but they were very kind to me and took me on many outings that I would never have had because of the frugality of our family life. Guy eventually became Chief Medical Officer of Health for Ayrshire, and lived in a very nice house in the grounds of Ballochmyle Hospital.

We both had an idea that if we came up with good fund-raising schemes we could get time off from lessons. I thought up a scheme to sell "laddergrams," which were the rage at that time, and Guy ran raffles for grocery prizes donated by his Dad and other valuable prizes donated by his brothers.

We were so successful that we were publicly commended for our efforts, but the down-side was that we neglected our studies to such an extent that we failed our exams and got kept back for a year. By this time I was beginning to be more confident; I gained my place in the rugby First Fifteen and I was very active in the Dramatic Society, playing some leading roles. Every Friday night I took part in the Debating Society, and in our final year Guy and I won the prize for the leading debate of the year which was: "Is the Face the Mirror of the Soul?" Guy argued the case for and I the case against.

During the seven years leading up to 1933 the Cadet Force played a major part in my early development. It was started by a diminutive Latin and English teacher, known to all as 'Daddy' Farrar, who was a bachelor and had been a Captain in the First World War. He really was a marvellously dedicated man, very strict but very fair. He had great enthusiasm, and had as his lieutenants a teacher of literature-*cum*-amateur pyschologist, a maths master, a Latin master and the redoutable janitor Alex Keddie.

We wore the Black Watch kilt, a khaki tunic and a glengarry, and paraded once a week. At weekends we had sessions at the local rifle range, and went for a week's Camp at Bourtree Farm on the Earl of Glasgow's estate at Fairlie. Here we carried rifles and bayonets and went through all the routine army drills. Physical training and boxing were popular, and every year we competed in the Lucas Tooth Shield, a national competition.

This Shield had first been presented by a General Lucas shortly after the end of the first World War for a competition to include all Cadet Companies in Great Britain. The programme covered army drills, including rifle drill, precision and sequence marching, physical training routines, shooting, boxing, and of course Pipe and Drum Band contests. These started locally on a knock-out basis, with each winning team progressing to area, then region, then to the semi-finals and finals, which were held in London at one of the prestigious Guards Regiment barracks.

We never normally got beyond the 'area' stage, but in 1932 we reached the semi-finals, thanks to the excellent performance of the boxing and shooting teams and the splendid effort of the Pipe Band. This meant a visit to London; the excitement was terrific and the support from the whole school was superb. We caught the train to London and stayed in the Horse Guards' barracks. The final stage was the Pipe Band competition; this we won, and we were through to the Final. Everything was even until the last event, boxing, and even after three events it was still a draw – the winner of the Lucas Tooth Shield depended on the result of the middle-weight event of three two-minute rounds.

As I was the contestant it all depended on me. I just managed to survive the first round by back-pedalling rapidly. My seconds were Lieuts Keddie and Mackie, and they told me that I must become more aggressive, watch my opponent's eyes and get in close. I tried, and got thumped – he was bigger than me, and had a longer reach. Keddie told me that if I lost the Lucas Tooth Shield I would never be able to hold up my head in Kilmarnock ever again. I rushed in and was slammed on the nose; there was blood everywhere and I thought the end was nigh. I saw red all right! The next thing I knew, everyone was in the ring and someone was holding up my arm: I was carried shoulder-high – we had won the Shield for the first time ever.

Everything thereafter was a blur; I do not even remember the presentation of the Shield and Medals, and I could not eat because of my damaged nose. I vaguely remember going on a coach tour of London and sleeping on the train. We received a rapturous welcome in Kilmarnock and some weeks later the Council gave us a civic reception in the Town Hall. The following year we won the Shield again, but not in the same spectacular fashion. If you are wondering about the origin of the "Tooth," I have never been able to establish it – perhaps it could have something to do with those regularly lost by the boxing participants!

On the way to Camp at the Fairlie estate we would march through the streets of Kilmarnock in full uniform with rifles on our shoulders and the Pipe Band playing at full volume. The pavements were usually lined with fond parents and friends. We entrained at Kilmarnock Station and travelled to Fairlie, with the parade repeated, and again with a lot of support from local people and tourists. An advance party consisting of ex-Cadets always went to Fairlie the previous weekend to set up camp, pitch the tents, dig latrines, erect the cookhouse, and renew their friendship with the local village girls.

There has always been controversy as to what a Scotsman wears under his kilt. Well, we were taught that it was more healthy to wear nothing. The advantage of the kilt was that it provided warmth and good ventilation, thus preventing rashes and irritation common with soiled underwear. On the train to Fairlie there was always some horseplay to find out if anyone was not conforming to the tradition. On one occasion a boy was found to be wearing trews under his kilt, so he was promptly stripped of them and the trews were thrown out of the railway carriage window, whereupon there were loud shrieks from the victim – his wallet and all his money were in his trews. A cadet with great presence of mind pulled the communication cord, the train ground to a halt and an irate guard was soon in our carriage raising hell, but when he was told the story he had a good laugh and did not enforce the £5 fine for improper use. The trews were recovered and all was well, apart from a severe reprimand from 'Daddy' Farrar.

The first Camp that I attended was when I had just turned 13. The first night no one slept very much and there were many pranks. We slept in bell tents, 12 boys to a tent. The beds were straw palliasses filled at the farmer's barn. The ground sheets were army issue and doubled as a cape. Each cadet had his own kit-bag, which was used as a pillow. Two blankets were supplied for each boy, and we slept with our toes pointing towards the central pole. Smells bring back vivid memories, and I can still recall the scent of wet canvas, straw palliasses, rubber groundsheets, and human bodies.

The day started at 07.30 with the *Reveille* bugle call and the NCOs going round the tents banging the canvas with their canes and singing in tune with the bugle call: "Get out of bed, get out of bed, you lazy heads." Then we had breakfast parades, starting with the bugle call: "Come to the kitchen door, lads, come to the kitchen door," and the smell of frying bacon and eggs sharpened our appetite.

After breakfast we had kit inspection, and marks were awarded to each tent. Tents with the lower scores had to provide the fatigue details for all the less popular jobs, such as latrine disinfecting, spud peeling and helping in the kitchen. This was followed by all kinds of marching drills, and competitions between the platoons. The Cadet Company was made up of four platoons each with 18 cadets, plus a sergeant and a corporal, making a total of 80. In addition there was the Band with 12 pipers, six drummers, a Pipe Major and a Drum Major making a grand total of 100, plus one Captain and four Lieutenants.

Then came the distribution of mail collected from the village post office. The post detail was most sought after and was always awarded to the cadet of the year. This award depended on a points system based on reliability, leadership, performance at physical training, boxing, and athletics, and finally at a parade to pick out the best turned-out and smartest cadet. Uniforms were supplied free of charge, and consisted of a tunic, kilt, sporran, belt, hose, garters, spats, and of course the glengarry. The competition was intense: buttons, badges and belts had to be polished, spats had to be blancoed, kilts pressed, glengarries fettled. Footwear was supplied by each cadet from his own resources. All kinds of 'old soldier' tricks were employed, e.g. soap or beeswax was applied to the back of the pleats on the kilt which was then ironed to make the kilt hang more neatly. The glengarries were stiffened with cardboard and the red and white checks were chalked to make the colours more vivid. The tunics were shaved with a safety razor to remove any roughness and make the nap smoother. Spit and polish added to Brasso made buttons and badges shine brighter, and the spats were toasted to make the blanco adhere better. The plumes of the sporran were washed and combed carefully, and the hose were starched so that wrinkles were eliminated. The winner always wore a red sash from right shoulder to left hip.

Now more about the annual camp. As I said the position of postman was much coveted and privileged, as the chosen cadet was relieved of all morning parades and duties and went off to the village each morning, not only to collect the post but also to order supplies for the camp, and to do personal shopping for some of the cadets. He also arranged dates with the village girls, but more of that later. He was also the recipient of presents from the village shopkeepers, as there was strong competition for business, which for over 100 campers was quite considerable. These presents were always handed over meticulously to the quartermaster's store, and were used as prizes for the various sporting events and other competitions.

Every afternoon there were two or three hours free time and cadets were allowed to leave the camp and 'do their own thing' provided they were back for the evening meal. Food was excellent. Every evening at 19.00 there was the "Beating of the Retreat" with due ceremony. The Colours were struck and the band played the usual stirring music. Then came the Changing of the Guard. Every night a guard was posted at the gate into Bourtree Field, where a guard hut had been built. The guard detail was on duty from 20.00 until *reveille* the following morning. Full uniform was worn with rifles and bayonets and each cadet did one hour on guard. It really was great fun as there were many attempts made to take the guard unawares by diversions so that the guard hut could be entered and points scored.

On my first camp, like many others I was very homesick: I faked tummy pains and wrote asking my mum to come and take me home. The officers were very caring and understanding, and gave sympathy plus threats of a large dose of castor oil if the patient was not better in the morning. That usually worked wonders. There were many pranks, one of two favourites being to try and extract kilts or other units of uniform stealthily by lifting the skirts of the bell tents in the night and hanging the items from the top of a tree; the other was to loosen the guy ropes so that the tent collapsed on top of the occupants. The cruellest trick of all was to drag a cadet through the skirt of the tent and cover his private parts with black boot polish. I was terrified of this happening to me and I always slept with the handle of a tent mallet in my hand. One night when I was chosen as the would-be victim I lashed out and broke the forearm of the culprit. As the officers took a very serious view of this disgusting prank, the boy with the broken arm claimed that the break was the result of a fall and that particular activity ceased from then on.

Wednesday was Parents' and Sports Day, when families and friends visited the camp laden with goodies for their loved ones. In retrospect these Sports Days were marvellous – bands playing, flags flying and all the cadets competing vigorously for prizes and praise, especially from the girls. I still cherish a pair of 18-carat gold cufflinks and a military compass won all these years ago. Wednesday night was the night of midnight feasts when we enjoyed all the goodies from our parents and friends. One of the favourites was cake mashed up with peach slices and covered with Nestlés milk, another was mashed-up bananas with strawberry jam and cream.

Friday night, our second last night in Camp, was "Pyjama Parade Night." This was a night of great revelry in the village, looked forward to by the villagers and cadets alike, but especially the village girls. Everyone dressed up and vigorous Scottish dancing took place in the streets. Every cadet had to be back in Camp by midnight. Saturday was preparation for striking Camp, and on Sunday we had the last Church Parade, then lunch, after which we all entrained to return to Kilmarnock. Our arrival was quite an occasion, with a full parade through the streets of the town.

Intelligence testing was in its infancy during the 1920s. However one of our teachers, James Mackie, was intensely interested in the subject and could never get enough volunteers to undergo testing. Most of us thought it was a bit of nonsense but we co-operated, especially when it freed us from lessons or parades. However Mr Mackie soon became an authority on the science and much of his work was published. Some of his predictions proved to be uncannily accurate. He believed that by measuring IQs and studying other psychological aspects of character he could predict the kind of lifestyle the person would have. With hindsight in a number of cases, I can quote examples. In one case he tested two brothers; one had an average IQ but little ambition, but the other brother, the younger one, had a high IQ and great ambition, and went right to the top as a chartered patent agent. The elder one spent all his life as a bus conductor.

In ten other cases he forecast high-flyers who, he predicted, would be very successful. Nine of them reached high positions in their chosen profession, one of them went to jail for fraud. In another case two brothers had the same IQs and the same ambition; one became a famous surgeon, the other remained a motor mechanic. Mr Mackie pondered the reasons but never quite found the answers. The son of the motor mechanic is now the owner of a very successful motor agency in Prestwick: the son of the surgeon works in a carpet warehouse. Life is strange.

The old cliché "Schooldays are the Happiest Days of Your Life" did not apply to me. However looking back over some 60 years, I realise now that Kilmarnock Academy provided an extraordinarily high standard of liberal education and instilled into its pupils the importance of self-discipline and respect for one's teachers and elders. Of course children were mischievous and rowdy and sometimes bullied others, and played truant. The 1920s and 1930s were years of serious depression, unemployment and deprivation. However the viciousness, the violence, the crime, the casual sex, alcohol abuse and drugs were absent. No parent ever complained if a child got beaten at school, and any suggestion that a beating would cause the child trauma or encourage violence would have been laughed out of court. Every teacher knew why any pupil was absent, and if there was not a good reason the school attendance officer called on the parent. Discipline at home and at school turned out people who became good citizens. I cannot recall a single person being expelled during my 13 years at school. There was no sex education and I can remember only one case of a girl getting pregnant while still at school.

This did not mean that we were all angels, far from it. There was still the urge to fight, bully, be rowdy, even break things or steal, but we knew that retribution would quickly follow, and in spite of the do-gooders' views corporal punishment did very much act as a deterrent. There was no possibility of the beatings being savage, or classed as abusive, because the strap was always administered in public, before the whole class or before the whole school if the behaviour was bad enough. Some examples were as follows.

There was a snooker hall at the bottom of Tankerha' Brae and many boys missed a period or two to play snooker. Punishment before the whole class was six of the best on one hand. One evening some boys broke into teachers' desks and stole all the tawses, and hung them all from the lightning conductor from the school tower: punishment, six on one hand before the whole school, plus the parents having to pay for the damaged locks. On a Friday evening after the Debating Society, it was found that the room where all the document copying was done was left unlocked. In these days the copying was done by typing on a waxed master which was then passed through an inked roller turned by hand. It so happened that these waxed masters were for the Preliminary Exams for the Highers. Copies were taken and distributed to those in the know, but this was never discovered until after the Prelims were over. However so many pupils had performed so far above their expected standards that the teachers smelt a rat, and there was a thorough enquiry. The culprits owned up and got six of the best on each hand before the whole school. The Prelims had to be held again, so the culprits were not very popular.

An incident in the chemical lab was the nearest case considered for expulsion. One of the 'in' things was to obtain a door key with a hole in the stem, the bigger the key and the bigger the hole the better. The hole was filled with a mixture of sulphur and other ingredients easily obtained from any chemist's shop. A nail approximately the same size as the hole was tied to the handle of the key with string, and pushed into the hole. The head of the nail was banged against a wall, and there was a great big bang – the bigger the key and the hole the bigger the bang. This practice was seriously discouraged and the chemistry teacher read everyone a lecture on the dangers, but two boys and a girl set a similar device in his desk, so that when the lid shut there would be a big bang. However the culprits overdid the strength of the mixture, and the desk was blown up and set on fire. There was an almighty row and the perpetrators were suspended for a month, narrowly missing expulsion.

It seems extraordinary to me that for years now, there has been debate about falling standards in education: a complete breakdown in discipline, both at home and in the classroom, about illiterate – and innumerate – children, about league tables, about bad teachers, and lack of accountability in schools and universities. The low pass levels in examinations, common today, would never have been tolerated in the 1920s and 1930s. The press and the media give great coverage about what should be done, and there is great speculation on the solution, but nothing changes and standards continue to fall. Why on earth can we not revert to the methods that made Scottish education the envy of the world? Teaching was not just a job, it was a dedicated vocation, and those in it were respected and admired, and enjoyed it. One has only to look at the standards of dress and behaviour of some of the teachers seen regularly on television at conferences to recognise what is part of the trouble.

My sister Betty was a dedicated teacher for all of her life. She used to tell me about the system of inspection carried out regularly, by independent "His Majesty's Inspectors of Schools." Any teacher receiving a substandard report had to undergo further training, and if that failed then dismissal followed. The system was highly effective. Today there is plenty of talk and little action, so no wonder standards are below other countries in Europe. My sister died in 1967, and a few years before her death she was beginning to have doubts about the future of education. Following the war the educational standards for entry into the teaching profession were relaxed, and a university degree was no longer a requirement. Mastery of the three "Rs" was no longer paramount, and teaching and learning methods were changed to give children an allegedly broader education on social issues. Control was becoming too liberal and too political, and the authority of head teachers and departmental heads was being eroded.

We have seen the fears expressed by my sister and others multiplying over the past 30 years. Of course there are still good schools and good dedicated teachers, but overall no one can doubt that today's average standards are not good enough. If it took 30 years to descend to the present level, then how long is it going to take to put it right again? The will seems to be lacking.

There can be no doubt that the decline in standards throughout the country stem from failures in the home and in schools. Excuse after excuse is presented: too large classes, inadequately trained teachers (and some politically motivated), unemployment and no hope of a job, absent fathers and single mothers, or working mothers and fathers, giving little supervision and, because of too much television, lack of communications and relationships in families. Unless this decline is halted then this country has no future either socially or economically. This government keeps telling us how good we are, how we are better than other Western economies, and yet the trade balance steadily declines, the PBSR continues to rise, there is no sign that the promised cut in Government spending is being achieved and the cost of national health and social security is out of control. Now that Parliament is being televised we see only too dramatically how much time is being spent on superficial issues, petty quarrels, efforts to make cheap capital by trying to score off each other and, worse, ranting, ill discipline and bad behaviour.

No wonder that Japan and the emerging Pacific Ring Countries are doing so much better and making so much of an inroad into our manufacturing industries. Take Singapore as an example. Towns, streets, roads and beaches are immaculately clean, everyone is courteous and polite, the economy is booming and crime, when it takes place, is dealt with firmly, quickly, and, when necessary, forcibly, and effectively. Nick Leeson was tried, convicted, and jailed all within 10 days. If he had been extradited here the trial would have dragged on for months.

But to return to my school days: we were all so busy that we had no time for serious mischief or worse. School lasted from nine till four, Monday evening was drama classes, Tuesday evening was boxing, Wednesday evening was Cadets, Thursday afternoon and evening was for rugby or other sports, Friday evening was Literary and Debating Society. Saturday morning I played rugby for the school and in the afternoon rugby again for the Kilmarnock Colts. Sunday was church and, in the afternoon, rifle shooting. All the teachers played an active part in all these activities, and there were numerous contests, sporting and otherwise, between teachers and pupils. In the summer we had country walks and hill & mountain climbing, including some adventurous rock climbing, all supervised by teaching staff.

Each year there were at least two hill walks and/or mountain climbs. The favourite climbs were Ben Lomond or The Cobbler, plus all the exciting and beautiful hills in Arran. Loudon Hill near Darvel in "the valley" was the training ground for rock climbers. Alex Duncan and Elkie Clark were very proficient and experienced mountaineers and rock climbers. The former taught mathematics and the latter was a form master and taught English. The pitches ranged from easy to severe on Loudon Hill, and the training there was very good. Guy Scoular and I were very keen and became quite proficient rock climbers.

One day in early summer we were with an expedition to Arran. The plan was to climb Goat Fell, then to proceed to Coire nam Fuaran, then to the summit of Cir Mhor, 2,618 ft, then to Coum na Caillach and finally to Suidhe Fhearghas and back down Glen Sannox. Messrs Duncan and Clarke were in charge. The day was baking hot and Guy and I decided we would have a dip in the Rosa burn. We both knew the hills of Arran well as Guy and family used to stay at Corrie and I was always invited. We fell well behind but we knew we could take a short cut by climbing a chimney on the Stachach. It was not a very severe or long climb and we had done it before. Halfway up Guy was leading and I was following. We were climbing by feet pushing on one side and the back sliding on the other. Guy took cramp and was stuck. I supported him on my shoulders, and shouted for help. As good climbers we both had whistles and blew them furiously. Before long a rope came snaking down, and we were hauled up the chimney by Messrs Duncan and Clark, who just happened to be within hearing distance. We were very lucky and got a good ticking off, which we well deserved; we were thoroughly ashamed of ourselves. That was a lesson we never forgot and we never took chances on mountains ever again.

CHAPTER 3

THE CRUISE

In 1932 I had the privilege of going on a Scottish schoolboys' cruise to Northern Europe. I was very envious of older boys who had been on such cruises before but had been careful not to embarrass my parents because I was only too well aware of their financial constraints. It came as a great surprise, therefore, one evening when my mother asked if I would like to go. She said that she had been saving carefully and had money put by to pay for me. I was flabbergasted and delighted.

The cruise, in *SS Neuralia* (a converted troop-ship), proceeded from Leith first to Oslo, then to Copenhagen, then through the Kiel Canal to Ijmuiden, then Amsterdam, Zebrugge, Bruges, Menin, and so back to Leith. Schools from all over Scotland were represented, and there was a good contingent from Kilmarnock Academy, how many exactly I do not remember, but what I do remember was that the Cadet Pipe Band was invited at preferential rates as it was famous throughout Scotland because of the Lucas Tooth Shield Competitions. Those of us who were Cadets wore our kilts, sporrans, hose, tweed jackets and white shirts, and of course our school ties. These ties had maroon and gold stripes and were nearly the same as the official ties of the MCC, so were the subject of some favourable comment.

As we set off by train for Leith the excitement was intense. We needed to get there early as the Pipe Band had been asked to play on the quay, which was crowded with boys, parents and friends. We duly embarked and were allotted sleeping quarters. The cabins were reserved for teachers and officials, and the boys were given hammock space and were shown how to sling their hammocks and where to store their belongings. We set sail with the ship's hooter hooting, the Pipe Band playing *Over the Sea to Skye* and those on the quayside cheering and throwing streamers.

We all set off to explore the ship, make friends and compare notes with those from other schools. The sea was calm and the sun was shining, but soon it was dinner time. The mess deck contained tables and forms bolted to the deck. Each table sat 12, and a rota was made up with two boys from each table who acted as stewards and brought the food and utensils from the galley. The rotas changed each day so that the work was shared. Empty dishes had to be returned but all the washing-up was done by kitchen staff.

There was great fun getting unpacked and climbing into the hammocks, and trying to tip each other out again. There was little sleep that night and most of the boys went on deck to see all the sights that could be seen. Supervision by teaching staff and officers was very evident and any horseplay was soon dealt with. Dawn breaking was a lovely experience and soon it was breakfast time – porridge, bacon & eggs, and lots of toast, marmalade and hot tea; the food was good and plentiful.

Announcements were made over the Tannoy about the planned activities for the day. The organisation was excellent; there were games, competitions, physical training, tug-of-war teams, deck hockey, shuffleboard, quoits and deck tennis. The philosophy was clearly "keep the boys busy, and they will not get up to mischief." After two days and two nights we arrived in Oslo, and the weather was still sunny and bright.

Tours were all organised beforehand with packed lunches, and combined educational visits to museums, ski jumps and of course the famous Roald Amundsen exhibition. There was also time to enjoy the scenic beauty of the fjords and surrounding country, and shopping for souvenirs before heading back to the ship for high tea.

The next night and day were not so pleasant. As soon as the ship cleared the Oslofjord and entered the Skagerrak, the wind got up and soon we were in a Force 8 gale. At first we all thought it was fun, but before very long we all took to our hammocks, where we tried to sleep and fight off the first attacks of seasickness. Hammocks were actually a great help as the pendulum action countered some of the pitching and rolling. The hardy ones went off for breakfast, and – guess what – the menu was porridge and smoked kippers with chips. Out of bravado I ate the lot. A friend then offered me a Fry's milk chocolate bar and I ate that as well. I soon became queasy and retired to my hammock with a book, but I was doing all right until the fellow in the next hammock vomited all over me and I consequently lost the lot. But there was still worse to come.

We expected better weather in the Kattegat, but the storm was blowing from the north, and the pitching and rolling was exacerbated and most of us were very ill. Some took their blankets onto the deck and huddled down behind benches or any other protection available. There is nothing worse than being sick on an empty stomach and those of us who could went to the mess deck and ate bread and jam. Suddenly the wind dropped and we were in sheltered waters.

It is amazing how quickly one can recover from seasickness, and shortly we were up eating a hearty breakfast and looking forward to enjoying the sights of Copenhagen. The Danes were very friendly people; most of them could speak English and we got a great welcome. The Burgomaster had invited the Pipe Band to give a concert of pipe music in the famous Tivoli Gardens and all those of who wore the kilt gave a demonstration of Scottish Dancing. The Danish girls soon learned the routines and joined in and a great time was had by all. The usual question was constantly asked: "What do you wear under your kilt?" The dancing was so energetic that they soon found out.

The Tivoli Gardens at that time were one of the most delightful entertainment areas in Europe, and we enjoyed every minute of it there. We were then entertained to dinner in the main restaurant in the Gardens at the Burgomaster's expense. At least, the Pipe Band and those closely associated with it were invited: others had to make their own arrangements. Teachers had a difficult time collecting us and prising us away, and it was the wee sma' hours before we returned to the ship.

Next day we toured the city and did our shopping, then the ship sailed for the Kiel Canal. The passage through was most interesting, particularly the sight of so many naval vessels and the massive submarine pens, all of which were going to do so much damage in the war which, unbeknown to us, was only seven years away.

The next stop was Ijmuiden, which is the main port for Amsterdam. The tours there were most impressive. The old city was fascinating; we enjoyed the water barge trips on the canals, we saw the bulb fields, and were amazed at the numerous dykes and the amount of land that had been reclaimed from the sea. What impressed us most of all was the flatness of the land and the number of people in traditional dress including clogs, as well as the incredible number of bicycles.

We left Ijmuiden and sailed down past the Hague to South Holland with all its creeks and waterways, past Zeeland, and then we eventually berthed at Zeebrugge, which is linked by canal to the city of Bruges. Zeebrugge is famous for the naval exploits there during the first World War, and we were thrilled by the tales of derring-do related by the tour guides of all that happened during the invasion of Belgium by the Germans in 1914. The next day we went on a conducted tour of Bruges, which was famous for its lace, glassmaking, brassware, and ship repairing; it was a mediaeval town, and my most lasting memory was old churches and the marvellous sound of their bells. We bought a lot of lace and brass souvenirs.

While we were there a remembrance service was held at the Menin gate for all the men killed at Ypres, Mons and other fierce battles in that area in the Great War. It was the most emotive and memorable occasion of my young life. Scenes of great carnage were shown projected on a large screen in the square, and the memorial service was most touching. It ended with the *Last Post* bugle call and *The Flowers of the Forest* played by our Pipe Band. We had to stand for a long period in very hot conditions and it was the first time that I ever fainted.

Thereafter the *SS Neuralia* sailed back to Leith and the cruise was over. It was a wonderful experience for all of us and I was particularly grateful that my mother had made such a big sacrifice so that I could go.

CHAPTER 4

AN EARLY INTRODUCTION TO BUSINESS LIFE

I arrived home full of excitement, ready to pass on all the news of the cruise, and to hand out all the souvenirs that I had brought home for my family and friends. I thought that Mum and Dad were rather quiet and withdrawn, and I quickly learned that Dad's business was in serious financial trouble and that the creditors were applying for a petition in bankruptcy.

My whole world fell apart. My sister was in her third year at Glasgow University, and there was no money coming in at all apart from what Mum was getting from her lodgers. I knew a little about Dad's business as I used to help him during the school holidays, so off I went to see the accountants, James McMurray & Co., to try to find out how bad things really were; Dad was in such a nervous state that he was unable to cope and needed medical treatment. James McMurray turned out to be a very caring man, and was obviously sorry for the family. He asked if I was prepared to step in and run the business. He would try to come to a deed of arrangement with the creditors and get the bankruptcy petition withdrawn. He explained that as I was technically a minor, being only 18, I could not make any legal arrangements on behalf of my father. He would try to get the creditors to agree to a trust deed with him as a trustee, so that the debts would be repaid over a period of years, at so much in the pound depending on the success or otherwise of the business.

I just did not know what to do. After a few sleepless nights I realised that there was no chance of my pursuing a medical career, which was what I had set my heart on, and that the only thing I could do was to follow the accountant's advice and get stuck in. He persuaded the creditors to accept a deed of arrangement. He would be the trustee until I was 21, and he would prepare quarterly accounts for the creditors' committee and put in one of his juniors to keep the books and advise me on financial matters. My father's bankers were most unhelpful, demanded repayment of the overdraft and refused credit. I changed to another bank, the Clydesdale, and the manager there was quite different; he was an old school friend of Mum's, was obviously sorry for the family, and was a tower of strength to me with his helpful advice and encouragement.

The next two years were the worst in my life. I was depressed and ashamed and withdrew from all my friends and social activity. I used to get to the office in John Finnie Street at 7.30 every morning including Saturdays and Sundays. I hardly dared look at the post, as there were many dunning letters [demanding money] and refusals to supply goods on credit. Everything had to be paid for in advance or Cash on Delivery. I laid out a programme of calls, a different town each day, and then set off with my big bag of samples trying to drum up business. Many of Dad's old customers were very understanding and I am sure gave me orders out of kindness. Others could be quite cruel, and kept me waiting in reception for what seemed like hours before they even sent someone to see me. I quickly worked out each day how much I had to sell to pay expenses, make a profit and leave something over for the creditors. Each Sunday I totted up the figures, and although I managed to stay in the black, I quickly realised that the turnover was not high enough to make the business viable. All my travelling was by public transport, so I went out and bought a motor-bike; it was an old 1926 belt-driven Triumph, and it cost me ten shillings.

The turnover soon doubled, but that was still not enough, and I knew that selling small tools and equipment, particularly during a bad depression, gave me no chance to pay off the creditors.

My father had a store at 38 John Finnie Street, lit by gas, of which he had let a part to a Mrs Stewart who operated two knitting machines and sold her wares. Her husband Dougald was a marvellous engineer and the son of a wealthy family from Helensburgh. At one time he had been chief engineer on the *City of Paris*, but drink had been his downfall and, like thousands of others, he was now out of work. He was also a keen fisherman and made his own rods and tied his own flies; before the troubles I had gone fishing with him. One day he came to see me to find out how things were going, and I nearly cried on his shoulder.

He said: “Look, laddie! Why don’t you get yourself qualified and then do some real engineering?”

He told me to go to night school and enrol in the National Engineering Certificate Class, and then go on to the Royal Technical College in Glasgow and get a Higher National Certificate. He said that if I paid him ten shillings a week I could be his apprentice and could then be a journeyman engineer.

This was a bit confusing, but he explained that he intended to beat the drink habit; then, as a qualified engineer, he could take me on as an apprentice and sign the necessary indentures, and I could then qualify as a trained engineer. I asked how he could do this when he did not have a job. He said he would work for nothing apart from the ten shillings and that I should go out and get some maintenance engineering jobs and together we would do them. He said that there were many hand-knitting machines that needed overhaul and that, as new ones were difficult to get as they came from Germany and Switzerland, he could rebuild them as new and we could make some money.

I took his advice. I paid him his ten shillings but he was soon drunk and I did not see him for a week. This did not help my depression, but I enrolled in the ONC Engineering course. I used to get home at 6 pm, have my tea and then go to night school four nights a week. I found this most therapeutic and enjoyed it.

I managed to get the Certificate in two years rather than the normal three, and then enrolled in the HNC course at the Royal Technical College, Glasgow, now Strathclyde University; I used to roar up there four nights a week on my motor-bike, now a 500 cc Sunbeam. I had no difficulty in getting my HNC at the end of another two years.

To return to my drunk engineer. He appeared, bright and well-dressed, full of apologies, and swore that he would never let me down again. Dad had many customers who were knitwear manufacturers, and I asked them if they had any machines that needed overhaul. The answer was yes, but they were reluctant to give them into my care. Nevertheless I persevered and got an order for two from a company in Kilmaurs, which were delivered to the store at 38 John Finnie Street.

Flat-bed knitting machines got clogged up with ouse [fluff] in the needle slots and in the cam boxes. The cams got worn and the flat beds containing all the slots bowed so that the cams scored the beds, which in turn wore the cams still further. My engineer, Dougald Evan Stewart, was highly educated and very intelligent, and had learned a great many engineering skills. He had noticed the problems on his wife's knitting machines and had fettled them. There were no machine tools at John Finnie Street, only a hand grinder, but I was amazed how Dougald Stewart improvised. The knitting machines were dismantled and boiled in the copper used for washing clothes in the wash-house at 23 Charles Street. The beds were straightened by ball-peening with an engineer's ball-pane hammer; this stretched the skin of the metal on the back side of the beds, which made them resistant to bending again. We acquired a metal-spraying outfit, which made the beds and cams look like new, and we then reassembled and painted the frames with black lacquer. The customer was delighted, the news spread and orders became easier to get. However as all the work had to be done by hand we could not charge enough to make a decent profit.

With the depression prices of knitwear were cuthroat; many small firms went bankrupt, and their assets were sold at auction. I used to go to the sales and learned to bid not for the good machines, but to wait for the ones going at knockdown prices; these were then rebuilt and sold at a good profit. Unfortunately we had neither the space nor equipment to do as many as we would have liked. We had no money to expand, but fortunately I met a knitting machine mechanic called Arthur Collins who was out of work but had been left a small engineering workshop in Mill Road. He had no work and no money, but I persuaded him that we could use his workshop for free, and we would give him a share of the profits. We were thus able to increase our output of rebuilt knitting machines.

One day the knitwear manufacturer who had given me the first order told me about a new power-driven knitting machine that was being sold by Dubied et Cie in Switzerland. It was very expensive and he had bought it on hire purchase. He took me to see it, and he thought it would reduce his labour costs and make his goods more competitive. I thought and thought about this and came to the conclusion that it might be possible to convert the hand machines to power. I made some rough drawings and discussed the idea with

Dougald and Arthur. We made a prototype from bicycle chains, sprockets and a 1 hp electric motor. After weeks of effort it worked and we were then in a more lucrative business than selling small tools.

Dad had a number of customers who were in the joinery business and now and again he would sell them a circular sawbench or a bandsaw. I was interested to see how these small joiners cut mortices for their doors and windows. They were either cut by hand or by a hand-morticing machine, which was slow and cumbersome. Big companies manufacturing wood-working machines, like Wadkin or Sagar, were selling morticing machines, which cut the mortices with a hollow chisel with a drill inside, but they were too expensive for the small joiner. Again I had the idea of converting the hand morticers to hollow chisel machines. Again Dougald and Arthur built the prototype and it worked. Manufacture of the parts were too complicated for our limited resources, but I got them made at Glenfield & Kennedy.

In those days woodworking machinery had phosphor-bronze, white metal or even *lignum vitae* bearings, and the heavy cutter blades on planers were mounted on square blocks. Bearings wore out and cutter blocks not only became unbalanced and caused ripples on the wood but were dangerous, and many machine operators lost fingers or even hands. More modern machines were all fitted with ball or roller bearings, and the cutter blades were narrow thin knives mounted on a cylinder. Those machines could run faster, vibrated less, gave a much smoother cut, and were easier to set. I designed conversion kits and fitted them, and soon more lucrative business was developing nicely.

Of course this all took time and great effort, and meanwhile I had to make ends meet and find the money to meet quarterly payments to the creditors as agreed in the trust deed. Regrettably Dougald Stewart could not beat his drink problem and from time to time he would go on a binge and vanish for days. He always returned very ashamed and very contrite. I persuaded him to let me pay his wages and share of profit into a savings account, but he would always find the money to buy drink. He would pawn his gold watch, his wife's jewellery, and even his tools. But he always came back and redeemed all his belongings from the pawn shop, and for spells was the perfect engineer, teacher, taskmaster and friend.

My first success in securing new business had been with Johnny Walker's, the world-famous whisky makers. Their cooperage and bottling plant were in Croft Street, just behind my office. The head cooper lived in South Hamilton Place, 100 yards from our house in Charles Street, and he had known me since I was a wee boy. He told me that they were reorganising and re-equipping their cooperage, and was instrumental in getting me the job, which was by far the biggest I had ever tackled. I was excited but concerned; could I do it successfully?

In those days it was possible to hire skilled engineers from the Labour Exchange on a daily basis without penalty if they were laid off. Six weeks later the job was completed successfully at a substantial profit; I was delighted and my confidence was greatly boosted. However weeks elapsed without my finding another job and soon I was back tramping the countryside again looking for work.

One day I called at Laird & Co., Admiralty contractors in Irvine. I had been calling there for years, had never got an order, and was left standing in the corridor for ages. That morning I was so depressed that I burst into tears, but the Managing Director, passing by, took me to his office and asked all about me. Several weeks later I had a contract to re-equip and refurbish their woodmill; that was another great success and a very profitable one too.

Thereafter the work kept rolling in, and I gained contracts to overhaul a soap factory in Irvine, to provide a new sawmill for Lord Howard de Walden's estate at Dean Castle, and to instal a diesel generating set for a knitting mill in Kilmaurs, to mention but a few.

One major job went badly wrong in a way. I had contracted to repair a Lancashire boiler at a laundry at Doonfoot on a fixed price, and the job had to be done during the Hogmanay New Year holiday with the boiler being back in service thereafter, otherwise the laundry could not operate. The repair was much more difficult than estimated and involved continuous working for three days and four nights without sleep. What a test of stamina! However the owner was very considerate and paid most handsomely for our efforts. I felt my confidence growing and meanwhile my reputation was spreading, mainly by word of mouth.

Looking back, I was fortunate in a number of ways; for example, my innate 'drive' generally resulted in my eventually finding suitable work. But in general the years from 1926 to 1936 were years of depression and deprivation, when many people were on the dole. Books have been written over the years about the inner cities, *Love on the Dole, Cathy Come Home* etc., and they all display the desperation of no work and no prospect of work.

The shipyards were the most important labour-intensive industry in Glasgow, and their excellence provided stable employment for father and son right up to the end of the first World War. After that most civilised families managed to survive; engineers became door-to-door salesmen, and the wives went charring or into service in the big houses, but as always there was an unruly element that caused trouble. Betting was illegal, but bookies, moneylenders and pawnbrokers flourished. Bookies controlled life in the poorer districts, and there was great competition for territories. Illegal bookies' runners took bets and the bookies and moneylenders lent money at extortionate rates of interest. Gangs were employed by the bookies to protect their territory and collect debts.

Depression encouraged heavy drinking, and "red biddy" was a favourite; this was a mixture of cheap red wine and methylated spirits, or even brush wash or paint thinners. Such mixtures were pretty deadly, and eventually sales of meths were restricted and a colouring agent was put in it to identify it. The next bad habit was a "milk shake." All Glasgow tenement closes were lit by high-pressure gas jets. Gas mantles were never supplied by landlords as they got stolen or broken. Milk was cheap to come by, so the flame of the jet was blown out, the swan neck was twisted round and the milk bottle was positioned over the jet until the milk effervesced, whereupon the contents were quickly drunk. This provided a quick high with violent effects. Certain neighbourhoods became "no-go" areas and the police could not cope until a new Chief Constable, Sir John Sillitoe, was appointed.

I can well remember one day being in a tram passing Glasgow Green when everything came to a stop. Rival Glasgow gangs had decided to settle their territorial differences and were marching to Glasgow Green. *The* weapons favoured by the gangs in those days were cut-throat razors and cloth caps with safety razor blades sewn into the skip; when slashed across the face, arms or legs, dreadful cuts were inflicted. The gangs would line up and each would provide a contestant. Open razor in one hand and the cap in the other, the battle was waged in old gladiatorial style. When one contestant retired hurt, another pair would take over, and so it continued. The injuries were horrible and there would be blood everywhere. Then the police would arrive (often mounted police as well), followed by ambulances to cart off the injured; arrests would be made, while others would flee from the scene.

Sir John Sillitoe introduced very tough policing methods. He formed groups of young fit policemen which today are known as Rapid Response Units. His philosophy was that those who inflict violence on others are cowards at heart and that fear of violence in retaliation against them is a dramatic deterrent. It is alleged that he briefed his officers with these words:

"Anyone arrested for violence must not be brought to any of my charge rooms until he has been in hospital. Anyone carrying a razor, break his arm: if he is carrying a razor and a bunnet [cap] with blades in the skip, break *both* arms."

That has gone down in Glasgow folklore and it may be true or not, but one thing is certain: violence and gang beatings disappeared from the streets of Glasgow within a year. There was some criticism of the methods but they certainly worked.

Great stuff, but the do-gooders have eventually won. Now there is no death penalty, there is no flogging, the stocks are uncivilised, corporal punishment of any kind is barred, parents can't even smack their children, the tawse is barred from schools, and indiscipline and bad behaviour are steadily escalating. One cannot pick up a paper today without reading about children totally out of control. I can't help wondering if common sense will once again take over, with a return to methods that have proved effective in the past.

CHAPTER 5

SOCIAL LIFE AT CHARLES STREET

23 Charles Street, Kilmarnock had a small front garden with a stone wall, iron railings and a wrought-iron gate. The outer front door was in two halves of heavy oak, with a mounted letter box also of oak. The inner door had a stained glass panel (which is still there). The hall was long and narrow, leading to a wooden staircase. On the left was a large dining room, and a large bedroom. Between these were two capacious side-by-side walk-in cupboards each about 6 ft square. Built out at the back of the house was the kitchen. Above the kitchen was a bedroom, which was the office and store mentioned earlier as Dad's business premises. Upstairs was a large bedroom and a drawing room and the bathroom was above the hall. There was a long narrow garden at the back which contained outbuildings, a coal house, a wash-house, a WC and a small workshop with bench, vice, and tools where Dad did all his work. Dad had built a lean-to roof between the end building and the boundary wall and that was where later I kept my motor-bike. There was a narrow passage about 3 ft wide between the gable end of the tenement building and the houses, ideal for cricket practice by the children in the neighbourhood.

The house was beautifully furnished, all paid for by grandfather. Lighting and cooking was all by town gas. There was no natural gas in those days, it was all manufactured from gas coal and stored in large gasholders (often referred to as "gasometers"), which floated on water and rose or fell dependent on the volume of gas in store. Our house had gasoliers in the main rooms; each had four burners with incandescent gas mantles, which could be pulled up or down dependent on where one wished to concentrate the light. The mechanism consisted of two metal cylinders, one sliding inside the other, and filled with water to prevent gas escaping.

The bathroom was well equipped, too, with a wash-hand basin, a flushing lavatory and a bath, and a very superior shower cabinet, which was built on the end of the bath; all were encased in beautiful mahogany. There was also a large hot water copper tank inside an airing cupboard. There was no electricity supply, and the water was heated by back-boilers behind open fires. There were fireplaces in every room, including the bedrooms.

The first lodger (or, as Mum called them, "paying guests") I can remember was a Miss Janet Tullis from Stirling. She was doing a course at the local agricultural college, known as the Dairy School. She was slightly mannish and always wore riding breeches, shirt and tie. She had the upstairs bedroom, with a beautiful brass double bed and handsome mahogany dressing table and wardrobe, plus a washstand with china bowl and large ewers. At first her meals were served in the drawing room, but when she saw how much extra work this caused she asked why she could not eat with us all in the kitchen. This was agreed and she became a family friend. She had first use of the bathroom and we used the outside loo. In these days things were so frugal that Dad used to cut up newspapers into squares and string them on a nail in the loo in place of expensive toilet paper. In the wash-house there was a huge copper built over a brick fireplace. On washdays the fire was lit and stoked up for two days, so that we could bath in two large wooden tubs. One of these contained a wringer, and there was also a mangle. I used to turn the handle and Mum or Betty fed in the sheets, blankets, and towels, which if properly done saved ironing. In our kitchen there was also a ceiling-mounted clothes airer (the traditional sort with rope and two pulleys). At that time coal was delivered at £1 per ton; it was dumped in Charles Place and for one shilling the coalman would wheelbarrow it into our coal-house. When I got big enough I did the barrowing and got the shilling.

When Miss Tullis departed we had a Miss Fairweather from Edinburgh. She was really hoity toity and had her meals upstairs on her own. She insisted in having supper brought up to the drawing room, and never mixed with us. She also was at the Dairy School and fortunately she did not stay long.

She was followed by two schoolteachers; one taught English and the other mathematics. They slept in the same bed, and had their meals in the drawing room. They were very nice ladies and when they saw how tired Mum got fetching and carrying up and down stairs, or had two children to do likewise, they too asked to eat in the kitchen. Mum of course was delighted to be getting double money from them. All the time they were with us there was never a cross word. They were very kind to Betty and me, and helped us with our homework. Later on in life I wondered what kind of relationship they had, as they were always quite affectionate towards one another.

Our final lodger came from Alloa, and taught French at Kilmarnock Academy. She was our longest-staying paying guest, and really became part of the family. More of her later.

My sister and I were brought up to share the housework on an equal basis. We made the beds and did the washing up and drying. We switched the carpets (no Hoovers in these days), did the dusting, polished the silver and brasswear, and learned to cook. I was also taught to sew on buttons and darn my own socks.

We made toffee, tablet and jam, and I even learned to bake. My favourite toffees were treacle twirls and bon-bons. Mum had an old recipe, the ingredients being sugar, condensed milk, treacle, and honey or syrup. One batch was boiled up with treacle, the other with honey or syrup. When the mixture cooled and became plastic it was rolled out into lengths, pulled and pulled by hand, and mixed with the other blend. The result was that one could develop different mixed and twisted colours and patterns. The mix could be rolled or moulded into many different shapes and then cut into different sizes, finally being sprinkled with icing sugar. We became adept at making tablet and fudge too, and sold many of our wares to the Stephen sisters (who also lived in Charles Street) who then did a roaring trade with them in their sweet shop in King Street, thus assisting our meagre family finances.

Twice a week a fishwife used to push her barrow round the local streets and sell 12 herring for sixpence. Herring were a very nourishing food and Mum used to pickle them, which is the way I liked them best.

I used to fish a lot and was able to bring home trout and even salmon when the fish were running, which further helped out the family budget. More of fishing later. Dad was a keen gardener and grew potatoes, onions, carrots, turnips, beetroot, lettuces and cabbages. We had apple trees, pear trees, gooseberry bushes, raspberry canes and loganberries. The garden was small but every inch of it was put to good use. We had a tiny pond for frogs, and we loved to see the frogspawn and tadpoles. Sometimes we even had newts. One winter we were horrified to find the pond frozen solid with two frogs in the ice; it may sound extraordinary, but they survived.

Before safety razors were invented and electric razors became popular, most shaving was done with open cut-throat razors. These were things of beauty with their shining steel blades and their ivory or ebony – or even gold – handles. For the affluent shaver they were sold in sets, seven razors packed in velvet-lined mahogany or oak boxes, each one labelled with the day of the week. Dad had built up quite a clientele sharpening razors. I used to be fascinated by all his oilstones and waterstones and his collection of leather straps, which were used to hone the final edge. One of these straps was kept specially to smack me if I misbehaved, but Dad never used it for that. Discipline was mother's prerogative as she was the dominant partner, and was by far the better organiser and manager of the family.

I had three different sets of friends, rugby friends, Cadet Force friends and neighbourhood friends. Of the latter, one of my two best friends was Bertie Robertson who lived at 6 Charles Place and was in my class at school; he was an only child and was not only clever but also good at sport. His father was a clerk in the wages office at Glenfield & Kennedy. The other was Andrew Ferguson, who lived at 5 Charles Street. He was three years older than me, and was a fount of knowledge, including sex. He was the son of a broken marriage and had three sisters, the youngest of whom was a real beauty. The mother and father had disappeared years ago and the family of four were brought up by aunts and uncles. The family were mill owners, but all of these had been closed down or sold, leaving the family comfortably off. They had a history of longevity – the grandfather climbed Goat Fell at 83.

Across the road were the Wilson family, with one son and two daughters. The father was Sam B. Wilson of Glenfield & Kennedy, who intrigued us as he was the only man we knew who had a nice wife and an even nicer mistress. The liaison was conducted discreetly and lasted for many years, but we were always agog to hear of any spicy news. James Burnett, who was also in the Cadets, lived at 1 Charles Street; his father was a director of Howie & Co. of Hurlford, who made china clay products including bathroom suites. James was popular because he had the only half-sized snooker table in the neighbourhood, and we all wanted to play on it. Olive and Hugh Bentley lived at 12 Charles Street. Their father was the head of the Electricity Station. Olive was pretty and had a sparkling personality. They eventually moved to a big house in Howard Street and later both children were sent off to private schools. To complete the group were Morton and John Clark, who lived in South Hamilton Place. Their father, who was quite religiously-minded, was also a Councillor and sales manager of a local printing and publishing company.

We were a close group, and of course there was always some bickering, but my memories of all the games we played together and all the pranks we got up to are happy ones. As well as football, cricket, handball and peevers [hopscotch], we had many street games, which are seldom heard of now, such as 'kick the can,' 'last across,' 'tick tag' and hide & seek. In those days there was little traffic on the streets. When motor cars became a little more numerous we were a little cross. I can well remember our little plot; we got two large tin cans and joined them together with a long piece of string, which was laid flat across the road. One of us then hid in a garden on each side of the road and when a car came we lifted the string and caught the front of the car, which pulled the cans along and caused a fearful racket. We did this several times before we were caught and got into a fearful row.

Some of the neighbours whom we did not like were targeted when we rang their bells and ran away. A more subtle prank utilised a piece of string, a large button, and a piece of putty. We would creep up to a lighted window, attach the putty, and retreat, then by pulling the string we could get the button to tap on the window and disturb the residents.

Of course there was no television and only a few of us had the wireless. Therefore there was much more interest in visiting one other and playing indoor games, as well as musical evenings in which the parents took part. Dad was very musical and played the violin, which he had made himself from timber from Loudon Castle. He had also made the violin case, lined with purple velvet and inlaid on the outside with scrolls and musical notes. Both were masterpieces of craftsmanship. I wish I had them today but they were probably disposed of when 23 Charles Street was cleared and sold in 1968. We also had a fine piano in the drawing room and Mum and Betty played it regularly.

Some of these friends faded into the past, others I kept in touch with, but regrettably they are all gone now.

TOP: Kilmarnock Academy's Cadet Pipe Band on parade outside Fairlie church, 1931.
BOTTOM: Myself and another climber at the top of Ben Nevis in August 1937, before we attempted the descent of the North Buttress.
Photos: author's collection.

TOP: The new Prestwick airfield in 1936, with flying school aircraft outside the original hangars. Photo: courtesy of the R.Ae.S.
BOTTOM: Another view of the pre-war Prestwick airfield.
Photo: via Prof. D. Cameron.

CHAPTER 6

CAMPING AND FISHING HOLIDAYS

The Ferguson family were lovers of Arran and used to rent a house on Lamlash seafront for the month of July. (This house is now the Carraig Mhor Restaurant.) The Scoular family were also frequent visitors to Arran and they used to rent a house on the shore at Corrie for the month of August. As mentioned earlier I was fortunate to be invited by both the Ferguson and Scoular families to spend a week with them, so I too became a lover of Arran, and even in later life, after a world of travel to many exotic lands, I still thought Arran the loveliest island of them all. When I was with the Scoulars I did a lot of climbing with Guy and got to know the mountains well. When staying with the Fergusons, Andrew and I concentrated on fishing, both sea and burn. We had prodigious catches of sea fish: cod, mackerel, sole, lobsters, crab and pollock. We fished the burns and it was not unknown to catch 20 or 30 brown trout in a day's fishing. They were not very big but made very tasty eating. We caught sea trout as well, spinning off the rocks at the mouth of the burns.

When I was 16 and Andrew was 19 he had the bright idea that we should go camping in Arran. Andrew had left school and worked for James Borland, a seed merchant and gardener's supplier who had a shop in St. Marnock Street. We booked a camping site at Blairmore Farm, Lamlash, just behind the cemetery and hired a bell tent from Black & Co. of Greenock, together with a latrine. A cottage tent was supplied by Guy. At the first camp there were six of us: Andrew, Guy, Bertie Robertson, Frank Chisholm from Catrine, Alex Wilson from Mauchline and myself. The weather was glorious, and we had a marvellous holiday. We spent most of the time climbing and swimming in the hill lochs and burns. The scenery from the mountain tops was fabulous and we could see the Irish coast quite clearly. We had a sketch of all the main peaks, published by V.A. Firsoft, and we planned to climb all 24 of them, but we only managed six on that first week, so we decided to go back the next year. We had five camps in all over the years, but of course the personnel changed for various reasons; however the main core, Andrew, Guy and myself, managed to climb all the peaks plus a few rock climbs as well.

We had some wonderful times, often along with the local girls, walking, golfing, swimming, picnicking, playing tennis, fishing, exploring, rowing across to Holy Isle, collecting white heather, photographing the wild goats, being shown round the lighthouse, and having high tea in the farmhouse. The teas were really great, with lots of home baking and homemade jam and wild honey, and all for one shilling each. We had barbecues on the beach and midnight parties. There was plenty of kissing and cuddling, and petting, but no sex – all good clean fun. Andrew Ferguson was very musical and played the banjo. He had a good musical ear and if you hummed a tune he could soon play it on his banjo. He eventually ran his own dance band and we used to engage him for Cadet and other dances. I had a ukelele, which I could not play very well. Alex was a good violinist and Frank Chisholm was pretty good on a concertina. We had some great musical evenings and singsongs round our camp fire.

We were teased by the girls about camping right behind the cemetery, and were asked if we were not scared of ghosts at night. We ridiculed any such scares and the girls challenged us to go separately to the old cemetery after midnight and see what happened. After much discussion it was agreed that the girls would provide six empty bottles, each with one of their names inside written on a folded piece of paper, and place them on top of the gravestones. The boys would then draw lots to determine who would be the first to go into the graveyard to choose a bottle, then second, and so on. We promised that there would be no lights used and the agreed prize was a romantic hour with whoever's name was in the bottle collected.

We could not have chosen a worse day – or a worse night – for our adventure: torrential rain, thunder and lightning. Earlier that afternoon there had been a burial of a well-known sea captain whose interment had had to be halted because of the thunderstorms. At midnight it was pitch black, and one literally could not see one's hand in front of one's face. I was first to go and I was away and back with my bottle like a linty [swallow]. Guy was next and he was away for ages; he got his bottle too but could not get out of the ruined chapel. He had to climb the wall and was muddy and wet. Andrew was next and had no trouble. Ronnie Smith was a relatively new visitor to Arran, a very good soccer player but a bit brash. He said he was going to shout to scare away any ghosts, and sure enough we heard him yell: "Arise ye dead, the judgement day is nigh." There was a shriek and then dead silence. We thought he was playing the fool and waited, but nothing happened and we became worried, so we got our torches and did a search. What we discovered was an apparition in white crouched by a gravestone, which turned out to be the sea captain's widow who had been praying at her husband's grave. When Ronnie shouted she had stood up, and Ronnie had got such a fright he had fainted.

As we could not revive him we wrapped him in a blanket and carried him to Lamlash Cottage Hospital, which was only a few hundred yards away. We took the old lady there also. All was well and they both soon recovered, but were kept in overnight because of shock. The following day Ronnie caught the boat home and never returned to Arran again.

During the summer family dances were held every week in the local village halls, each with a live band. The best was led by Bill Livingstone, whose signature tune was *Alexander's Ragtime Band*. We used to walk from Lamlash to Brodick or Whiting Bay to sample the dancing and then back again in the wee sma' hours after the dance was over. The dances at Whiting Bay were by far the most enjoyable, but we never made any new girl friends there, the Lamlash group seemed to stick together. Little did I know that a few years later I would meet the best girl of them all in Whiting Bay and that I would marry her and live happily ever after.

After buying my first old Triumph motor-bike, I became addicted to fast bikes, all bought second-hand. My second one was a 350 cc BSA; this was followed by a Velocette, then an Ariel water-cooled *Four Square*, then a Norton and, finally, the best of them all, a Sunbeam 500 cc. I became friendly with a knitting machine mechanic, Ronnie Black, who worked in Kilmaurs for Alexander Cunningham & Co., one of the biggest knitwear firms in Scotland; they sold their knitwear under the label St. Margaret and all the sons were reputed to be millionaires. Ronnie Black was an enthusiastic motor-cyclist; he competed in the Isle of Man TT Races and tuned his own bikes, and he passed on all his tips as to how to make the bikes go faster. To raise the compression ratio, the cylinder head was skimmed on a milling machine, slightly domed pistons and stronger valve springs were fitted, and every single part, particularly the valve ports, was polished to a mirror finish with calico mops and jewellers' rouge. Bypass systems were fitted to the silencers, and the bike was made as light as possible. Pure alcohol or other additives were added to the fuel. But the need to concentrate on my work to earn money prevented me from ever going to the TT Races.

On another holiday Andrew was staying in Lamlash while I was staying in a little cottage in Whiting Bay with Mum, Dad and Betty. On this occasion I had taken my Sunbeam 500 cc along, so first thing every morning I would pick up Andrew at Lamlash, he would mount the pillion and we would roar round the island, pretending that we were practising for the TT. We timed the circuit and the ambition was to do it faster each time. There was a straight stretch leading to the stone bridge over the Monamore Burn, where I could clock 100 mph or slightly more before braking sharply to negotiate the bend over the bridge.

One morning a man with a cow came out of a field, and I had to swerve slightly to avoid them; this spoiled my line, and I realised I could not make the turn. At times of crisis one's brain seems to be much clearer, and decision-making is much faster. I realised that if we hit the bridge we would be dead, so I braked fiercely and tried to turn into a slip road on the right. But I did not make it and the bike hit a fallen tree trunk and catapulted us both high into the air, after which we landed on our backs in a deep pool in the burn; that undoubtedly saved our lives. I do not remember much very clearly after that, apart from my lovely Sunbeam lying in the burn giving off clouds of steam. We both got taken to Lamlash Cottage Hospital, and Andrew was kept there as he had a badly damaged knee and head injuries. I went home and did not tell my parents anything about the accident, but said I had fallen into the burn. Later that day I collapsed – I had concussion and was taken back to hospital. Two days later I was out, but Andrew spent over two weeks there. Fortunately no serious or lasting damage was done and I was soon back rebuilding my bike, but that was the end of my motor-cycling days. I realised that it was unfair to continue as Mum and Dad were scared stiff I would have another accident. So I sold my bike and started to save up for a motor car.

The Monamore Bridge accident was remembered by my family for many years. Every time we passed it the question was asked: "What happened at this bridge?" The story was told again and again to and by my children and grandchildren, and may be told to my great grandchildren if I have any before I die.

The best thing that ever happened to me was to develop a love of fly-fishing, which has given me lifelong pleasure; it is the most relaxing hobby I know. When I was sad, depressed and unhappy, and could go fishing, all my cares would disappear. The gurgle of the streams and little waterfalls, and the enjoyment of studying the flora and fauna, I found most soothing, and even if I was not catching fish, I returned calm, peaceful and rejuvenated, and ready to deal with life and its problems with renewed courage and energy.

When I was 10 Dad had bought me a 9 ft 6 in Greenhart rod, reel, and line from Primrose McCririck for about 15 shillings complete. David Howie took me in hand and stated categorically that he would not take me fishing until I was proficient at casting. Many fishermen never learn to cast properly, and the arrival of the fixed-spool reel and spinning rods have done grievous harm to the sport. David took me into a field and taught me the rudiments. I cast with a single fly on the leader, and I had to land it on a pocket-handkerchief 10 times out of 10. Then it was a saucer with the same target. Casting is really quite easy once one develops the knack, but without it it is extremely difficult. Most bad casters try too hard, their action is too quick, they allow the rod to go past 12 o'clock on the back cast, and they do not make use of the flexibility of the rod. Once the timing is right, the rod does the work; it bends backwards on the back cast and forward on the front cast, thus providing momentum to the line and propelling the line straight forward. There are many other forms of casting, roll casting, spey casting and haul casting, but I will not go into the complexities of these here. Types of line and tippets are also important. Double-tapered floating lines are most common, but there are weight-forward, shooting heads, sinking lines, sinking tip lines, lead core lines and others. It is also important to match the weight of line to the rod, otherwise casting is more difficult.

When I started fishing nylon was unknown, and we used catgut or even horsehair for our leaders. Horsehair came from the tail of a stallion; hair from a mare's tail was no good as it was weakened by urine. Catgut had always to be steeped in water before tying the knots. When one had learned to cast and understand the equipment, it did not mean that fish would be caught. David taught me to read the river and the loch. Many times David would not even start fishing for an hour or even more; he would just scrutinise the water for any flies, hatching nymphs or midge pupas; he looked for fish movement disclosed by ripples and he studied depth of water, and as a result he caught more fish than many others did. He emphasised that depth and how the fly was presented mattered and how the speed and style of retrieve was important.

There are many hundreds of different flies on the market, and each fisherman has his or her own favourites. Over the years I am sure that frequent changing of flies is a waste of time. I carry no more than four of each type: wet, dry, nymph, midge, and lure. Colour does not matter very much, size and weight does. I reckon that I catch more than my fair share of fish.

It can be very frustrating when someone is catching fish and you are not. I have often seen two fishers fishing from a boat or from the bank using exactly the same equipment and identical flies: one is catching fish and the other is not. No one can explain it but I am sure that it has something to do with fly movement and fly depth. It has also been claimed that lady fishers catch more fish than do men, and that it has something to do with smell or female hormones. I consider this to be rubbish! It may be that the ladies move the fly in a different fashion.

I remember fishing once with a great friend of mine, Hugh Rowand. It was just after VJ-Day (so some years later) and we went fishing on the lochs in New Galloway. Hugh had a vintage Bentley, and we camped and lived rough and fished all the hill lochs. In these days all the trout were wild ones and difficult to catch. We decided to stay in a hotel for the last two nights, and finished up in the Anwoth Hotel in Gatehouse of Fleet, whose proprietor, Stuart Paton, was the champion flycaster for Scotland. We asked if we could fish, and he arranged a day's fishing on Loch Ordnochonoch. He explained that two doctors staying in the hotel had been fishing it all week and had caught nothing, so they had gone off to fish at Lairdmannoch.

The day was terrible, with gale-force winds and heavy rain. The wind was so strong that the boat drifted too fast and we could not fish. We found two buckets and some rope and used them as drogues to slow the drift down. I was fishing two flies, a Grouse and Green on the tail and a Peter Ross on the dropper, and by lunch time I had 16 lovely trout in the boat. Hugh had caught nothing. In the afternoon it was the other way about, Hugh was catching fish and I was not, yet we were both using the same flies. We went back to the hotel with 30 trout and laid them out on a big tray in the hall, and you should have seen the doctors' faces when they returned with no fish once again. I think they thought we had caught them illegally.

I have been following this same hobby now for more than 70 years, and it still has the same fascination for me as it did back then.

CHAPTER 7

COMING OF AGE

I was 21 years of age on 8th April 1936 and by then had obtained an Ordinary and a Higher National Certificate in Mechanical Engineering. Accompanied by Dougald Evan Stewart in his best Sunday suit, I went to the local office of the Amalgamated Engineering Union with my indentures and asked them if they would accept me as a fully qualified journeyman engineer. The local secretary said that this was very unusual and they had never been asked to do such a thing before. All engineering firms had their own procedures. I explained the background and he was very sympathetic, but said he would have to refer it to the area headquarters. Fortunately the area organiser lived in Galston, was a keen fisher and belonged to the local miners' angling club where I was also a member, so it all worked out well. In retrospect I cannot really understand why I went to so much trouble; I suppose I felt underprivileged because my hoped-for medical career had not even got started, and I needed something to boost my ego. God or Fate must have been guiding me and looking after me, because if I had not done what I did next my future life would have been vastly different.

Just before my 21st birthday all the creditors had been paid off, all the requirements of the trust deed had been met and for the first time I felt a free man, but there was another problem. Mr Yuille, one of the Trustees of the Turnbull Trust, came to my office and asked how things were going. He said that he had heard that the creditors had been paid off, produced a piece of paper and asked when he was going to be paid. This paper was an IOU for £400 which he had loaned to my father, who, he said, had pledged all the office furniture and stock. I asked why he had not disclosed this debt at the creditors' meeting when Mr McMurray had arranged the deed of settlement, but he claimed that the debt was a private matter and that he had not wanted to embarrass my father. He said that if we could not pay cash he was prepared to settle for a share in the business. I asked for time to think about it and went to see Mr McMurray, who said that he thought it very sharp practice, but as Dad had not said anything about the debt at the time of the threatened bankruptcy, and as it had not appeared in my father's statement of affairs, recovery was probably legal.

When I talked to Dad about it he broke down in tears and admitted that he had borrowed the money but did not have the courage to tell anyone about it. Another body blow! I had been thinking for some time about my future life and had been wondering if I wanted to continue running the business. I had not thought beyond the point of clearing off the debts and satisfying the creditors, and I still had a hankering that I might go to University one day and become a doctor.

During the years 1933 to 1936 I did nothing but work, study and worry. I had no time or inclination to associate with my friends, play rugby or even relax. At weekends I would go to the library and study all the *gurus* on management, efficiency, productivity, and philosophy. I just did not wish to meet people socially, and I used to retire to bed with my books and a bag of chocolates. It was a great relief when I felt that I had discharged my responsibilities to my father, mother and sister. I was able to give my mother £3 per week, and I was also able to pay for my sister's expenses at University. I bought my father cigarettes and pipe tobacco, but he did not even get pocket money. I only took what I needed to exist.

I still heard from Guy Scoular from time to time and he kept asking me to go to meet him in Glasgow and see how medical students lived. Eventually I was persuaded, so one evening I took a bus to the University Union to meet Guy and his friends. I enjoyed listening to all their tales, and we eventually retired to the Royal Hotel in Cathedral Street. I had learned to drink whisky by virtue of all the tots that I received for free when I was working at Johnny Walkers, but that whisky of course was not bonded and was very pure and very smooth and I have been an enthusiast ever since. However I never drank beer, whereas the medical students' favourite drink was a mixture of heavy ale and Guinness in a pint glass. After two of these I was definitely the worse for wear; I was poured onto the bus and was sick all over the floor on the way home.

That evening enabled me to make up my mind about the medical profession. I came to the conclusion, after very much reflection, that I had really done well in building up my father's bankrupt business, and I became determined to make a great success of it. Why should I give up all that I had done and waste all the experience I had gained in business? Frankly, I had found the medicos rather juvenile.

So here I was, at 21 years of age; business was flourishing, my sister was fully qualified and had a good teaching job, and Dad, at the age of 67, had returned to work and was able to visit many of his old customers and bring in a little business. By now I had a full time secretary, Bessie Simms, who came from Stewarton, and I had also employed a young lad, James Lamberton, to do the office work and a little bit of sales promotion together with some selling. In addition Dougald Stewart and Arthur Collins were on hand to help out on the major engineering jobs. At last financial pressures had eased, and I was able to contemplate the future with a little more confidence.

However when the Trustee heard that Dad was back at work, he was soon on the doorstep asking for his money plus interest, plus £80 for money he had loaned to pay the interest on the North Hamilton Street property mortgage. The property was always in debt but if the interest had not been paid then it could have been repossessed. I left him standing in the public office and called Bessie into my private office, where I dictated a full and final settlement receipt and wrote a cheque for the full and final amount less the interest. I then asked him to sign the receipt, and he was so surprised that he signed it straight away and did not even query the interest. I told him that I was taking over the management of the property and that he and Austin Turnbull could get lost; up till then they had been the factors.

I was also able to spend some money on 23 Charles Street; I installed electric power and light and put in a new bathroom suite, but kept the old shower as it was far superior to the single-headed unit that was the modern trend. I also put in new fireplaces in the kitchen and dining room, bought Mum a new three-piece suite, and transferred the couch and an armchair to my office. The next year I bought my first car, a Riley Nine, from James Bickett, who had a garage in Riccarton; this cost me all of £48.

My secretary Bessie Simms had been in my class at school. She was a highly intelligent and efficient secretary; she was also attractive and had a nice figure. As sometimes happen when two people are in close proximity to each other they become attracted and a relationship can develop. This happened to us and when there was no one else in the office we had some heavy petting sessions. She was very passionate and wanted to go the whole way, but for some reason I was reluctant, which was just as well, for some time later she became pregnant by the manager of the local picture house, who was married. The thought passed through my mind that as an up-and-coming young tycoon with good prospects it was me that could have been blamed. However when Bessie, in tears, broke the news to me, I felt very sorry for her and I told her that she could stay on for as long as she wished. Fortunately the father accepted responsibility and promised to meet all expenses plus maintenance – abortions were illegal in those days. Bessie continued to work with energy and efficiency until she went off to her aunt in Motherwell to have the baby; I never heard from her again.

CHAPTER 8

SCOTTISH EXPEDITIONS

My sister Betty and I decided that we needed a holiday, so we decided to explore the border country and stay in youth hostels. We joined the YHA, where the annual subscription was one shilling per annum and the cost of a night's stay was also one shilling.

The French teacher who had lodged with us since 1930 asked if she could join us. A prematurely grey and rather prim spinster in her mid-thirties from Alloa who taught French and German at Kilmarnock Academy, she had two sisters, also teachers, who lived with their mother. She never spoke of her early life, and we suspected that there must have been some tragedy and sorrow which she would never speak about. Over the years she had become a close family friend, and had been great help to me in coaching my French. When she bought a second-hand Ford I was allowed to not only choose the car but also teach her to drive, and before I had my Riley Nine she used to let me use her car quite a lot. We had formed a close relationship and when I was depressed and could not sleep at night I used to tiptoe upstairs and crawl into her bed, where she comforted and soothed me. I often wondered what my family would have thought if they had known, but as far as I know they never even suspected.

We agreed that she could come with us and studied the YHA handbook to plan our route. We took the bus to Galashiels, where the hostel was rather spartan although the beds were comfortable. We bought and cooked our own food, and there was a rota for the use of the kitchen. Rules were carefully observed and everyone was very friendly, and in all the youth hostels I visited over many years I never observed any rudeness or bad behaviour. Sadly that is not the case today. First we explored Abbotsford, Sir Walter Scott's home; then we walked to Melrose and inspected Dryburgh Abbey, then proceeded to Selkirk and visited Halliwell's House Museum and finally we visited Bowhill, the family seat of the Duke of Buccleuch, where the house and grounds were most extensive and beautifully kept. My life so far had been nothing but worry and hard work and I could not but envy such grandeur and wealth. Little did I know that some years later my wife and I would be dancing an eightsome reel with the Duke's son the Earl of Dalkeith. The Earl succeeded his father and was crippled for life as the result of a hunting accident. Little did I know, either, that I would spend many happy years fishing for salmon on the Nith at Drumlanrig Castle. The Duke owned most of the land surrounding Thornhill and district, indeed at one time he owned the whole village and all the property in it.

We walked along the Yarrow valley heading for St Mary's Loch and the famous waterfall, the Grey Mare's Tail. The weather was beautiful, the Yarrow water was flowing smoothly after the previous week's rain, and the conditions were idyllic. Of course I put up my rod and caught some beautiful trout, which provided our evening meal and breakfast the following morning.

In these far-off days there was little traffic, but local buses would transport us on our way when we had had enough walking. In the country districts the post buses which carried the mail, parcels and supplies to outlying farms and cottages also took passengers. The people were very friendly and we listened to all the local news and gossip. Hitchhiking was in its infancy then and it was very unusual for tired youth hostellers to be refused a lift – how things have changed. I also fished St Mary's Loch but caught nothing. We finished up at Moffat and spent the night in the youth hostel there before proceeding home by bus. A wonderful holiday, enjoyed by us all.

We promised ourselves that the next year we would go again, and when the time came we were a little more ambitious and decided to head north. We caught a train to Achnasheen where there was a beautiful youth hostel on the shore of Loch a'Chroisg. The first morning before breakfast I decided to have a dip in the loch. The sun was shining and it was warm, but I did not realise how cold these hill lochs could be, and when I dived in I was almost paralysed by the ice-cold water. I could not get out fast enough but was left with a bad headache for an hour or two. We walked to Achnashellach on the shores of Loch Dughaill, spent the night there and then proceeded to Loch Carron, and after a day resting and a night's sleep continued to Shieldaig on Upper Loch Torridon where we were joined by Aunt Effie and Uncle Lionel. The scenery was starkly beautiful and imposing. Most of the locals spoke only "the Gaelic." The next morning was a Sunday and I called at a local farm to try to buy milk and some eggs, but the door was shut in my face. It was not that the locals were unfriendly, they were just very devout and belonged to the "Wee Free Church" whose members did nothing but pray and attend church from midnight Saturday to midnight Sunday; they did not even milk the cows on a Sunday.

The only other visitors to the youth hostel were two young men from London who were studying at Oxford University. One of them was very withdrawn and looked ill. His friend explained that the isolation of the area and the mountains had had a profound and depressing effect on his friend, and that they were returning to London civilisation.

I can recall that we could not get the large kitchen range to work. When we lit the fire there were clouds of smoke which permeated all the rooms. However the range was the only method of cooking, so I went into the nearside wood and cut a long whippy branch from a mountain ash, returned and pushed it up the chimney. After strenuous efforts I dislodged a huge ball of soot that had been clogging the chimney. The soot went everywhere and we spent the next hour or two cleaning up, but all was well and we enjoyed our supper even more. The next day we walked round Upper Loch Torridon to the hostel at Inveralligin, a walk of some 15 miles. I did not think that Aunt Effie and Uncle Lionel would make it but they got there – with difficulty. Uncle

Lionel was very distressed and breathless so retired to bed. Betty and Eleanor cooked the evening meal and gave Uncle Lionel his supper in bed. The next day we rested and I took a boat out on Loch Torridon with Betty and Eleanor and caught some sea trout.

The day after that we swam, picnicked and rested and had an early tea. We then decided to climb Beinn Alligin, just under 3,000 ft, as we were told that the views from the top were spectacular. We had an enjoyable and not very strenuous climb, and the view was certainly worth the effort. After some biscuits and tea from our Thermos we started the descent, but as sometimes happens in the evening the mist came down. Fortunately I had my map and compass, which no experienced hill walker should ever be without. However an argument developed between myself and Uncle Lionel about the correct route. With his army experience he claimed he could map-read and navigate better than I could, so I deferred to his superior knowledge. However I had a gut feeling that we were heading for danger, so I pressed on alone to reconnoitre the territory ahead. When the mist lifted momentarily I found I was right on the brink of a sheer precipice, and shouted as loudly as I could for the others to stop and sit down. We then had to retrace our steps and eventually found the correct route, arriving back just before midnight. Relations were more than a little cool between Uncle Lionel and myself, and I thought that that was the end of a happy holiday. However in the morning he was very contrite and apologised.

We went to the Countryside Centre at the head of the loch, had lunch there and caught a bus to Kinlochewe. I had bought a pair of new climbing boots from Black's of Greenock especially for this holiday. Climbing boots in these days were of leather with the soles and edges of the soles heavily nailed to give a good grip for rock-climbing. They were very heavy and the theory was that they provided a pendulum effect and were just the thing for walking as well as climbing. But by this time my heels were so sore that I could hardly walk, so I discarded the boots and bought a pair of sandshoes at a store in Kinlochewe, which I wore for the rest of the holiday. Sixty years on I still have the boots and a box of the special nails for the edge of the soles: I never wore them again. It just goes to show how wrong some theories can be as modern climbing footwear are lightweight shoes with special rubber soles.

After a further day's rest we walked up the shores of Loch Maree to Talladale. We had an evening meal in the Loch Maree Hotel, paid for by Uncle Lionel; the prices frightened me! We then went on to the youth hostel right on the banks of Loch Maree. I was very interested to see the number of fishing guests in the hotel and to watch them with their ghillies going off in their boats to fish for salmon. I did not think much of the fishing as the boats were powered by outboard motors and ploughed up and down the loch trawling lures. They certainly caught lots of salmon and sea trout but I could not approve of such unskilled and unsporting ways of catching fish.

Next day we walked to Gairloch. The youth hostel there was at Cairn Dearg, an old country house right on the point. The weather and the scenery were again spectacular. We explored, went to the Heritage Museum, and on our last evening had dinner at the Gairloch Hotel again as guests of Uncle Lionel. The next day we caught the train to Glasgow and Uncle Lionel and Aunt Effie continued on to London while we returned to Kilmarnock. It was a truly memorable holiday.

The following year I was able to rent Gowanhill in Whiting Bay for the month of August so that Mum, Dad and Betty could have a longer holiday than usual. I spent the first few days there with them but then returned home as I had other things in mind. I had in fact arranged a cycling holiday with Guy Scoular, and for this I had bought a second-hand bike for 12/6, nearly new and with a Sturmey-Archer three-speed gear. I had designed and made special carriers over the back & front wheels and panniers, which hung from the crossbar, and these were fitted to Guy's bike as well to carry our tent and other equipment. We intended to camp and live rough and fish and climb. I still had this bike till two years ago, when I gave it to my son-in-law Dave.

We set off from Kilmarnock and cycled to Crianlarich. We had our lunch at the side of Loch Lomond and fished a wee burn, but caught nothing. We stayed in the youth hostel and set off for Ben Nevis. Guy was a member of Glasgow University Mountaineering Club and we stayed in their hut. We climbed Ben Nevis by the easy route, but on the summit we met two boys from Newcastle who were planning to descend by the Great Buttress route as they thought the ascent that we had both taken very unexciting. So we joined up with them; they thought we knew the route and we thought that they did. The climbing map for Ben Nevis showed the route as difficult but not severe. We had all the correct climbing gear, but less than halfway down we were in more than a little difficulty. One of the Newcastle boys was leading, but the route terminated in a pitch which was not just 'severe,' it was 'impossible.' We were all scared to death but Guy, who was last on the rope, kept his head and found that we could retrace our route and get onto an easier pitch. We never did complete the Buttress descent and were glad to get back to the summit and come down the easy way. Never climb with strangers! After a day's rest we cycled west and along the side of Loch Linnhe; we stopped at Fort William for lunch and then continued past Neptune's Staircase to Gairlochy and thus to Spean Bridge, followed by a run up Loch Lochy to Invergarry. We pitched our tent there and did some fishing on the Garry River – that was before the damming of the river for the hydroelectric scheme. It is a beautiful place and in the twilight we saw the evening rise and caught some sizeable brown trout. There is nothing more exciting than to hear the plop of rising fish, to make contact and listen to the reel scream to a running fish eventually coming to the net. We saw one or two salmon as well; early one morning we were tempted and we each landed one before anyone was abroad – or even awake.

We struck camp and cycled to Invermoriston, and thence to Cluanie where we camped again. Glenmoriston is a magnificent valley and we continued to Shiel Bridge on the shores of Loch Duich. Seeing the five sisters of Kintail against the setting sun is one of the most beautiful scenes that one could ever imagine. We swam in Loch Duich and pitched our tent once more. Everything was still and peaceful and one could imagine being in Paradise. The next part of our journey was the most testing of all, up and over Màm Ratagan. The incline was 1 in 4 and it was impossible to cycle on our well-laden bikes. It was a case of 'walk and push' all the way, but when we got to the summit the view was well worth all the effort. Looking down into Glenelg and the Sound of Sleat, with the Cuillins of Skye in the background, was a sight that can never be forgotten – it was magic, it was mind-blowing. We had a rest and then freewheeled all the way down at speed into the village. After shopping and finding a place to camp we went for a drink in the local pub and met a charming man who turned out to be the gamekeeper of the Gleann Beag estate, which was owned by a wealthy stockbroker in London. When he heard that we were fishers he invited us to spend a few days with him and see what country life was like. It was a very isolated spot and he had no telephone and no electricity. He told us that when he received a telegram from his boss it was usually a request for Scottish salmon to be put on the night train for one of the stockbroker's lavish dinner parties.

He showed us some aspects of fishing that we had never heard of before. He knew the burns and Kylerhea like the back of his hand and was an excellent caster of the fly. He always tried to catch salmon on the fly, but if that was not successful he showed us clear water worming. He knew all the lies, and clear water worming meant crawling through the heather and keeping out of sight. The water was gin-clear and one could see the salmon and their reaction to the worm. Sometimes they would pay no attention at all, even when the worm was dangled on their noses. At other times they would play with it, even taking it in their mouths and spitting it out again. Then occasionally they would go for it in a great rush, and the salmon was hooked.

If this worming did not produce a salmon, then the rabbit snare was used; this was a noose of braided brass wire mounted on the end of a long pole. Again stealth was essential; the noose was put in the water and carefully and gradually it was slipped over the salmon's tail. A great yank was made, the noose tightened and the poor salmon was on the bank. Failure disturbed the salmon, who became nervous and were then even more difficult to catch.

Another technique was the bottle and carbide method. Calcium carbide when mixed with water produces acetylene gas, and this in the early days had been used to light bicycle and car lamps. A lemonade or beer bottle with a screw top was obtained and about two inches of carbide was placed in the bottom of the bottle, followed by dry sand. The depth of the sand acted as the timing device, the more sand the longer before the explosion. The bottle was then filled with water and tightly corked. A length of string was attached to the neck, and again the bottle was manoeuvred stealthily close to the salmon lie. When the bottle exploded the water hammer created stunned the salmon and they were easily netted at the run-out of the pool. This method was a great favourite of poachers and was a very successful one. There was little noise to be heard as the water greatly reduced the sound of the explosion and there was no damage to the fish. During our visit the ghillie never failed to catch salmon – it was an enlightening experience.

Talking of poaching, the ghillie related a case of two wealthy yachtsmen who had been sailing in the outer isles and had anchored their yacht in Loch Alsh. They had seen the salmon running into Loch Long and into the river Elchaig, and one evening they had been tempted to take some salmon illegally. The next morning they had a visit from a man who claimed to be the water bailiff; he said that he had been watching them through his field-glasses and would have to report them to the police. They were horrified as their reputation could be severely damaged and pleaded with him to turn a blind eye as they had meant no harm and were only having a bit of fun. He said that if they handed over the fish he would see what the riparian owner would say, and he would try to prevent a prosecution. So they gave him the fish and a bottle of their best malt whisky and off he went. Two days later they were having a drink in a pub in Strome Ferry, and there was the water bailiff. They plied him with drink, and when he eventually left they asked the barman who he was; he responded: "Oh! That's old Jock; he's the best-known poacher in the district."

At the end of our stay we caught the ferry from Bernera to Kylerhea on the island of Skye. Our luck ran out and we had high winds and torrential rain. During our first night on Skye our tent was blown down and everything was soaked. We stayed the next night with a charming lady in an old cottage. Bed and breakfast cost us 5/- all in for the two of us, and the breakfast was superb. We cycled on to Portree and camped once again. The weather did not improve and we were soaked again. We had dinner in the Portree Hotel and were allowed to have hot baths as well. Next day we set off for Dunvegan and found the weather there still dreadful, so we tried to find a cheap bed and breakfast, but it was the English holiday season and everywhere was full.

We bumped into the minister in the village and asked if he could recommend accommodation. He must have been sorry for us with our bedraggled appearance and insisted that we should come home with him. He had a son and daughter who were at Glasgow University, the daughter reading Medicine and the son the Law. We had a lovely dinner, hot baths and a gigantic breakfast, and the minister and his wife refused to take a penny. They recommended that we should go to the little clachan [hamlet] of Claigan six miles north as the estate joiner there might have some accommodation.

By now it had stopped raining and the sun had come out. The burns had been in spate and in the falling water we saw trout rising. Up went the rods and we started catching fish. As we moved up the river we saw a lady and two children fishing too. They had caught nothing and we showed them our fish. The lady was duly impressed and asked who we were, and pointed out that we should not be fishing at all as the water was private. We were very apologetic and said she must have the fish. It turned that she was the Duchess of Dunvegan Castle, the Lady McLeod. We told her who we were and how kind the minister had been at Dunvegan and it finished up with us being invited to the Castle for tea.

It was an unforgettable experience, a stately home, a wonderful picture gallery, lovely home-baking with bramble jam and all kinds of cakes, and of course tea from a silver tea service. When we mentioned to Lady McLeod that we were heading for Claigan she told us something about the family who lived there. The husband, Andrew McGregor, had been a history teacher at Kilmarnock Academy until he became ill with tuberculosis. He recovered but was told by his doctor to move to a country area. He had married a Margaret Campbell from Kilmaurs and they had moved to Skye, and as he was skilled with his hands he had become the estate joiner. Margaret's brother Jim was in my class at school, and I had sold knitting machines to the father who had a small hosiery business in Kilmaurs – it's a small world!

When we arrived at Claigan we were made very welcome and we stayed for four days. The only coral beach in Europe is at Claigan; the coral got there because of the Gulf Stream, and we were able to pick up a selection to take home. Andrew's neighbours had a son who was celebrating his 21st birthday the day after we arrived. In the islands there were a few illicit whisky stills, but provided the distilling was done discreetly and the whisky was not sold on, the authorities turned a blind eye.

It was the custom when the first son was born to bury a keg of pure malt whisky in the peat and leave it there until the son reached 21, when it was then dug up for the birthday party and the ceilidh. We were invited to this occasion and it was one I will never forget. The minister was there to bless the boy and we all prayed for a long and happy life. Presents were given, the keg of whisky was broached and everyone got drunk or at least very merry. It was a fine evening and most of the celebrations were out-of-doors. The pipe music, the fiddlers, the accordion players and even a harpist made fine music, and the dancing was energetic. The party lasted until dawn, followed by a traditional Scottish breakfast.

The next day everyone rested and the day after that we went sea-fishing with Andrew in his boat. We saw a family of otters, seals and porpoises galore, and basking sharks, and caught some fish, mainly cod, haddock, herring and mackerel. We were sorry to leave and once again the McGregors would not take a penny.

I went back to Skye with my wife Joy in September 1985, nearly 50 years later. We visited all the old places, and things had changed dramatically. Dunvegan Castle is in the hands of the National Trust and we were given a conducted tour. The Macleods still live in the Castle but were not in residence during our visit. I did see the picture gallery and recognised some of the portraits. I also recognised a photograph of the Duchess who invited us for tea, and in the drawing room I am sure that the silver tea service on display was the very one from which we were served tea. We went to the coral beach but very little coral was to be seen, and at Claigan all the cottages were in ruins.

Guy and I took the ferry from Kyleakin to Kyle of Lochalsh and cycled round Lochcarron and past Loch Kishorn to Shieldaig. The weather was atrocious and I began to feel unwell. I was shivery and coughing badly and was running a high temperature. Guy was in his final year of Medicine and thought I had pneumonia. He got me to the nearest railway station, put our bikes in the guard's van and we caught the train home – a somewhat sad end to a glorious holiday.

I was seriously ill for three weeks. Jim Allardyce, our local GP, confirmed pneumonia and perhaps rheumatic fever. I was alone in Charles Street, but Betty came home from Arran and nursed me with great care and loving attention. Fortunately, when I recovered I did not suffer any long-term effects.

CHAPTER 9

FALLING IN LOVE

Then were to come the most momentous years of my young life so far. I fell seriously in love, I joined the RAFVR and on 3rd September 1939 war was declared. All these played a vital part in my future personal life, in fact they changed it dramatically. Following the sad end to my cycling holiday with Guy and my illness, the next year I bowed to the wishes of my parents and sister and joined them in a holiday in Whiting Bay, Arran. Once more I had rented Gowanhill Cottage for the month of August, and Babs and Will Wilson also came for the month.

A Glasgow family had rented Little Gowanhill, the cottage next door. The father had been blind from birth and was a music teacher; he had fathered two beautiful blonde daughters, and I was quickly intrigued. The elder daughter, Lillian, I found to my sorrow was engaged to a weather forecaster, who was working somewhere in the South of England, although that did not prevent her engaging in a little dalliance; but when things became a little overheated she reminded me that she was an engaged girl and had to be true to her fiancée, so I switched my attentions to her younger sister, Helen, where they looked more promising.

I played a lot of golf with a handsome blonde boy, Hugh Craw, whom I had met before. He was a well-off corn merchant from Glasgow, running the family business there. One morning playing the ninth hole we caught up with two nice young ladies who were looking for a lost ball; one of them was Shennah Turner, who had been in my class at school and came from a very wealthy family who owned a soft drinks business. I had always fancied her at school but because of my lowly status and family worries I never thought I had a chance. We chatted them up and suggested we meet at the dance that evening, but Shennah was catching the evening boat home, so my luck was out again. But the other girl was going to the dance, so Hugh and I turned up, and there she was, along with Helen. We had a pleasant evening and escorted them home. Betty Foster, the golfing girl, was staying with her family in Silverburn right opposite the Golf Club entrance. At the next dance Betty was there with her younger sister and her cousin, and we all went back to Silverburn for coffee and biscuits, and had a very interesting time talking in the front porch, and trying to find out about each others' background. Betty's sister was called Joy, and I was immediately impressed by her beauty, startling vivacity and personality.

At the next dance the girls and cousins were all there; Hugh and I had a wonderful evening, and danced every dance. I took Helen home and Hugh took Joy home. I had a very passionate time, but when I asked Hugh how he had got on he told me he could not even get his arm round her, let alone a kiss!

I then had to return to Kilmarnock to deal with some pressing business matters. One evening I had a telephone call from Helen saying that she was home alone in her parents' flat, had just climbed out of the bath and would I like to come and have supper with her? So I bought a bottle of sherry and some malt whisky and set off in the good old Riley Nine. It was soon clear that I was expected to stay the night and I was sorely tempted. Fortunately the sherry was too much for Helen and she eventually passed out. I put her to bed and thought of climbing in beside her, but thoughts of the other girl – and the state of the bed linen – deterred me; discretion was the better part of valour, and I took myself home.

On my return to Arran, Joy and I saw a lot of each other; we golfed, danced, fished, picnicked, swam together and quoted poetry to each other. I realised that I was truly in love, and worried that perhaps I was not good enough for her. Her family had a lovely house, 'Trees' at Lochwinnoch, and her father was secretary of the great industrial empire India Tyres. I sailed home on the *Glen Sannox*, and wrote Joy a postcard asking if she would like to go with me to visit the Bellahouston Park Exhibition in Glasgow. I was on tenterhooks until I got a reply, so was delighted when the answer was yes: I could hardly wait for the day. The Riley was serviced and cleaned and polished, and off I set. We had arranged a rendezvous inside the Exhibition grounds, but as I was collecting a ticket in the car park the engine stalled and when I tried to get it going again the starter motor jammed. I knew how to free it, but it meant sorting out my tools and getting underneath the car, so I finished up dirty, dishevelled, and very late. Fortunately my sister Betty was meeting her boy friend at the same place so all was well, but I had to find somewhere to wash my dirty hands, which were greasy to the elbow. We had a great day, so enjoyable in fact that Joy missed her last bus home, and she finished up being taken home by Betty's boy friend Rob, while I wended my way home with my sister.

Our next meeting was when I was invited to Trees for the weekend. The weather was cold and frosty and we were able to go skating on Lochwinnoch, but had to drive back in a terrible fog. The next morning all the pipes leading from the outside supply were frozen, and I had to use all my engineering skills to thaw them out, which took most of the morning.

Some weeks later Joy invited me to go as her partner to India Tyres' Annual Ball at the Grosvenor Hotel in Kilmarnock. What a thrill that gave me, especially as I had just received my first suit of tails. I travelled up to Lochwinnoch all decked out with my tail coat carefully folded on the back seat to prevent creases, and a heavy sweater over my stiff shirt, collar, and white bow tie. This I tied myself; in those days anyone wearing a ready-made tie with an elastic band was thought to be a bit 'low class'! At dances we used to pull at the bow ties to see who was top quality and who was not. The ball was a huge success and I enjoyed every minute of it. Afterwards I spent the weekend at Trees.

Joy worked at Register House in Edinburgh and was studying at the University there for a Law degree. She used to come home for most weekends by train, returning on the Sunday night. I suspected that I was not the only boy in her life, and that she had other interests in Edinburgh, but I had decided that she was the only girl for me, and tried all I knew to impress her and her family.

CHAPTER 10

FLYING LESSONS

Every time I passed the airfield at Prestwick I used to stop and watch all the activity there: Tiger Moths taking off and landing, Ansons going off on longer journeys doing training flights for navigators and radio operators, and occasionally larger aircraft which, I learned, were Fokkers. I was fascinated by the young men strolling around in their Sidcot suits, flying helmets and gloves. The roar of the engines and the smell of petrol was exciting, and I wondered what it would be like to soar up into the sky. The airfield had no runways in those days, it was just green fields with a little country road leading past a farmhouse. I used to park in this little road and watch the aircraft landing just over my head, and started thinking seriously about joining the RAFVR.

Prestwick airfield had come into existence only a short time before, partly as a result of friendships forged during the Houston expedition to Mount Everest in the spring of 1933. David McIntyre and the Marquess of Clydesdale, both with No. 602 City of Glasgow Auxiliary Air Force Squadron at Abbotsinch, had been selected as the pilots for this attempt to overfly the mountain, which at nearly 30,000 ft above sea level was only just within the capabilities of the two biplanes chosen. David had flown Westland PV.3 G-ACAZ with observer Lt. Col. Lathan Blacker, while the Marquess had flown a modified Westland Wallace, G-ACBR, together with the Gaumont-British ciné-photographer Stanley Bonnet. Flt. Lt. Richard Ellison had been the RAF Liaison Officer for the expedition, and he and David McIntyre had formed a close friendship.

After the successful outcome (which had not been made any easier due to political complications at the time), David McIintyre had been looking for ways of pursuing his aviation aspirations, so when he heard that the government was prepared under certain circumstances to issue contracts for approved firms to open flying training schools, he and the Marquess, in association with de Havilland's, set up Scottish Aviation Ltd in 1935. Both Richard Ellison and Francis Burnard, the engineer from Westlands who had been responsible for the maintenance of the expedition's aircraft, later played a major role at the company.

When the airfield was first opened, David is reported to have said that "in ten years' time you will see here an international airport and an aviation industry," but although there was no doubt that he fully intended this to happen (as it indeed did) it is unlikely that too many others would have taken him seriously at the time.

The humble beginnings of Prestwick airfield were well described in a lecture given by Noel Capper to the Prestwick Branch of the Royal Aeronautical Society early in 1975, and this was reproduced in the February 1975 issue of their journal *Aerospace*. Noel Capper had been involved with

Prestwick right from the start (in fact he had been the Chief Flying Instructor with No. 12 EFTS before the war and had checked me out for my first solo), and by the time he left in 1965 was Scottish Aviation's chief test pilot.

I am indebted to the RAeS for permitting me to include relevant extracts from his lecture here:

"To begin with the airfield occupied 157 acres . . . and another 191 acres were bought . . . to allow for future expansion. Accommodation, including a hangar, offices, lecture rooms and a little control tower, was built by the end of 1935 – it was a copy of the buildings at de Havilland's School at White Waltham – and the small airfield was ready for No. 12 Elementary Flying School to open on the 17th February 1936. For a time, an area remained that had not completely recovered from growing a crop of turnips and wooden planks had to be laid for aircraft to taxy out onto the main airfield. There were 16 Tiger Moths, eight instructors and between 30 & 40 pupils."

When I started to make some personal enquiries at the airfield, I was very interested to hear that Scottish Aviation Ltd had started up a factory to modify aircraft and make components, and I thought that maybe I could get some work from them, so I started paying calls but at the time no one seemed to know anything about who was in charge.

After serious deliberation, and with the growing probability of war, I decided to try to join the RAFVR rather than eventually be called up for the infantry. I went to the Instructors' room and asked for details, and was told that I would have to apply to RAFVR headquarters at Bothwell Street, Glasgow. So I applied there and filled in all the papers, and two weeks later was called for interview, which was a thorough and searching one, as everyone wanted to be a pilot rather than other types of aircrew. One week later I was accepted subject to the 'medical,' which also was very thorough. I was told that the glasses I was wearing were unnecessary and that I should throw them away. Mum and Dad were somewhat distressed as they depended on me to run the business, but as I explained I was only a weekend trainee and would not be called up unless there was a war, and if that happened I would be called up anyhow.

It was a great thrill to take the oath and to be registered as Sergeant Pilot u/t Service No. 745746. I was looking forward to my flying training, but was disappointed to learn that that was a long way off, as I had to complete theoretical studies first. This meant two nights a week studying Flying Training and Air Navigation, learning how to drill and salute, studying Conditions of Service, and how one could claim travelling expenses and – where necessary – subsistence allowance. The first surprise was to learn that the Instructors were certain that war was inevitable, and so we had to learn survival techniques, and what to do – and not to do – if captured.

There were 25 entrants in my group, including Bill Rodgers, who was in my class at school, and Tom Campbell, who was three years our junior. The three of us travelled together to Glasgow in my Riley, and claimed three sets of expenses. I enjoyed all my studies and longed for the day when I could commence flying.

We were able to go to No. 12 Elementary Flying Training School at Prestwick during weekends, mix with those doing their flying training and listen to all the gossip in the Mess afterwards. I took the opportunity also to snoop around the factory area to examine the prospects of doing business; I thought they were excellent if I could only make the right contacts. I learned that the Deputy Chief Flying Instructor, Dick Ellison, was also keeping an eye on the factory on behalf of Group Captain David McIntyre.

I was also told that the factory manager (who had been Chief Inspector at J. & J. Weir of Cathcart, a world-famous engineering company) operated from the old farmhouse. One Monday I was able to get an appointment to see him, so I told him who I was, that I was in the RAFVR awaiting flying training, that I ran an engineering and merchanting business, and asked if there were any chances of getting some work. I found him very helpful; he took me for a tour of the factory, and soon I was getting orders for tools and machinery.

But I did not think that the factory was well run. The organisation seemed to be non-existent, and nobody seemed to know where to buy tools and equipment, particularly when these were in short supply due to the growing rearmament programme. This was a perfect situation for me and I started spending more and more time at Prestwick, getting bigger and better orders. I also wrote and intimated that if they would treat me as their main supplier I could offer Scottish Aviation a discount. More about that later.

Then early in 1939 my flying training started. I duly reported to the Adjutant and was entered into the programme, which gave half an hour's instruction every other weekend. I went to the Quartermaster's store and was fitted out with my flying gear, Sidcot suit, flying helmet & goggles, earphones for communication, and silk socks & gloves (worn inside woollen socks and leather gloves to alleviate the cold); all these I put in my newly allotted locker. I was shown how to buckle on my parachute and how to use it if necessary, and at last I was allowed to get into a Tiger Moth for instruction on the controls. I was then allowed to taxy the aircraft to get the feel of things. What a thrill, but that was all – until the following Saturday.

I was invited to Trees shortly after Christmas and again had a wonderful time. Joy's father was a very fine golfer (he had a handicap of +2) and through this had become very friendly with a Scottish entrepreneur, Andrew Melville. Together they started India Tyres and from small beginnings it mushroomed into a large enterprise that became a threat to the big boys like Pirelli, Michelin, and Dunlop. Eventually, Dunlop bought up India Tyres so, inevitably, directors and management changed, and one of the last survivors was Joy's father. He was offered a job at Fort Dunlop in Birmingham, but he turned it down and as a result was sacked. In those days there were no redundancy payments and no compensation, and so another job had to be found and Trees was put up for sale. In modern society there would have been a huge golden handshake and massive share options, as Melville and Foster had built the business and were substantial shareholders. So my expectations of marrying a wealthy wife did not materialise, but that did not weaken my endearing love for Joy who, I found out, had been born in Memphis, Tennessee and whose full name was Frances Virginia Marshall Foster.

I thought that next Saturday would never come, but in due course I strapped on my parachute and climbed into a Tiger Moth once again. The parachute acted as a seat cushion. I was taken through the pre-flight checks. Magneto switches "off" while the ground engineer rotated the propeller in the reverse direction to prime the carburettor, check that chocks at the wheels were secure. Switch on ignition, set throttle, thumbs up to the engineer, who would swing the propeller, and hopefully the engine would start. Check that all the controls worked properly, run the engine up to full throttle, check each magneto, then chocks away and we taxied out for take-off. Check controls again while waiting for clearance signal and then we were off. Bumping over the grass, then airborne and climbing at 1,000 ft per minute. The instructor sat in the front seat and communicated with his pupil through the Gosport tube, plugged into a socket and connecting the earphones in the respective helmets. I could hardly believe it, airborne at last. To those who have never flown in an open-cockpit aeroplane, it is difficult to describe adequately the sensations; they are fantastic. Soaring up in a clear blue sky, the fields rapidly falling away, the size of everything becoming diminished, the wind rushing past, and the slight disorientation felt at first: this was an exceptional, exciting experience that I will never forget.

Then the voice of my instructor: "Put your hands on the joystick and your feet on the rudder bar and get the feel of the controls. No – not like that, you are gripping too tightly – relax. Can you recognise any landmarks? Do you know where we are?"

"Yes, I think so."

"Well, I want you to do some gentle turns and banks. OK. No, you are still too tense – relax. The rudder will do the turns, the ailerons will do the banks. That's better. Now do some climbs and descents. No! No! When you are climbing, open the throttle; when you are descending, close the throttle. Keep the rudder and ailerons straight or you will generate a spin."

I was beginning to get the knack when my instructor said: "I have her now, it's time to land."

I could not believe we had been in the air for 35 minutes. I could hardly wait till my next lesson.

The next few months were very hectic. Business was booming. I was scouring the country to find machine tools and equipment for Scottish Aviation, which they so badly needed. Deliveries of new plant were very extended, so I used all my connections to find the whereabouts of the necessary requirements, particularly turning lathes, milling machines, power drills, grinders, guillotines, metal-forming machines, rivetters and hand &

power presses. I found them in many odd places: garages, blacksmiths, lace and textile factories, schools, and even linoleum and flax works. Many had not been used for years, and required overhaul and rebuilding. Dougald Stewart and Andrew Collins were very busy doing the overhauls and we took on two apprentices. Meanwhile our sales promoter James Lamberton found another assistant and a girl clerk. I was spending more and more time at SAL and was becoming involved in production problems. The modification on the long-range Wellesleys was going well, but production of parts was not.

SAL had received an order from the Hawker Aircraft Co to manufacture Hart variant rudders, but could not get the prototypes passed due to lack of jigs and lack of skill, so I was asked if I could help. I designed new fixtures and supplied new Desoutter drilling and rivetting equipment, and showed the operators how to tension the skins and maintain the contours. I also developed a contour-checking gauge and the prototypes then passed inspection at Hawker's Kingston Factory. The Chief Inspector there was a Mr Jefferson who was known to be very strict; I got to know him fairly well and he was quite complimentary about my efforts. Many years later I got to know his son George Jefferson very well and we travelled the world together when we served on the Government's "Expert Committee."

Every alternative weekend when I was not flying I spent with Joy when she was home for the weekend. I did the washing up, gave the cooker a good clean and polish, and generally tried to show the family that I would make a good husband for Joy. We went for long walks, golfed and went to the pictures, and thoroughly enjoyed each other's company. On Sunday I used to drive her to the station and send her off to Edinburgh with a box of *Black Magic* chocolates. Little did I know that another boy met her at Edinburgh, entertained her for the evening and gave her another box of chocolates. I invited her to go to the Former Cadet Dance in the Grand Hall, Kilmarnock, which I was organising. I introduced her to all my friends, and they told me how lucky I was to have such a stunner for a partner.

My flying training was also going well; I felt that I was mastering all the exercises, and the time came when I had to do a week's intensive training ready for my first solo. I had told Guy Scoular when it was likely to be, and he promised to come with his brothers and watch from the little road passing Newdykes Farm. It was a glorious clear day and I was a little nervous. I was so anxious to make a good take-off that I forgot to adjust the trim, and took off far too steeply. The trim lever, nicknamed the "cheese cutter," was on the left-hand side of the cockpit and I quickly realised what had happened and made an adjustment. All the other manoeuvres went off well; my instructor was quite complimentary and said: "Do a circuit and make a landing."

Just as I was coming in to land I saw the Scoulars and waved to them, whereupon I lost concentration and stalled; the instructor immediately took over, and we had made a safe landing he said he could not authorise a solo flight and would have to report me to the Chief Flying Instructor. I was very distressed. In due course I was seen by the Adjutant, who tried very hard to persuade me to transfer as a navigator. I told him I would not even consider it as I had joined the RAFVR to learn to fly, and pleaded for another try.

The next day I drove up to Renfrew and joined the Civil Air Guard. I was accepted and did my first flight on 15th August 1939; the aircraft was a DH.60G Gipsy Moth, Reg. No. G-ABZV and my instructor was a Mrs Fairweather. I had further flights in the same aircraft on the 17th, 19th, and 22nd and flew solo on 23rd August 1939. My logbook was endorsed: "Solo completed satisfactorily."

Full of glee I set off for Prestwick, but my instructor said there was nothing he could do, and that I would have to see the Adjutant. He was not very pleased and stated that what I had done was highly irregular; then he tried again to persuade me to change to navigator or radio operator status. He explained that the RAF had more pilots than they could train but were short of navigators. I was emphatic that as I had already gone solo I should at least have another chance, but he did not want to know.

Because of my other activities at SAL I had met Dick Ellison (who was also the Assistant CFI) and we had got on well together, so I persuaded him to take me up on a flight and do a simulated solo with him in the instructor's seat. He did so and said he could find nothing wrong with my flying, but as he was acting unofficially he would need to talk to the Chief Flying Instructor. A few days later I got my second chance and the CFI gave me a pretty exhaustive test, including going into a spin and recovering from it. That frightened me a little, but I succeeded. I was then told to do a circuit and landing. Following that the CFI climbed out of the aircraft and told me to do a solo. So I took off, did the required circuit and made a perfect landing. I then taxied to the parking area and climbed out, whereupon the CFI shook my hand and said "Well done!"

Five days later, on 3rd September 1939, war was declared, and I received my call-up papers instructing me to report for duty.

PART II: THE WARTIME YEARS

CHAPTER 11

SCOTTISH AVIATION LTD

The autumn of 1939 was, weatherwise, a glorious one – long hot days of sunshine. Everything seemed to be in suspended animation, all waiting for something to happen. Sergeant Pilots under training were paid 1/- per hour for an 8-hour day, plus subsistence of 10/- a day, which totalled between £5 and £6 each week. They reported in at 9 am, were dismissed, and spent the rest of the time sunbathing, swimming, or playing golf or football. I was the exception.

It was now that I met David McIntyre for the first time. He was tall, broad-shouldered with iron-grey hair and with a somewhat grim-looking face, but he had great charm and a beautiful smile. He said that he had heard of the help I had been on the manufacturing side and he hoped that I could continue to assist full-time until further notice.

On 28th September 1939 I received a letter from the RAF Record Office, Ruislip, Middlesex, enclosing a Certificate of Discharge, endorsed to the effect that the discharge was because I was unlikely to become an efficient pilot. I was absolutely shattered and very angry; I had received my call-up notice on 1st September 1939 after doing my successful solo on 25th August, and had heard nothing since. What made it worse was that all the other 24 pilots in my group received their postings on the 30th September.

In high dudgeon I went to see the Group Captain and asked for an explanation. He promised to investigate, and a few days later he told me that there must have been bad communication between Ruislip and RAFVR Headquarters in Glasgow. As I had been officially mobilised on 1st September I could not be discharged for something that happened previously, particularly when the CFI of No. 12 EFTS had confirmed that there was nothing wrong with my flying. He then turned on his well-known charm and suggested that I should think very seriously before going back to flying. He told me that I could do very much more for my country working as an engineer for Scottish Aviation Ltd. (SAL); in that way I could make a very much better contribution to the war effort than if I went back to the RAFVR and got myself killed.

I was in a dilemma; I had a business to run and my parents were dependent on me for financial support. On the other hand there was the glamour of flying in a fine uniform with wings on my breast. However, most telling of all was that as a self-employed person I would have to register with the Manpower Board, and in view of my youth I would not be in a reserved occupation and I would be called up anyway. On balance I thought it best to stick with the RAFVR.

But I had become involved with Dick Ellison and Stewart Kennedy (the Company Secretary) in all kinds of things apart from just selling equipment. Stewart was a chartered accountant and a director of the company from the early days. Two of his wealthy aunts had invested originally, and Stewart joked that he was only there to look after their money. Both he and Dick tried very hard to persuade me not to go back to flying. I was not convinced but promised to think about it.

That Sunday I went to a Church Parade with the Cadets and Former Cadets, and when I got home Mum said there was a telephone call from Prestwick and I was to go there as soon as possible. It was then that I met W.E. Nixon; he was Chairman of the de Havilland Group of Companies as well as being a director of SAL, and was highly thought of throughout the industry. He gave me a good pep talk and said that although he understood my problems he would strongly advise me to reconsider my decision. The country had more pilots than it could train and not enough aircraft for them to fly. It might not always be so but he considered it was my duty to use my proven engineering skills rather than my limited flying ones. When aircraft outnumbered pilots then there might be a case to resume active service in the RAFVR.

It was convincing stuff. The next day I was offered a full-time consultancy with the company at a retaining fee of £300 per annum, plus reasonable fees & expenses and the use of a company car when required. It was an offer difficult to refuse, but I asked about the prospects of my existing business. I got a quick reply: if I was to go back to the RAFVR, what would happen to my business then? Stewart Kennedy said that he thought he could find someone to manage it, provided that my staff agreed, and came up with a lady called Constance Yuille, whose husband was in the Merchant Navy; she was a remarkable woman and ran the business efficiently throughout the war.

I was thus able to concentrate all my energies on Scottish Aviation. Talk about excitement, challenges, adversity, adventure, achievement and fulfilment – they were all there!

The current extent of SAL's manufacturing activities was a series of contracts to modify long-range Wellesleys, repair Rocs & Skuas, and manufacture Hart rudders; one would have thought that, with a war on, work would have been more plentiful. But the Earl of Selkirk had been told that the Ministry did not consider the Prestwick site as suitable for establishing an aircraft industry.

Late in 1939 Stewart Kennedy, who was an excellent negotiator, went down to London for a meeting with the Ministry of Aircraft Production. He took me with him and we stayed in the Waldorf Hotel in Aldwych, which was owned by a Scottish consortium. It was the first time that I had had a haircut in a London barber's. It was quite an experience: first a haircut, then shaping with a razor, a shampoo, a blow-dry, a friction rub, a shave, and finally a facial with hot towels, all for the sum of 12/6. The final touch was a bottle of *Ideal* hair tonic for £1. The barber was a cockney called Mike Smith and he had had to buy the concession from the hotel; I patronised him for many years until the Waldorf was taken over by Forte, when he disappeared from the scene.

We spent two days at the Ministry arguing strongly for the virtues of Prestwick. Some officials who had never even been to Prestwick had the mistaken idea that the workers on the Clyde were all "Bolshies," not to be trusted with aircraft production. We discovered that the biggest contract planned was for the production of Lysander aircraft, designed by Westlands. By the time we left we were promised a share of the contract on the understanding that we could provide factory space at our own expense, and have it commissioned within the time scale. The Board approved of our plans.

SAL were very strong financially as they had made excellent profits from No. 12 EFTS and No. 1 AONS (Air Observer and Navigation School). The weather and flying conditions were so good at Prestwick that the flying hours were about three times better than any other station. In addition, Group Captain McIntyre began negotiations with the Dutch to purchase Fokker 29-seater aircraft from KLM, as Noel Capper recalled in his lecture:

"Towards the end of August 1939 . . . Stewart Kennedy . . . phoned to ask me if I had a passport. After a short conversation I asked him when he wanted me to go to Holland and he said: "Now." I said: "What for?" and he said: "To fetch a four-engined Fokker." I was on the night train that evening with another pilot. We flew to Schiphol next day, had a 'briefing' with KLM pilot Parmentier of Melbourne Race fame, were given a circuit and landing by him and then flew a Fokker 22 and a 36 to Croydon. We were held at Croydon for three days while the government argued the toss about whether Scottish Aviation should have them or whether they should be commissioned for the RAF. McIntyre had set his mind on getting them and he won, so the AONS received their Fokkers."

Costs for AONS training were based on Anson aircraft, which could accommodate four pupils, whereas the four-engined Fokkers could teach up to 26, so the profits were substantial. At that time instructors were paid a basic salary plus a bonus based on flying hours per pupil; no wonder the instructors wanted me to transfer from pilot to navigator!

Where could we find a factory? All contractors' quotations were not only extortionate but deliveries were way out. Suddenly I had a brain wave. What about the Palace of Engineering at Bellahouston Park? When I was there with Joy earlier in the year I had been very impressed with the structural design of the Palace; it was the largest single-span building in Europe, and had been standing empty ever since the Exibition. Stewart and I paid a visit and went to see the Town Chamberlain of Glasgow City Council. After some tricky negotiations we bought it; we then had to find a contractor to dismantle it and re-erect it at Prestwick. That was a magnificent effort, ably supervised by Jack Dickie, the civil engineering manager at SAL.

The contract for Lysander production was then confirmed, leading to the formation of the Scottish Aircraft Group comprising SAL, Scottish Motor Transport (a bus company owned by John Sword, who had large premises in the West of Scotland), a large group of garages in Perth, and a linoleum factory in Kirkaldy (J. & J. Nairn). A further visit to the Ministry persuaded them to finance the capital cost of both the purchase of the Palace and the plant, tools and equipment, provided that SAL supplied the working capital thereafter. That was a good deal for SAL as it reduced capital outlay and helped cash flow.

Our next visit to London concerned the Orangefield Hotel at Prestwick; this was privately owned and the owners would not sell. David McIntyre had the vision to realise that it was in a strategic position for future development, and applied for a requisition order. This was granted and the owners were paid a generous price; the hotel then became the flying control centre, reception area, officers' Mess and restaurant for the massive arrival of 'Lease-Lend' aircraft towards the end of 1940.

The next few months were hectic. The Palace of Engineering was completed, but it had to be equipped and commissioned; jigs and fixtures had to be designed and made; labour had to be engaged and trained. Everyone was working a 16-hour day seven days a week. Management was under strain, and I could see that they were not coping. Heavy bombing raids had started, and losses of pilots and aircraft were heavy. The Ministry of Aircraft Production (MAP) had formed the Civilian Repair Organisation (CRO) whose headquarters had been established at Merton College, Oxford. The Lysander programme was going very slowly, there was hardly any production work and the Palace, now called No. 3 Factory, remained virtually empty apart from jigs and fixtures.

We had to find other work quickly, and negotiations started with CRO for the repair of Hurricanes and Spitfires at Prestwick. On the night of 1st February 1940 Dick Ellison and I set off in his Riley Kestrel for Oxford in a snowstorm. It was an exciting journey, as there were air raids around Birmingham and Coventry with searchlights criss-crossing the sky, together with heavy anti-aircraft gun bursts, the drone of bomber engines and the higher-pitched sound of fighters chasing them, but we arrived in Oxford safely and after a few hours sleep we reported to Merton College where we concluded by signing a substantial contract.

Dick Ellison had been a surveyor in a colliery before he took up flying, and on the way home we stopped at Northallerton, where he had worked. I had never been down a mine before, let alone one of the deepest mines in the country, and Dick arranged a tour of the workings. We were fitted out with hard hats, overalls and lamps, and stepped into the cage. It plunged down at breakneck speed and I thought we would never stop. The deceleration was terrific; I felt that my stomach was going to come out of the top of my head, and I could feel the pressure building up in my ears. Once safely down, the first thing I noticed was the heat, and I was soon pouring with sweat. Miners stripped to the waist; conveyor belts carrying coal to the trucks; miniature railways everywhere; pit-props supporting the roof; alleyways becoming narrower and narrower; coal-cutting machines screaming away; dust everywhere; it looked like a scene from Dante's *Inferno*. That was the era of "Bevan Boys," when young men who did not wish to do military service could volunteer to be a "Bevan Boy" and go down the mines. I thought that anything was better than that, but as one wag said: "At least we don't need air raid shelters."

The bombing of our cities intensified. At the same time the Battle of the Atlantic was being fought; we were losing, and our shipping losses were horrendous. Top priority was being given to equipping aircraft, particularly flying boats, as submarine hunters. Thanks to Robert Watson Watt we had superiority in Anti-Submarine Vectoring (ASV), a form of radar which could track submarines. Aircraft had to be fitted with depth-charges, radar, special navigation devices, long-range tanks and new armament, usually Oerlikon 20 mm cannon with tracer ammunition. Churchill and Roosevelt had signed the 'Lease-Lend' agreement, and plans were laid to fly Lockheed Hudsons, Consolidated-Vultee Liberators, Catalina long-range flying boats and Boeing Flying Fortresses across the Atlantic. With its excellent weather record, Prestwick was chosen as the main reception airfield, and the workload became even more frantic.

To make matters worse, the main administration block between the Tiger Moth hangar and the Anson hangar caught fire and was totally destroyed. I will never forget the horror of this fire. I was in my office and at ten in the morning I looked out of the window and saw flames coming through the roof of No. 1 AONS classrooms. I shouted to everyone to evacuate and dashed out to my car, which was parked just below the flames. People were jumping out of windows and one young man, hanging from the windowsill with his clothes on fire, dropped at my feet. I beat the flames out, lifted him into my car and drove him to the first aid centre. He was in hospital for some time but fully recovered after plastic surgery, and I then discovered that he was Joy's Edinburgh boy friend – what a strange coincidence. In all there were seven fatalities and a number of serious injuries.

New runways had to be planned and built, dispersal areas had to be found and tarmaced, more land had to be requisitioned, and new hangars had to be acquired and erected. David McIntyre, whose father owned the Ailsa Dockyard, had heard of a derelict shipyard, Cairds at Gourock, and this was quickly acquired for seaplane reception and conversion to modify the flying boats as submarine hunters and, hopefully, submarine killers. Saunders-Roe from the Isle of Wight was the main contractor, and SAL were subcontractors. Management being scarce, a civil servant from MOD was seconded as manager.

I was sent to Cairds shortly afterwards to report on what was happening. The place was a shambles; the poor manager was totally out of his depth and did not know what to do. I was asked to go to Gourock for three months, but as I was still only a consultant I thought that my position would be untenable. Again David McIntyre used his charm and I agreed, providing I got written agreement from the Ministry of Aircraft production (MAP), Saunders-Roe and SAL that I would have complete control, and that all my expenses were paid. Everyone was so desperate that they agreed, and I also got allotted a Humber Snipe motor car. For the first week or two I stayed in the Bay Hotel, then I remembered that George Brown, an old Cadet friend, was at Ferguson Brothers, Greenock, so we made contact and I moved into his digs.

Some weeks before I went to Gourock, I had been invited to a party. Due to the long hours and hard work there was a lot of stress and some friction between managers and staff, so a party was arranged at the Burns Monument Hotel at Alloway to provide relaxation and and hopefully get people co-operating together a little better. I still have the photograph which was published in the *Ayr Advertiser*; there were no fewer than 35 people in the group, including representatives from the Government Inspection Agency (AID), disrespectfully known as the Artificial Insemination Department. It was a great party and the food was excellent; everyone relaxed and some got very merry.

I had driven the factory manager and a maintenance engineer called Jack to the party. They were great friends as they had both worked together at J. & J. Weir's. Jack's wife had bought him a new three-piece suit for the party, but he had had a little too much to drink and was sick in the gutter on the way home. When I got to the factory manager's house, he could not get his key to open the door. He banged on the door but no one answered, so I threw some pebbles at the bedroom window. In a few minutes an angry man's face appeared – it was the wrong house.

Jack had soiled his suit rather badly, both with vomit and diarrhoea, and the story goes that, rather than tell his wife, he wrapped the suit in newspaper and burned it the next day in the boiler-room fire. Worse still, he had lost his false teeth in the gutter, but as I remembered exactly where I had stopped to let him be sick I took him back there and was able to retrieve them, to his great joy.

My first few days at Gourock were difficult, but George Fordyce, an accountant, had been there from the start and was a tower of strength. Direction of Labour was in force and the Manpower Board had drafted in loads of skilled labour, many of them experienced engineers. I walked around the shops and talked to as many of them as possible. A few superintendents and foremen had been brought up from the Isle of Wight, but they could not cope with broad Glaswegian dialect.

I called a meeting and explained who I was and why I was there, and got immediate co-operation. I said that the men from Saunders-Roe were very experienced on flying boats, but would act only as advisors, and I called for volunteers for foremen and chargehands. I said there would be 24-hour shift working, that I would pay AEU wages and overtime rates, and that I would set targets which, if met, would warrant a bonus of 10%. The improvements were dramatic and soon all the Short Sunderland boats in the slipway were ready for operational service and were flown away. Then the Catalinas, including amphibians, began to arrive and every buoy in the bay was full, as was the yard. Conversion of Catalinas was more difficult as we had to redesign all the bracketry etc. to fit American-built aircraft. But the Clydeside engineers showed great ingenuity and when bits did not fit they improvised. Robert Watson Watt came to the yard to give us a pep talk and told us how vital it was to win the Battle of the Atlantic, otherwise we would have no fuel and no food and we would starve.

Efforts were terrific and soon 10 aircraft were completed; however they could not be tested because of (a) a shortage of special co-axial cable to wire the ASV, and (b) – a silly one – all the sparking plugs sent as spares for the engines and the auxiliary power units were the wrong size. Phone calls to MAP only brought excuses, but in the meantime we pressed on with the rest of the work.

One evening at 23.00 I was having a little rest in my office when the phone rang. It was a 'loud-mouth' from MAP, raging away as to why no aircraft had been delivered. Did we not know that ships were being lost, that sailors were being killed, and we had not delivered a single aircraft?

I was tired and a little depressed and shouted down the phone: "If only people like you would get off their lazy arses and get us the supplies we need then we would deliver some aircraft."

The response was: "Don't you dare speak to me like that. Don't you know who I am?"

"No, and I don't care either."

"I am Beaverbrook and I will have you removed from your job."

"I couldn't care less, and what's more I don't even work for SAL."

However, we eventually both calmed down; he asked for details of what we needed, and his secretary came on the line and took a list. Beaverbrook then came back and said that his personal assistant, Air Commodore White, would be with me first thing in the morning.

Sure enough a flying boat landed in the bay about 11.00 and shortly afterwards the Air Commodore was asking for me. He was efficient and courteous, and said that Lord Beaverbrook (a very dynamic individual) had instructed him to remain at Caird's Yard until all the shortages had been cleared. Late that evening cars and lorries were arriving loaded up with co-axial cable. I showed the Air Commodore the 10 aircraft that were virtually completed, and he wanted to know when they would be delivered. I quoted two days, but said that the first had to be flight-tested and the ASV checked by the RAF radar operators. The very next morning a Catalina flying boat arrived with a consignment of sparking plugs, and I phoned Dick Ellison so that he could come and do the flight-testing. The next day Dick arrived; the Air Commodore and I went on the test flight and all was well. On the way back the tip of the port wing struck the cable of a barrage balloon which had drifted out of position, but Dick made a safe landing and the damage was minor. The

10 aircraft were delivered by the end of the week and a further five were ready on the following Monday. We got a telegram of congratulations from Beaverbrook, and at the end of each shift all those who had worked so hard were given a generous tot of rum.

Two weeks later Greenock, Gourock, and Glasgow were subjected to a severe air attack with heavy casualties and great damage. Fortunately damage to the Yard was superficial, but many of the workers had family casualties, and my digs had shrapnel through the roof. By this time the civil servant had been recalled, and now I had established a competent management team I returned to Prestwick on 7th June. Seven submarines had been destroyed by Coastal Command flying Catalinas and Short Sunderlands, and we often wondered if a German spy had targeted Gourock.

When I got back to Prestwick I found many changes. The factory manager had been demoted to maintenance, and a new works manager had been appointed. I was asked if I would terminate my consultancy agreement and become assistant works manager at a salary of £800 per annum. I would in addition be expected to pay regular visits to Gourock and would still retain my authority there. I accepted.

As for leisure activities at Gourock, there were none, but every other weekend I was able to spend at least one night with Joy's family at Southbrae Drive, Anniesland. I had a nice camouflaged Humber Snipe at my disposal with few petrol restrictions, and the drive from Gourock to Anniesland was very convenient. I had decided that if Joy would only marry me then all things would be possible.

So I plucked up courage to ask her, and she accepted. One Saturday we went off to a posh jeweller's in Glasgow, Edwards, and bought the ring. We decided to keep the engagement secret and Joy wore the ring round her neck on a string.

In spite of the extortionate hours and strain I enjoyed my months at Gourock. We had many parties with delivery crews and visiting 'brass' from MAP, and we occasionally managed to get to a night club in Glasgow. Good whisky, indeed any alcohol, was in very short supply, and rationing was very strict. We were spoiled as the ferry pilots kept us well supplied with good whisky and other luxuries, including silk stockings and perfume, which were in great demand from the ladies. The favourite drink at that time was called a "Depth Charge"; very appropriately it consisted of Navy Rum and Italian Vermouth, filled up with cider and with a slice of lemon on top. It tasted quite innocuous at first, but when it exploded . . . oh boy!

Lockheed had an establishment at Abbotsinch assembling, modifying and repairing the Lockheed range of aircraft. It was run by Tex Nixon from Texas, handsome, charming and a bit of a tear-away. He was a great ladies' man and he, I and Stewart Kennedy used to go night-clubbing together. In spite of the fact that he was reputed to have a wife and family in America he got shacked up with a beautiful Scottish lass from Paisley. When the war was ended he threw a terrific farewell party in his flat in Glasgow. A discussion developed about the physical impact of parachute landings, so to demonstrate Tex jumped out of the window one storey high and fractured both his ankles. When we saw him off on his way home to Texas some weeks later, he was still on crutches.

Nearly 50 years later, I saw an announcement in the *British Aerospace Magazine* from a Tex Nixon asking for information about his friends from the last war days. When I replied, I discovered that it was the same Tex Nixon, and we corresponded for nearly six months. It was nostalgic stuff; we compared notes of all we had done in the past, and then brought each other up to date with our later lives. The Scottish lass was called Diana; he had married her and had three strapping sons by her, and as there was never any mention of an American wife, maybe we had misjudged him. Sadly Diana died of cancer after 46 years of a happy marriage. I think his letter to the magazine was a way of getting over his bereavement, and he was living the past over again. My last letter to him in June 1989 was never answered, so I presume he had died. That is one of the joys of writing one's memoirs, one can live one's life over again, with all the happiness, sadness, achievements and set-backs.

As I said, when I returned from Gourock, there had been many changes. All flying training had ceased, and those engaged in it had either been called up, transferred or absorbed into the SAL organisation. SAL was a major player in repairing Hurricanes and Spitfires. It was also assembling aircraft which had been crated and sent by sea from America, such as Mohawks and Tomahawks (Grumman and Curtiss-Wright fighters). Success at Gourock led to a contract for the modification of Consolidated Vultee B-24 Liberators and Boeing B-17 Flying Fortresses. The No. 3 Factory, in which not a single Westland Lysander had yet been built, was the only building which could accommodate the wingspan of these huge aircraft. It was fitted with electrically operated sliding and folding doors, which had to be widened by 12 feet to enable the aircraft to be towed in and out.

On the 29th November 1940 a Hudson arrived directly from Newfoundland; this was a significant event, although not appreciated as such at the time. Before America's entry into the war aircraft were being moved by land over the US-Canadian border and then flown over the Atlantic, normally to Aldergrove, but the pilot of this Hudson had lost contact with the other aircraft in the formation and finished up landing at Prestwick. Before too long Prestwick was selected as the main arrival airfield for all aircraft flying over from Canada and the US throughout the war.

A flying control tower had been built on the roof of the Orangefield Hotel, and the hotel itself had been extended to provide accommodation and messing facilities for the air ferry crews. Plans had to be made to get these crews back to America, and so the North Atlantic Ferry Organisation (ATFERO) was set up in May 1941, operated initially by Liberators flown by BOAC crews and staff. Noel Capper recalled:

"To cater for this increase in heavy traffic, it was obvious that a runway must be built. McIntyre demanded that it should be 2,200 yd long and 100 yd wide. The Air Ministry's standard was 1,700 yd by 50 yd and they resisted any increase, but fortunately a member of the Air Ministry Aerodromes Board, a Canadian, supported McIntyre's recommendation and threatened to resign if the bigger specification was not approved. The runway was made 2,200 yd long and 100 yd wide."

An Air Transport Auxiliary had also been formed to ferry both new, repaired, and modified aircraft across the UK; most of the pilots were civilian pilots and a growing number were women, the most famous of whom was Amy Johnson. New buildings had to be put up for them, including sleeping quarters, messing and offices.

Group Captain McIntyre was not only Station Commander but was MD of SAL. He concentrated mostly on the overall administration and left the organisation of the factory to Dick Ellison who had been made General Manager, but also retained his responsibilities as Chief Test Pilot. The workload was really heavy; the factory manager could not cope and had been made chief of maintenance, and a new works manager had come from Hawker Aircraft, well recommended by a senior official at MAP. I was quite content to work under him, but it soon became clear that he could not cope either. He was supposed to have experience of factory organisation, but he spent most of his time in his office planning new systems and increasing the paperwork. He was seldom if ever seen on the factory floor, and he was totally inadequate at motivating his staff. Also one of Sydney Camm's bright young designers, Robert McIntyre (no relation of David McIntyre) had been engaged from Hawkers', where Camm was designer of the Hurricane among many others, and brought his brother Jim with him.

Liberators were now beginning to arrive, urgently required by Coastal Command for patrol work and as submarine hunters and killers. My experience at Gourock proved invaluable, as I knew what the modifications were and how to make the parts, but according to the works manager everything had to stick to the system and we were bogged down by paperwork. We were also getting severe criticism from MAP for failing to meet our deliveries. The factory manager, who was very disgruntled at his demotion, was stirring up trouble, and he and the works manager were accusing Dick Ellison of incompetence, and me of having no engineering training or experience. Matters came to a head when David McIntyre received a letter from T.C. Westbrook, an official at MAP, stating that a letter had been received via one of SAL's production departments complaining very seriously about the organisation at Prestwick. It emerged that the works manager had been conniving with the ex-factory manager and others, and had been writing to Westbrook, but had asked to have their identity kept secret. The result was inevitable: David McIntyre summoned them to his office and summarily dismissed them.

He later explained to Dick and myself what had happened, and added that, in view of the underhand way that things had been done and the collusion of certain people in MAP, he expected further problems. In view of this he was appointing F.W. Hopkins as Works Manager, and would I continue as Assistant Works Manager?

I was not very pleased, in view of all the efforts I had made, and I said so.

He replied: "Bill, you are only 26 years of age and no one is denying that you did an outstanding job at Gourock. But serious allegations have been made against you, and I and my fellow directors think that it would be wise to have an older and very experienced engineer as Works Manager. Fred Hopkins was Deputy Service Manager at de Havillands, he has served us well as Chief Service Manager at our Flying Training School, and he is very experienced in aircraft production, so until we see what is happening it will be in your interest to accept. We are going to give you a 25% increase in salary, and I hope you will understand and accept. Dick will concentrate on his duties as Chief Test Pilot, which are already onerous."

What could I say? But when I met Fred Hopkins I was very impressed. He was in his early fifties, he was kind and considerate, and very understanding. I felt that I could trust him and work with him.

However I had never been impressed with the new works manager. He was small in stature and, like many small men, very arrogant. He treated me with consideration but I always felt that he was trying to catch me out all the time, and I did not trust him.

In accordance with the Manpower Act, I registered on 9th March 1940 at Kilmarnock Labour Exchange as a Consulting Engineer and Machinery Agent and was allotted the registration No. KGB/1403. On 20th March 1940 I was called to Ayr for a medical examination and was passed Grade 1. My previous experience was documented and I was advised that the work being done for SAL was of paramount importance. The necessary paperwork was sent to the Under-Secretary of State for Air, Department ZA, Harrogate and form NS.100 was lodged with the Manager of the Employment Exchange in Ayr.

I was requested to visit the Manpower Board in Edinburgh, where I saw a Mr Scott. He advised the personnel office at SAL that I should be reregistered in a reserved occupation. Many weeks later I was interviewed again at Prestwick by the Manpower officials; it transpired that this interview was due to a complaint that had been raised at a general meeting of the Labour Supply Board by the ex-factory manager, who had been appointed as a Manpower Board Inspector.

Due to the enormous number of American aircraft arriving under 'Lease-Lend,' a separate department had been set up within MAP called Director of Production [Canadian & American] (DPCA). The first head of DPCA was Sir Eric Bowater, seconded from the famous paper company. His deputy was Wing Commander E.A. Whiteley, a distinguished pilot with DFC and bar. I had met them both several times, and when the matter of my registration was raised again by the Manpower Board, a signal was sent telling them that the matter of Mr Neill's military service had already been settled and no further action was necessary. But that was far from the end of the story.

TOP: The aircraft production factory in August 1940.
Photo: via Prof. D. Cameron.
BOTTOM: A wartime view of the Scottish Aviation complex.
Photo: courtesy of the R.Ae.S.

TOP: Ansons of the No. 1 A.O.N.S. Photo: via Prof. D. Cameron.
BOTTOM: The Prestwick team on their way to investigate the 1941 Liberator crash near Goat Fell, Arran; myself 2nd from R.
Photo: author's collection.

Where it all started! A rare photo of David McIntyre flying over Everest in 1933. Photo: author's collection.

TOP: Prestwick pioneers – from L. to R. David McIntyre, the Duke of Hamilton & Carlyle Gifford. Photo: courtesy of the R.Ae.S.
BOTTOM: The new control tower built during the war on top of the requisitioned Orangefield Hotel. Photo: via Prof. D. Cameron.

CHAPTER 12

THE MCNAIR SNADDON LETTERS

McNair Snaddon was the Member of Parliament for Ayr and District, and he received a 60-page dossier compiled by four individuals who asked him to protect their identity.

This dossier made very serious allegations against Scottish Aviation, and particularly against Group Captain McIntyre, Stewart Kennedy, R.C.W. Ellison, and W.T. Neill. These covered charges of fraud and false accounting in respect of flying training, arson in respect of the destruction by fire of the administration building, dereliction of duty by McIntyre who, it was claimed, was putting his ambitions beyond the war effort, aggressive and interfering behaviour by Ellison, and conspiracy by Neill, Ellison, and Kennedy in buying tools, machinery and equipment, then selling at exorbitant prices and sharing the profit. It was claimed that I had never served an apprenticeship and had no experience, and that the company had been party to my illegal registration with the Ministry of Labour.

McNair Snaddon had to take these charges seriously and raised the matter in Parliament. The Minister of Aircraft Production at that time was Sir Stafford Cripps, renowned for his integrity and strictness. A committee of enquiry was set up, and we were all subject to scrutiny and cross-examination. It was a worrying time but we all continued to do our job with as much energy and enthusiasm as we could muster. Then the harassment started; I received white feathers through the post, together with abusive anonymous letters. My parents received similar insults, and one day a parcel was delivered with a severed chicken's head and a note: "This is what will happen to your chicken-cowardly son." A fire was started in a cupboard just below my office, but fortunately it was discovered before any serious damage was done.

It was at this stage that the wise head and experience of Fred Hopkins came into play. He held a series of meetings with senior management & staff, and told them who he was and that he had spent all his life in the aircraft industry. He informed them that a well-orchestrated campaign was under way to try and discredit the notable achievements of SAL and how the efforts of these evil people could harm the war effort. He said that those who had any doubts about the management should resign now, and if they didn't they would be found out and dismissed, and could be prosecuted. In general his speech was well received, but quickly he too was subjected to an attack by another letter to McNair Snaddon, claiming that he had got the job only because he was a friend of David McIntyre and his old job of Chief Service Manager had ceased to exist with the termination of all flying training. Clearly there was still a traitor in the camp.

The McNair Snaddon letters referred to the four informants as A, B, C & D, but of course the first thing the committee of enquiry demanded was the identity of these individuals. These were supplied but here I shall refer to them just as 'A,' 'B,' 'C' & 'D.'

'A' was a filing clerk in the drawing office who had been dismissed. He was a South African who came to England in 1939 claiming to have been a detective in connection with diamond mining. He had already been investigated by Scotland Yard Special Branch and was understood to be mentally deranged.

'B' was the ex-factory manager, dismissed 24.2.41.

'C' was the ex-works manager, dismissed 9.7.41.

'D' was the chief production engineer, who resigned 4.11.41.

'A''s report contained 12 allegations, 'B''s 35, 'C''s 31 and 'D''s 8. In all there were 27 appendices and seven letters.

Detailed responses to all of these were given in writing to G.S. Knight Esq., Secretary to the Ministry of Aircraft Production, by D.F. McIntyre on 29th August 1942. On 22nd October 1942 Ben Smith, Parliamentary Secretary to the Minister, wrote to McNair Snaddon, confirming that all allegations had been thoroughly investigated and that the charges were inaccurate and misleading in the extreme, the subtle innuendos were quite unjustified and were frivolous and indeed libellous, and that when the malcontents were dismissed things improved immensely. All reports confirmed that output at SAL was satisfactory and in some cases was very good.

Those four people were warned that if they did not desist, they could be charged under the Defence of the Realm Act and could be prosecuted and jailed. We considered issuing writs for libel but our legal advisors, considering that the allegations were so ridiculous, advised them it was not worth proceeding, especially as not one of us then had the resources to pay damages. From October 1941 to October 1942, 13 months, busy people's time had been wasted to no avail. All of us were relieved but it was not over yet.

Before the Ben Smith letter was received on the 23rd June 1942, less than two months after my marriage, I received an enlistment notice from the Army Recruiting Section, Salisbury Green, Dalkieth Road, Edinburgh, enclosing a travel warrant and instructing me to report for service to the General Service Corps, 233rd Light A.A. Training Regiment, R.A. Saighton Camp, Chester. Also enclosed was a Postal Order for 4/- in advance of service pay. The letter went on to say that if I failed to report for any reason I would be arrested by the Military Police. This triggered some very irate telephone calls from Stewart Kennedy to the Minister of Labour and from David McIntyre to the Principal Private Secretary to the Minister of Aircraft Production, plus a telegram to the Commanding Officer of the 233rd Light A.A. Training Regiment in Chester. He replied on 1st July 1942 granting 28 days' postponement. I was pretty angry and disgusted, but David McIntyre told me to pay no attention to these disgraceful carry-ons, and that he would take care of it.

I did not tell Joy anything about all this as I did not wish to worry her. The evening before my scheduled departure to Chester I had organised a football match with 'management' against 'foremen.' We had a great game and the 'management' won 2-1. I drove two of the foremen home to Ayr and when I got back there was a line of cars outside the flat, so I thought that maybe the Hopkins were entertaining friends. But no, there was a party in full swing in my flat, and Joy had risen nobly to the occasion and was playing the piano and leading the singing. All the lads had decided to give me a farewell party before I joined the Army. They all thought it was a great joke, but Joy was not very pleased – not about the party, but because I had not told her about the call-up notice. She was worried and I was worried and, believe it or not, 20 days later I got another call-up notice with another travel warrant and another Postal Order for 4/-.

I went to see David McIntyre; I was not angry, I was absolutely raging! He told me to calm down and wait in his outer office while he made a telephone call. He then told me that my discharge from the RAFVR had been an error, I was still in it, and he was immediately remobilising me. He sent for the Adjutant of the Station and I was sworn in again and told I was being promoted with immediate effect from Sergeant Pilot to acting Wing Commander, and would I please forget all the nonsense and get back to work.

I was flabbergasted, but in due course David McIntyre showed me a letter from G.S. Jackson, Principal Private Secretary to the Minister, that the enlistment notice had been cancelled. However there was still more to come.

Ten months later we were advised that Sir Stafford Cripps was planning to visit Prestwick to be shown round the factories, and that he would also like to meet the Joint Production Committee. Sir Stafford had recommended that these should be set up with management, staff and shop stewards and that they should meet regularly to co-operate together to further the war effort. I chaired the one at Prestwick and generally found the shop stewards helpful. Sir Stafford duly arrived and was taken for a tour by Group Captain McIntyre, accompanied by Stewart Kennedy, Dick Ellison, Fred Hopkins and myself. He was most impressed and very complimentary. Then we had the meeting of the Joint Production Committee chaired by myself, which was quite innocuous and passed off well, or so we thought. We lunched Sir Stafford's party in the management Mess, and afterwards Sir Stafford showed David McIntyre a note he had been given by the shop steward convenor. This was a repetition of all the old allegations, which had already been fully investigated.

On his return Sir Stafford had all the papers re-examined and he himself enquired into the matter. Thereafter he sent a telegram to all members of the Joint Production Committee and to the management, the full text of which which is reproduced in full over the next two pages.

CIRCULATION DATE 21ST DECEMBER 1943

TO: THE SHOP STEWARDS CONVENOR SCOTTISH AVIATION LIMITED PRESTWICK.

FROM: THE MINISTER OF AIRCRAFT PRODUCTION (MAP) LONDON 191300A

AP385 19TH DECEMBER 1943.

When I was recently at Prestwick you handed me a note found to contain certain allegations against the management.

I was disturbed to note that these were in the main repetitions of accusations circulated by certain evilly-disposed persons which had been currently disposed of after a most thorough enquiry by my Department many months ago.

I regard this repetition, no doubt instigated by the same evilly-disposed persons, as most unfortunate and ill-advised. It can only have the effect of creating an atmosphere of distrust and suspicion and so interfering with production, thereby assisting the enemy.

However, in order that there may be no possible excuse for their further repetition I have had all the papers re-examined and have myself enquired into the matter. I will deal with the four points you raise in the order in which they appear in the letter you handed to me.

1. The Assistant Works Manager, in whom both I personally and my Department have complete confidence, was originally registered as a consulting engineer, in which capacity he served the Scottish Aviation Company during 1940. Later at the Company's request and on the advice of the Ministry of Labour official in Edinburgh he applied for his reclassification as a jig and tool draughtsman as he was largely employed on that job at that time. There is no question whatsoever of any false registration.

2. The Scottish Aviation Company have had dealings with Messrs W.T. Neill of Kilmarnock. The accusation in your Paragraph 2, which equally formed part of the earlier accusation to which I have referred above, was specially investigated by the cost & investigations section of my Department and was proved to be entirely false.

3. The difficulty as regards spares was explained at a meeting of your Joint Production Committee in June 1942, at which time it was suggested by my Department that Scottish Aviation should take on a contract from Supermarines Limited for these spares. It was not until September that this contract was placed and then it was only for a small quantity, and as a result it was a very considerable time before production could be got under way.

4. The work done by Scottish Aviation is such that it is exceedingly difficult to plan it ahead. A large part of it concerns American aircraft, the arrival dates of which are bound to be uncertain due to American deliveries and

Atlantic weather. We do not consider that the firm is to blame for the consequent difficulties that arise.

I very much hope that after these explanations you will assist to suppress this evilmongering which is being instigated, I believe, by certain evilly-disposed persons outside the factory.

It is unfair to the management, the workers and the country to encourage attempts to upset the flow of production by creating suspicion and mistrust in the Works. I had, as you know, a long talk to the Joint Production Committee when I was at Prestwick, but not one of the workers' representatives raised any of these points when I was at that Committee.

CRIPPS

I am sending copies of this to Management and the Joint Production Committee.

The most gratifying part of this telegram, as far as I was concerned, were the words: *"Both my Department and I personally have complete confidence in the Assistant Works Manager."*

I had never had any cross words with the factory manager, indeed I had rather liked him, and it came as a surprise that he should be so malevolent and that I should be the recipient of his hate, particularly as I had never said a word against him or done him any harm. However even in 1948 he was still campaigning. In an article in *Practical Engineering* he was railing against the Manpower Board and managers of Labour Exchanges. He had been a Grade 'A' Inspector for two years, and went on to criticise the system and to explain that, if he and his colleagues had only been allowed to use their own knowledge and experience, many more men would have been placed in the right job and thus the war effort would have benefited. He gave several examples, the main one being how an unqualified young man with no engineering experience had become an assistant works manager, and in spite of all the efforts by the Manpower Board inspectors they had been overruled by Sir Stafford Cripps, and that this young man was still in the engineering industry, and so it was no small wonder that we could not compete in world markets when men of this type were still in executive positions.

He must have died an embittered old man. If he had put as much effort into being an energetic works manager as he did during the "Hate Campaign" then maybe he would not have lost his job in the first place.

It turned out that one of the Manpower officials used to live in Charles Street. He had been chief draughtsman at Andrew Barclay & Co., the locomotive engineers in Kilmarnock, but had lost his job because of what nowadays would be called sexual harassment. He went to the Carron Ironworks and the same thing happened there, and he ended up at the Manpower Board, another bitter man.

CHAPTER 13

THE TRANSFORMATION OF PRESTWICK

I must be one of the few people still alive who saw the transformation of a small country flying training school into one of the largest and busiest airfields in the world. It is an incredible story, which has never really been told. Even Alan Robertson's book *Lion Rampant and Winged* failed to capture the spirit and determination of those involved, or to convey the tremendous effort by a few people who had the vision and made it happen. Without Prestwick we could well have lost the war. The vast effort of all those who worked there has never been properly documented, and recognition of – and award for – their dedication has never been given. This was possibly due to the aftermath of the "Hate Campaign" plus the fact that David McIntyre was in constant contention with the Government over the future of airline operation and the bitter litigation over who actually owned the airfield and all the buildings thereon.

The place was pulsating with life and energy, a heterogeneous, kaleidoscopic assembly of thousands of people from many countries, speaking different languages and with different life-styles and behavioural patterns. Manufacturing activities accounted for over 8,000 people. Airfield administration, flying control, transport pools, catering and hotel accommodation accounted for some 2,000 others. Also to be included were Ferry Command, the Air Transport Auxiliary, and a weather forecasting station. When America entered the war, Adampton House became the headquarters of the 8th US Army Air Corps. At the height of influx of 'Lease-Lend' aircraft were landing every five minutes. Traffic was so intense that a further airfield had to be built at Heathfield, and Cairds Yard was so busy that another flying boat station had to be created at Largs.

Early on most of the flying crews were American and Canadian free-lance operators, but they also included Polish, French, Czechoslovakian and even German pilots who had fled to America to avoid the Nazi regime. All of them were paid substantial sums for what was of course a hazardous operation. The scenes in the Orangefield Hotel were not only cosmopolitan but were bizarre: jeans, plaid jackets, cowboy outfits with boots and hats to match, fur coats, fur hats, baseball caps, big cigars – you name it, it was there. While awaiting transport back to the USA, poker games, gin rummy, bridge and many other gambling pastimes were practised, the favourite, of course, with the many attractive girls on the airport, was strip poker. The money changing hands was substantial, and I know of one British pilot, a non-drinker, who made enough money to start up his own small airline after the war. Rationing was severe and all these crews bringing in the "goodies," ranging from booze & chocolate to silk stockings & exotic underwear were very welcome. I was able to acquire a Remington ·22 automatic rifle with telescopic sight and a large packet of ammunition.

There was tragedy too. On the 10th August 1941 a converted Liberator flown by Captain White, a very experienced BOAC pilot flying for Ferry Command, took off from Prestwick with 24 ferry pilots on board *en route* for the USA, but crashed on the mountains of Arran, killing all on board. He had done the same journey many times, the weather was quite good, and there were no aircraft faults. The court of enquiry found "Pilot Error" as the reason for the crash, and concluded that Captain White was so familiar with the route that he had been careless with his altimeter reading.

As I was very familiar with all the mountains in Arran, I took part in the enquiry, and led a team to examine the wreckage of AM261. We went across in one of the flying boat tenders from Troon to Brodick. With me were McKeown and Robinson of Air Inspection Directorate, Bob Pasulovitch, the Technical Representative of Consolidated-Vultee Corporation, and Tom Sunderland of the Air Registration Board. It was a rainy and somewhat cloudy day, and the climb was strenuous for those not used to the mountains. I found the wreckage, which was spread over a wide area, and it seemed clear as to what had happened. Captain White had flown many times over the saddle between Glen Rosa and Glen Sannox with Goat Fell to the left and Cir Mhor to the right. If the aircraft had been 10 ft higher there would not have been a crash; however it must have drifted slightly off course, whereupon a wingtip would have caught the rocky slope of Cir Mhor, causing the aircraft to cartwheel into the hillside. All the bodies had been recovered by an RAF Mountain Rescue team, but we found the compass and altimeter and took them back for examination. It was impossible to say if there had been any control defects; of course, in those days there were no "Black Boxes" and in wartime there was no attempt at reconstruction. We found a nice pair of fur-lined flying boots in the wreckage and decided to take them home as a memento, but there were two feet still inside: we threw the boots away in horror.

All the victims of this Liberator crash on Arran were buried in Lamlash Cemetery, and a memorial service was held in Lamlash church; I found it very sad and very moving. Some 60 years later, on the 11th August 2001, another memorial service was held there; obviously aviation enthusiasts have long memories and, even after all this time, it is amazing that there are enough people still alive connected with the accident in some way (maybe they lost relatives in it) to arrange a memorial service in such a remote place, and to have it so well attended.

The airfield was ringed by anti-aircraft guns, and a Company of the RAF Regiment was continuously on duty to protect the area. Detachments of the Air Observer Corps were on duty, and their headquarters were at High Street, Ayr. After my marriage to Joy she served with the Corps until the end of the war. A large carpet factory, William Gray and Co. in Ayr, was requisitioned and used as a training centre for semi-skilled work, mainly for women, some of whom proved outstandingly skilful. The craft unions had agreed a Dilution of Labour agreement, whereby unskilled and semi-skilled people were allowed to do skilled work. An outstanding example of this was a young lad who had been a butcher's boy; he had an aptitude for mathematics and became a jig borer in the toolroom, one of the most skilled operations there, and was acknowledged to be the best operator we ever had.

Most flying training was carried out in Canada and America, and as the crews completed their training and became proficient in navigation, they gradually replaced the colourful free-lance crews and undertook delivery flights to Prestwick. They flew from Gander, Newfoundland to Goose Bay in Greenland, or to a new American air base at Meek's Field in Iceland and thence to Prestwick. This built up the confidence of the crews and prepared them for the heavy bombing raids on Germany, which were so decisive in winning the war.

There were very few losses until Canadian-built Mosquitoes started to disappear over the route. This was very worrying and no one could explain it. However one day a Mosquito landed at Prestwick with a large hole in the fuselage. The pilot had had a strong following wind and his journey was much quicker than usual. As he was approaching Prestwick he heard a loud bang and a great hole appeared in the fuselage. He landed with some difficulty, and his Mosquito came into the hangar for inspection. The Mosquito undercarriages were operated by a compressed air system, and we found that the pressure vessel had exploded. Further research led to the discovery that the pressure relief valve on certain aircraft had been assembled the wrong way round so that, instead of relieving the pressure, it increased it – hence the explosion.

In spite of all the hard work and long hours, there was still time for partying, and what parties there were! The inward traffic to Prestwick was so heavy that loads and loads of "goodies" were brought in to such an extent that a Custom & Excise Division was set up, with everything supposed to be declared. As can be imagined, Customs had no hope of stopping the deliveries, especially when the Customs Officers were always invited to the parties, but they carried out their duties to the best of their abilities while at the same time displaying integrity and common sense. With the arrival of the 8th US Army Air Corps life became even more exciting and intense and in the various Messes liquor was never in short supply. The effect of all this on the economy of Prestwick and the other towns in Ayrshire was very beneficial. Never a weekend passed without a dance or a party of some kind. Everyone lived life to the full. There was great competition to get a job on the huge complex, particularly from young unmarried girls, and married ones too whose husbands were serving overseas. Unsuccessful people who failed to get a job jibed that SAL stood for "Scroungers and Loungers" or "Safe at Last." There was sadness too: many affairs and unwanted pregnancies, broken marriages, jealousies and bitter disputes. An enterprising butcher's son from Newmilns set up a brothel and made a fortune before he went to jail.

The air terminal saw many famous names passing through, such as Eleanor Roosevelt, Bob Hope, Clark Gable, Yehudi Menuhin, Eisenhower, de Gaulle, Leslie Howard and Glenn Miller and his band. These latter two both perished in aircraft crashes. We had many Russian visitors too including a Petlyakov-8 bomber carrying Molotov to a meeting with the American President Roosevelt in Washington. In retrospect I was a very fortunate young man to have gained such excellent experience so early in life and to have survived the traumas and adventures.

Indeed I was very lucky still to be alive at the end of the war. After VJ-Day, of the original 25 young men who were in my group, only four were still living. Bill Rodgers flew Wellington bombers and safely returned from over 50 missions. His aircraft was badly shot up over the Ruhr on one trip and he made a crash-landing at his home base. Two of his crew were dead and he broke his back; he was awarded the DFC and eventually recovered. Another pilot, who worked for the Clydesdale Bank in Kilmarnock, had a distinguished career with Coastal Command and won the DFC and bar. The third failed his advanced flying training and returned to his father's business in Glasgow, and was never harassed or called up. I was the fourth and suffered harassment right up to the end of the war.

CHAPTER 14

GETTING MARRIED

I never had any doubts that I would like to get married and I was sure that I had found the right girl. However I had some qualms as to whether I could support a wife in addition to my parents, and I was uncertain as to whether I would be called up as a Private in the army because of the "Hate Campaign" which was still being waged. I wanted us to live in a home of our own, and although my parents would have been delighted for us to live in Charles Street, I did not think that a good idea.

My great friend Guy Scoular was married in 1941 to a lovely Edinburgh girl, and I was best man at his wedding; Guy was by then a Captain in the RAMC and was about to be posted overseas. My sister Betty got married in March 1942 to a brilliant doctor, Robert Tatlock Thompson; he had a Master of Arts degree and then an M.B. and Ch.B., followed by a Diploma in Public Health. He was brought up by his mother and two maiden aunts, and I thought that he was pompous and spoiled, and that my sister deserved someone better. After the honeymoon he was posted to India, with the rank of Major in the RAMC.

With these two weddings, Joy wanted to get married too, and became a little impatient with my indecision. I can remember the occasion only too well; we were returning from a long walk on a glorious day, and Joy told me that if I did not marry her soon, she was going to join the WAAFs. Fred Hopkins had met Joy, and he also knew of my concerns; he gave me sound advice and said: "Marry the girl, you will never get a better one." He went on to state that the flat above him had become vacant and was to let fully furnished at a rent of £10 per month, and that I would be a fool not to take it.

So Joy and I got married on the 18th April 1942, and it was the best thing I ever did. Robert James Anderson, one of my friends in the Cadets & Former Cadets and a camping buddy from Fairlie, was delighted to be my best man. All my friends and colleagues also were delighted and I was showered with congratulations on having a lovely, charming and vivacious wife-to-be.

Knowing the kind of parties that could take place at Prestwick, I made it clear that my "stag night" must take place at least two nights before the wedding. David McIntyre organised a party in the Orangefield Mess, and promised that we would not drink spirits but would only imbibe Pimm's. It was a fantastic party and most people did indeed drink Pimm's. All was paid for by David McIntyre, and there was no horseplay or bad behaviour. Pimm's is a very innocuous drink while one is drinking it, but oh boy, does it have a latent kick! As soon as I got into the fresh air, my head spun and my legs were gone. Fortunately a kind driver from the transport pool drove me home, but the next morning I had a terrible hangover. My Mum always believed that the day should start with a good breakfast, porridge and bacon & eggs. I could not face it that morning, but fortunately someone came to the front door at that moment and I was able to dispose of the lot down the sink without Mum noticing. I arrived at work on time, feeling very grim, but I was not the only one. Pimm's has the effect of causing further nausea whenever anything is drunk or eaten. Some of those at the party did not arrive for work at all. Stewart Kennedy was sick all over the hall carpet when he got home – his wife was not very pleased. When I looked into Fred Hopkin's office, he was holding the telephone in one hand while being sick into the wastepaper basket.

The same evening I was expected to go to Glasgow to attend a rehearsal for the wedding. I went by train with Robert Anderson, and just about managed to cope. All was well but the next morning I was as nauseated as ever and wondered if I would make the marriage ceremony. I drove to Glasgow with Robert, all dressed up in our morning suits, and arrived at Jordanhill church in plenty of time. As I stood before the altar awaiting the bride, I thought I was going to be sick again and I felt giddy. I asked Robert if he would stand in for me if I disappeared, but in the event that was not necessary, and I survived – just. The ceremony was performed by the Reverend Allison, minister of Jordanhill church, ably assisted by Joy's uncle, the Reverend Jim Baillie, minister at Strathavon.

The reception was at the Ca'Dora Rooms in Gordon Street, Glasgow. Knowing the kind of things that happen after weddings, I parked my car in a garage near the Ca'Dora and Robert and I took a taxi to the church, leaving all our honeymoon luggage safely locked in the boot. I don't remember much about the reception as I had neither eaten – nor had a drink – for two days. I did manage to make a short speech, and everyone had a good time. It was the custom to send greetings telegrams and we received well over 50, some of which I still have. Some were very clever and amusing, e.g. "Return gown immediately, another client being married tomorrow," "Neill Willie to Foster Joy," "He made her Neill to Liberator" and "The bachelors of Bourtree mourn another blank file but welcome the added Joy. May you have many joyful nights and no sorrowful mornings."

There were a few high jinks; I lost my shoes and socks and nearly my trousers as well, and Stewart Kennedy jumped into the driver's seat of the taxi that was driving us to the hidden car, but the driver kicked up such a fuss that he had to desist.

I had booked six nights at the Bridge of Lochay Hotel near Killin in the wilds of Perthshire, and off we went in glorious spring sunshine. A lot of Commando training was going in the mountains of Glencoe and we were stopped twice by Military Police, and I had to show my travel permit and SAL pass. We arrived in time for dinner, which I particularly enjoyed as, at last, I was feeling better and was very hungry. We had a lovely room overlooking the river. We had both agreed to remain celibate until we were married, and although we had been tempted many times we had never succumbed. The old saying "If a thing is worth having it is worth waiting for" was very true in our case.

We had an idyllic six days and nights. The weather was unseasonably warm and we were in shorts most of the time. We walked, golfed, fished, and explored the surrounding country, which is fabulously beautiful, especially the Falls of Lochay, Dochart, and Glen Lyon. There was an interesting 9-hole golf course at Finlarig, and 18-hole courses at Killin and Taymouth Castle. Around the hotel we made friends with a lovely kitten whom we christened Lochay – he used to follow us everywhere.

I think it is a great shame that so many young people today wish to sleep together and live together, and either forego marriage or get married in a registry office; they do not really know what they are missing. The self-discipline required to maintain celibacy until marriage is an excellent character-builder. I have never joined the church, and am a non-believer, but a church wedding meant a great deal to me, and the wedding vows were meaningful too. How can a wedding be pertinent or a honeymoon be really exciting when you have done it all before? It is a sad reflection on modern society when tax laws make it financially beneficial to live in sin rather than to get married, and then we bemoan the facts of rising divorce, single parenthood, absent fathers, more abortions and a dramatic rise in Social Security payments, which are steadily and inexorably ruining the economy. If parents do not start off right and cannot or will not accept the responsibility for disciplining and bringing up their children properly, no wonder there is juvenile delinquency and rising crime & violence.

And so, the honeymoon over, we eventually arrived home and took up residence in our top floor flat at 6 Victoria Terrace, Prestwick; I went back to work, while Joy began learning to be a housewife.

CHAPTER 15

WARTIME WORK FOR PRESTWICK

The B-24 Liberator was one of the most efficient flying machines of its generation. The design of the Davis wing gave not only exceptional lift with its flaps and slots, but had such a low drag coefficient that it also contributed to high speed and long range. The Pratt & Whitney radial engines were fitted with turbo-superchargers, which enabled the aircraft to fly at high altitudes. The Liberator had long-range capabilities, and was used as a bomber (both day and night), as a submarine hunter & killer and as a troop carrier, and eventually some were converted into long-range passenger airliners. All of these roles required considerable conversion and, even with all the expansion at Prestwick, we could not cope with the ever-increasing influx of aircraft; there were Liberators parked everywhere. In America the might of mass production in the automobile industry was being applied to aircraft production, and the Ford Company had built a mass production factory at Willow Run.

DPCA decided that the possibility of having the modifications incorporated during manufacture should be explored, so Wing Commander E.A. Whiteley and I were asked to go to Fort Worth. Fortunately this was before I was married. We flew out in a Liberator with other returning pilots and, having seen what had happened in Arran, I was more than a little nervous, but we landed safely at Gander, Newfoundland, and flew on in a Lockheed aircraft to Willow Run. The sight was amazing; the hangar was colossal, and production lines of aircraft were moving on tracks, as per auto production. The plant was a mile long and a quarter-mile wide. The man in charge of production was the legendary Charles E. Sorensen, Vice-President of Ford, and he showed us around.

When we explained what we were after, he said categorically: “No way! I am not going to have my production lines messed up with modifications. Mods are a death knell to production, and I will not tolerate them.”

Henry Ford himself was totally against war. Sorensen had started life as a pattern-maker in one of the Ford plants, and had worked his way up to the top job; he was one of the few people who got along with Henry Ford, until 1944 when he resigned. His book *Forty Years with Ford* tells it all. Production of B-24 Liberators from the Consolidated-Vultee Plant was only a trickle and Sorensen was sent in to examine the situation. The plan was to produce one aircraft a day, but that was never met, and Sorensen concluded that it never *could* be met: they had neither the plant, the production methods nor the management skills. Sorensen went back to his room in the Colorado Hotel and spent the night thinking, drawing up plans and making sketches, and so Willow Run was born. It was planned to produce one B-24 Liberator every hour. Sorensen had terrible trouble as the Consolidated drawings were totally inadequate, and the design was unsuitable for mass production.

Sorensen's drive and energy had overcome all these difficulties, so one can imagine his feelings when an Australian and a Scotsman arrived wanting substantial modifications incorporated.

E.A. Whiteley (often called "Titch") was only about 5 ft 4 in tall , but was a bundle of fire and energy. He had previously been a schoolteacher in New South Wales, Australia, where he had taught mathematics, but he also loved to fly and before the war he had joined the Royal Air Force Auxiliary, doing weekend flying. On the outbreak of war he had then been called up and had since completed two tours of duty, had flown over 60 missions, and earned the DFC & bar, and had been fighting in the defence of Malta when he was posted to be Deputy Director of Canadian & American Production – for a rest.

There was an immediate clash of personalities and Sorensen and Whiteley were at it long into the night. Whiteley complimented Sorensen on his monumental achievements in building such successful mass production lines for aircraft, which had never been done before. Sorensen in his book admits that "this was the greatest challenge in his whole career." Whiteley went on to point out that this achievement was worthless if the aircraft were not fit for operational duty and killed their crews as a result. The arguments went on and on and I thought that we had reached an impasse, so I suggested that Sorensen should continue to produce aircraft as before, but should close down one of the lines and then recycle the aircraft through it to incorporate the modifications. I also pointed out that Prestwick had reached saturation point and we had neither the labour nor the space to increase production. Sorensen thought that this was a good idea and he would sleep on it.

Early next morning we sat down and examined the drawings and the photographs of the modifications. I suggested that Sorensen should start by incorporating the mods that required structural alterations to the airframe such as:

1. The fitting of an astrodome to the flight deck.
2. The fitting of new bomb- and depth-charge racks in the bomb bay.
3. The replacement of the bomb bay doors with a fixed structure and a floor for troop-carrying aircraft.
4. The installation of armour plate to protect flight crews and vital parts of the aircraft.
5. The fitting of self-sealing fuel tanks.
6. Mods to the gun turrets to give a better arc of fire.
7. Shutes to enable shell cases to be dumped overboard to prevent them cluttering up the turrets.
8. Provision of brackets to the wings to facilitate the mounting of ASV aerials and searchlights (Leigh Lights).

I also offered to send out a team of engineers to help in the initial stages.

Finally agreement was reached, and within 48 hours we were back home. This made a big difference to the work load at Prestwick. Shortly thereafter

Wing Commander E.A. Whiteley was promoted to Group Captain and became Director of DPCA, where he was a tower of strength for the rest of the war.

Much has been written about "Bomber" Harris and the morality of his saturation bombing campaign, but not so much has been written about those brave young men who risked their lives night after night and how they felt about what they were doing. Most of them were terrified every time they boarded their aeroplanes. German radar was very good, so good in fact that they could pick up bomber packs before they had even crossed the Channel, and were able to track them and estimate the possible targets, so that fighter and anti-aircraft guns could be concentrated over the target areas. The only defence we had against enemy radar was the dropping of strips of aluminium foil to combat radar scanning, but this was not very effective and losses were mounting; if a crew survived five raids without damage or death, they considered themselves lucky. Various jamming devices were tried but they were not good enough either.

The strategists, and those in intelligence who were experts in "dis-information," put forward the suggestion that we must devise some form of diversionary attacks. After much thought Robert Watson Watt decided that if he could develop a method of simulating a radar wave pattern in line with that created by a heavy bomber raid, and fly the device in an aircraft at very high altitude, he could achieve the desired diversion. These plans were top secret, and those involved had to sign a special secret declaration. The code word was "Air Grocer." Prestwick did the installation and modification work, and a B-17 Flying Fortress was chosen to carry the device. Everything possible was stripped out of the aircraft – armament, armour etc. – to reduce the weight. Everything that had been learned from high-altitude flying over Everest was put to good use, including maximum boost to the engines. The theory was that the aircraft would fly at heights well above the ceiling for anti-aircraft fire and fighter attack. I was able to go on some of the test flights with Dick Ellison and the results were impressive. I tried to talk myself into being allowed to go on the first flight over Germany, but that was very firmly ruled out.

I read all the casualty lists and hardly a month went by without there being someone on them whom I had known. I began to have qualms of conscience as to what I was doing, especially as the controversy in respect of my military service was still rumbling on and I was still being investigated and interviewed *ad nauseam*. However the "Air Grocer" project was a great success, and while the 1,000-bomber raids were causing havoc in industrial Germany the aircraft losses were being contained.

The Germans modified some Messerschmitt fighters and eventually the Flying Fortress got shot up, fortunately making it to Sweden and landing there safely. It was imperative that this aircraft, so essential to the success of "Air Grocer," was recovered and Watson Watt decided to go and inspect it. I volunteered to go with him and after much argument this was agreed. We went to Leuchars where a specially modified Mosquito was standing by to fly us to Sweden. It was a two-seater which had been modified to carry agents in the bomb bay. We were first fitted out with electrically heated suits, boots & gloves and communication headsets, and then we were strapped onto two stretchers which were winched up into the bomb bay, whereupon the doors were closed. We were told that there was nothing to worry about and that we would be perfectly safe as similar journeys had been done many times before without a single loss.

And so we took off. We were warm and comfortable, but I felt nervous and claustrophobic. Suddenly there was a burst of gunfire, and I thought the end had come. Then the Captain's voice sounded through the intercom:

"Sorry about that, Sir; I should have warned you, we were only testing our guns."

The rest of the flight was smooth and uneventful. The Swedes were wonderful, but security was total as there was a risk of spies. We were entertained royally in a safe house and next morning went to see the Fortress. It looked to me to be a complete write-off but the equipment was undamaged apart from one bullet hole in the casing. Coded messages were sent back to Prestwick and soon a Liberator was on its way with a team to dismantle the B-17 and fly the components back to Prestwick. Within ten days another B-17 had been modified and "Air Grocer" was back in business. This little adventure helped me no end in feeling that I was doing my bit for the war effort, and I tackled my duties with renewed zest and vigour.

1941 was quite a momentous year: on the 2nd May Rudolf Hess landed on the Duke of Hamilton's estate at Dungavel by parachute; on the 7th July American troops were stationed in Iceland; on the 6th October the Germans attacked Moscow, and on the 7th December the Japanese raided Pearl Harbour and the Americans entered the war.

Meanwhile David McIntyre was fully occupied with the administration of the airfield and all that went on there, but he was always available to listen and give advice when necessary. In the summer of 1941 the Air Terminal was requisitioned by the Air Ministry, but SAL was given a contract for the overall management of it. We provided all the accommodation and catering, ably managed by George Simpson, who recruited the head chef and waiter from the Central Hotel, Glasgow. All the maintenance was provided by Jack Dickie and his team, and all the fuelling, maintenance, baggage handling and – when necessary – repairs was handled by a Service unit under Jack Wilkinson, manned by the service engineers from No. 12 EFTS and No. 1 AONS. All transport – 24 hours a day, 7 days per week – was provided under the control of Stan Taylor who used to work in the garage in Troon where I bought my Riley Falcon. Dick Ellison was fully occupied with test flying, and Fred Hopkins was not only in charge of the Service unit but was responsible for a dispersal factory in Glasgow.

SAL had received a large order for the manufacture of 100 Queen Bee aircraft. These were based on the Tiger Moth, so of course no one knew more about them than Fred Hopkins. Being radio-controlled they flew without a pilot, and were in great demand for target practice for the Anti-Aircraft Regiments and both Fighter and Bomber Command. The result was that I was left very much on my own to run the entire manufacturing activities.

I referred earlier to "a traitor in the camp," but in fact there were two of them. The ex-factory manager had two sons, and one of them worked in the toolroom. Our expert butcher's boy-*cum*-jig borer had been called up by the Manpower Board, but SAL had had the call-up cancelled, and he now confided to me that there had been a set-up between the shop steward and the son and that I was next on the list for attention. The second culprit was the chief production engineer, who was interviewed and given the chance to resign or be fired: he resigned. We were advised to leave the other man in place in the toolroom, as he might unwittingly be a good source of information.

I began some reorganising. The factory under the former works manager had been run – or misrun – by strict systems, a mass of paperwork and interminable meetings. That could not work in wartime; I needed to find people with initiative and drive, and the ability to take responsibility without too much supervision. Frank W. Burnard had been the ground engineer from Westlands responsible for the aircraft on the Everest Expedition, and I made him Chief Superintendent. Bill Howgate, a brilliant young engineer, became Superintendent of parts manufacture, and a double bass player in a local band became foreman; after the war his music made him quite famous and rich.

I found another man, Frank Broughton, who was promoted to be Superintendent of the three dispersal units on the perimeter of the airfield, specially designed for Liberators. He was a great driver, an excellent organiser and a big success – more of him later. I also found an able planning engineer, George Finch, and we set up a progress department under Charlie Reid and a production control department under Alex Holland.

The Ministry architect was called George Grenville Baines, who had designed hangars based on the Nissen hut principle referred to as 'B' hangars. He came to see us, and Frank Burnard and I showed him the drawings of what we needed. The hangars were huge semi-circular structures 140 ft wide; as the wingspan of a Liberator was 120 ft they were ideal. In next to no time they were adapted and erected and were known as 'B1,' 'B2' and'"B3.' George Baines became famous and was later knighted. By now the management team was working well and everything was soon humming.

The London and Scottish Railway Company had a large workshop at Barassie, and had applied to CRO at Merton College for a contract to repair Hurricanes and Spitfires. They were given one, but were told they had to work as subcontractors of SAL; this added even more to our workload, but they recruited more women, who were trained at our training unit in Ayr.

We even had our own doctor on site, Dr Stephenson, who was a great believer in physical fitness and recreation. There were also a barber's shop, a ladies' hairdressing salon and a dental surgery, all of which could be used in working hours. A social Club was built, and two squash courts were added to the Orangefield Mess.

In spite of all this intense activity, there were very few accidents overall, although regrettably two Liberators crashed at Heathfield, not very far away, killing both their crews. But I do recall one particular occasion when we had installed a long-range fuel tank in the bomb bay of a Liberator for a special operation, and Dick Ellison was to do a test flight which I was to watch from the end of the runway; during take-off the two starboard engines failed and the plane careered off the runway into a culvert. I jumped into my car and tore down the runway, fearing the worst. Dick had jumped out, bruised and very shocked, and was in tears as he thought that as the plane was on fire all his crew would be dead. But the rescue service was there in minutes and got the others out; they were burned a little but they all survived.

Some while afterwards, Dick was coming in to land in a Spitfire and, due to a misunderstanding with an air controller, he landed on top of a Beaufighter which was taking off. Both aircraft were write-offs, but no one was killed. After the war Dick had a miraculous escape from a crash in Switzerland, and he and I, on a delivery flight of a converted Dakota to Lisbon, were very lucky not to crash into the sea. I will say more about these incidents in later chapters.

CHAPTER 16

SOCIAL LIFE IN WARTIME PRESTWICK

Joy had joined the Royal Observer Corps, and had settled in very well as a housewife, and we were very happy after the trauma of the "Hate Campaign." Betty Maliphant, the wife of Chuck Maliphant, the Chief Technical Officer representing MAP at Prestwick, had joined at the same time, so Joy was making friends. We decided that we should do some entertaining, so we invited David McIntyre and his wife, Dick Ellison and his wife Beryl, and Fred & Nancy Hopkins for dinner. Joy had talked to her local butcher, and he had promised her chicken or rabbit.

But it turned out that there was no chicken, no rabbit, not even a good bit of fish, so we were in a dilemma as to whether to cancel or not. However I had heard of a farm on the far side of Ayr which had some ducks for sale, so one evening we set off on our bicycles. We were shown some nice plump ducks but were told we would have to kill them ourselves. I had never killed a duck before and Joy did not like the idea at all. The farmer suggested that Joy should go for a little walk, and he told me to catch two and bang their heads against the wall. Very reluctantly I did so – successfully, I thought. But when we were cycling through Ayr, one of the ducks recovered and fluttered off. With the traffic I had quite a difficult time catching it, and a passer-by told me that the only safe way to kill a duck was to cut its jugular vein. When we got home I followed this advice with both of them, whereupon one of them fluttered away and spurted blood all over the kitchen – not a very auspicious start. Then I had to stay up late and pluck them and gut them. Joy had gone to bed, so I cleared everything up, and left them hanging. In due course Joy cooked them and our guests pronounced them delicious. Personally, I have never liked duck since.

The next dinner party was with the Ellisons, who lived in a detached house called Torvar at the end of the runway. We arrived in good time, all dressed up, and rang the bell. There was no reply and when we looked round the house it was deserted. We were just departing when a Riley Kestrel pulled up with a screech of brakes, and out jumped the Ellisons. They had been sailing and adverse tides and winds had delayed them. Dick poured the drinks while Beryl retired to the kitchen, and we partook of a makeshift meal which was excellent.

We formed a lifetime friendship with the Ellisons – over 56 years. Following a serious motor accident Dick died on 20th October 1996, leaving Beryl and four sons. Dick was a very likeable and talented man, and celebrated his golden wedding by flying in a hot-air balloon with his wife. He was a great sailor and sailed across the Atlantic with his son, winning the Round Britain race for small yachts. I played squash with him every week and he taught me to play chess.

We even kept bees together and during wartime days the honey yield was of great benefit to our families when there was strict rationing of sugar. In the early summer we used to take all the hives to heather country on the Carrick hills, all loaded onto Dick's trailer. But one evening one of the hives slipped and the bees became very angry. Dick was decked out in hat, veil and gloves, but I was so foolhardy that I did not wear any protection and I was very badly stung in many places. When I arrived home I went straight to bed. Joy was on night duty with the Observer Corps, and when she came home and saw me she was horrified; my face, head, arms and legs were badly swollen and I could hardly speak. Joy phoned for Dr Stephenson, who came and gave me an injection, and advised rest. I have been careful of bees and wasps ever since.

The Kennedys lived in a fine detached house called Rustwood in Fullarton Woods in Troon. One evening we were invited to a cocktail party there, but I was delayed at the factory and had to go home and change. When we arrived we were devastated to find that we were so late that all the guests had gone. But Stewart and Eleanor insisted that we stay for dinner, and that too was the start of a lifelong friendship.

David McIntyre had a lovely country house called Cushetts near Sorn. David had married a lovely vivacious lady called Marjorie Potts, whose family were wealthy sausage manufacturers. He was a great entertainer and socialiser, and we were invited to his house when he was entertaining some distinguished guests, including the Duke of Hamilton, his brother the Earl of Selkirk, Air Marshal Sir Fred Bowhill (Head of Transport Command) and Sir John Colville of MAP. On these occasions he always served generous drinks, and these were followed by a long-driving golf competition from the front lawn; following this we all made our way to Sundrum Castle Hotel for a sumptuous dinner.

The most elaborate parties of all were of course hosted by the officers of the 8th US Army Air Corps, not only at Adampton House, but also at Butlin's holiday camp, south of Ayr (which had been turned into a barracks for servicemen) and at Culzean Castle. There was great competition for the local girls and ladies, and with the prospect of a short but merry life every day was lived to the full and could be quite frenetic.

Joy and I spent our first wedding anniversary in Edinburgh, and stayed for three nights in the North British Hotel. Joy gave me a solid silver cigarette case suitably engraved; I smoked a pipe but never cigarettes, but it was considered very much the 'in thing' to be able to offer one's friend a cigarette from a handsome cigarette case. I still have it and it is very valuable to me. I gave Joy a sapphire necklace on a gold chain. Joy visited her friends at Register House and at her old digs, we went to the zoo, and had a very enjoyable and restful time.

In August we were able to have a week's holiday. We spent it at Weem Hotel near Aberfeldy on the banks of the Tay, and the weather was glorious. The hotel was owned by Donald Matheson, who was a bagpipe player of some renown. Every morning at eight o'clock precisely he marched round the hotel playing stirring tunes on his pipes. He also wrote and produced plays for the local dramatic society, and in addition was a good table tennis player. I thought I was good too (!) so we had some stirring matches. The food was, for war-time, excellent.

Joy and I were great lovers of poetry, and one of our favourite poems was *To a Gipsy Girl on Farragon* by J.B. Salmond.

We stood together by the blackthorn tree,
Children of one hill-mother, her milk dew
Splashing our minds to a wild happiness
Like swooning dreams above Schiehallion's head.
We too had gazed in throbbing silences,
And, with one long deep breath,
Taken our way o'er hills mist-carpeted.

As Farragon was just behind our hotel, we set off one morning early and climbed it. Joy was much fitter than I was, and I arrived at the summit puffing and panting, but it was well worth the effort. Farragon was not even a 'Munro,' being only 2,559 ft high, but the views from the top were spectacular. To the north there was Loch Rannoch and the Tummel Valley, with Schiehallion raising its noble head at 3,547 ft, while to the south was Ben Lawers at 3,984 ft, the famous skiing mountain still with snow on top, sloping down to Loch Tay with a glorious view of the whole loch as well as Taymouth Castle and golf course.

On the lower slopes of Farragon, just before we reached the tree line, we spotted a beautiful little loch teeming with trout. Donald Matheson told us that all that land was owned by an Englishman who lived in a large house on the road to Fortingall, so that evening after dinner we cycled along, found the house and rang the bell. We were received by the butler and were duly admitted into a fine library, where we were seen by a very old but dapper gentleman, who was quite charming and offered us sherry or coffee. We explained who we were and that we would like very much to have his permission to fish his loch.

When we told him that we were staying at the Weem Hotel, his manner changed, and he told us that no one at Weem would ever be allowed to fish his waters. He said he was sorry, as we seemed such a nice young couple, so that was that and we were ushered out. Later we learned that there had been a dispute with Donald Matheson because some of his guests had fished the loch without permission, and Donald had not deterred them as he considered that there should be no restriction on trout fishing in Scotland.

Another day we went fishing on Loch na Craig on the side of the road from Aberfeldy to Amulree. We caught nothing, but we met a gamekeeper who told us that there was excellent fishing in a loch about five miles into the hills. He gave us directions and said we could fish it any time. So the next morning Joy and I set off with our picnic lunches and eventually, after a strenuous walk, we found Loch Fender, a beautiful little loch nestling in a hollow in the hills. Fish were rising, but were too far out from the shore to be within casting distance. However we found a boat and baled it out, and soon we were catching fish with a fly called a Blue Zulu. We arrived back tired but very pleased with ourselves.

On our second last day we went to explore Glen Lyon; it was indeed a beautiful glen and the river Lyon was rocky with tumbling white water cascading down to deep still pools. It was a good spring salmon river but August was too late for them; nevertheless we fished for trout – catching nothing, – walked and talked, and made love in the heather.

The next day we set off for home and nearly had a tragedy on the way. As we were driving along the shores of Loch Lubnaig, we saw trout rising, so we stopped, and out came the fishing tackle. Once again I could not cast to the rising fish, so I went back to the car and put on my Wellingtons. A few steps into the loch and still I could not reach; then I was over the top of my wellies, but that did not matter as I was wearing shorts. A few steps more and I was nearly in reach, then I realised I was steadily sinking in deep slimy mud. The harder I tried to free myself the further I sank, so I shouted to Joy to get a rope out of the car boot, and throw it to me. She did so but could not pull me out, so I asked her to tie the rope to a tree and, by dint of lying flat on the water, I pulled myself free with a horrible squelchy sound, soaking wet and covered with mud. After a wash in clean water and a change of clothes, all was well, and so we came home, but I have never forgotten that lesson; never wade without a wading stick and never move without testing the bottom with the stick.

CHAPTER 17

OUTWORKING AND MORE FISHING TALES

To service and repair Coastal Command aircraft, SAL had working parties at Saint Ives, Beaumaris, Wigton Bay, Benbecula, and Meek's Field, Iceland. We also sent a special working party to RAF Station Lyneham. Lyneham was the headquarters of Air Transport Command, who were responsible for the movement of all servicemen and VIPs. They were quite separate from Ferry Command, who were in charge of all ferry aircraft crossing the Atlantic.

Churchill had decided that he wanted a personal aircraft, and it was decided that it should be a Liberator, not only because of its excellent record but because Churchill considered the name "Liberator" very appropriate. SAL were given the job of doing the conversion, and what a conversion it was! It had a well-equipped galley with a bar, a bedroom with shower, a luxurious lounge, and the most state-of-the-art VHF communications equipment.

Dick Ellison and I were invited to the handing-over ceremony. We planned to fly down to Lyneham in a Liberator, but as the weather forecast was bad I set off the day before in a Mercedes 3-litre saloon with Hugh Rowand, our Chief Inspector. To digress for a moment, this was one of the three cars that SAL had acquired as "war booty." A whole shipload of German cars had been captured and these three had been allotted to SAL. Stewart Kennedy got a super Opel sports car, David McIntyre got the top-of-the-range Mercedes, and the 3-litre was shared by top management.

Some miles from Lyneham we saw a Liberator overhead, flying low, and as it passed it waggled its wings. We thought that it was Dick, but it wasn't; he had been caught up in a test-flying problem, and the pilot was in fact "Titch" Whiteley of DPCA, who had been visiting at Prestwick and was also invited to the ceremony. Churchill was delighted and very complimentary, and we had an enjoyable lunch.

I had to visit all the out-stations from time to time, and the most exciting trip of all was to Meek's Field in Iceland. My first visit was in a Liberator and the view over the northern islands was fabulous: the Inner and Outer Hebrides, the Orkney Islands and the Shetlands, and then the coast of Iceland appearing on the horizon. Iceland was a very stark volcanic island with barely a tree in sight, the highest mountain being Oræfa Jökull at 6,952 ft. There were two renowned salmon rivers, the Hvita and the Hieradhsvötn in the north. Reykjavik, the capital, was a fascinating place, and the shops were full of all kind of things that could not be bought in wartime Britain. As I said earlier, the Americans had moved in in July 1941 and the economy had boomed as a result. The Icelanders were an inbred nation and it was alleged that the Americans were received with open arms and that liaisons with the beautiful blonde girls were welcomed rather than being frowned upon. There were many marriages and the Icelandic population expanded considerably during the war years.

I usually stayed in the Officers' Mess at Meek's Field, where I recall the favourite drink being a blend of whisky and apple juice. I was able to do some fishing on the Huita, and very exciting it was. The salmon and sea trout were plentiful and great fighters, and the Mess back at Prestwick benefited considerably. It was always my ambition to go back and fish in Iceland but I never got around to it. Fishing there became very expensive, and the catches, like everywhere else, steadily dwindled.

I shopped in Reykjavik and on one occasion brought home two hot water bottles, one aluminium frying pan and one saucepan, none of which were available in the UK for love nor money. I also bought a glamorous nightie for Joy.

My next favourite out-station was at Wigton Bay. One of the foremen at SAL was Sandy Bain; he was also a keen fisherman, and his father was gamekeeper at the Traquhair Estate near the village of Balmaclellan, made famous by the *Tales of Old Mortality* about a legendary stonemason who travelled the graveyards of southern Scotland maintaining headstones. Near Balmaclellan there was beautiful little Loch Een. The burn had been dammed, creating an artificial picturesque loch, and this was now full of brown trout from the Lake of Menteith (the only 'lake' in Scotland) and Loch Katrine. Sandy Bain, Hugh Rowand and I used to stop there on our way to Wigton to catch a few fish. It was a difficult loch to fish, as there were no boats and it was too deep and weedy to wade. However there were dry stone dykes and banks that had been submerged during the flooding, and when one knew where these were it was possible to wade on them and cover most of the water. Mind you, it was also easy to miss one's footing and fall into deep water. We also fished the Bladnoch and the Cree, and I cannot remember us ever returning without a good catch of salmon and sea trout.

Those days have gone for ever. The Ken Valley was very dear to me, as I had done much of my early fishing at Carsphairn with David Howie. That was the first watershed that had been dammed to create the hydroelectric power scheme from the rivers Deough and Ken. The huge dams and water control towers made an imposing sight, but they spoiled the natural fishing and the exquisite scenery.

Before I had ever joined SAL I had had good customers in Prestwick called the Lawrie Brothers. They had pioneered the making of artificial stone for ornamental purposes as well as mundane things like kerbstones and lintels for doors and windows, and they too were keen fishermen. We formed a syndicate with them, myself and Hugh Rowand, and leased some fine salmon fishing on the River Doon from a farmer on the Skeldon Estate for £8 per annum; that was £2 each and we had two miles of river. The year I was writing this, 1996, I noticed in the July issue of *Trout and Salmon* an article from which I quote:

"One small river which has an amazing track record for low water summer fishing is the Doon. Last year one good beat produced 800 salmon, most taken in August and September."

So I wrote to Skeldon Estate Office for details and records of catches: they were nothing near the figures quoted above. Indeed in 1995 the total catches were: August – 1, September – 38, October – 118. Charges for these months were £1,110 per week for four rods, i.e. £278 per rod per week. Talk about fishermen's tales, no doubt written to attract fishermen! Even in the 1940s there were never catches like that.

We used to cycle to Dalrymple village, park our bikes at the farm and fish all the way down to the Hollybush Hotel. At that time the Doon was a spring river and most of the fish taken were fresh run, bars of silver, still with sea lice on them, and running up to 30 lb in weight. We had been told that there were plenty of fish about, but when we got there on a Sunday they all seemed to have vanished. We heard on the grapevine that the river was being heavily poached by miners and "Bevan Boys" from Patna, and as there were no water bailiffs they had a free run.

We decided to stake the river out, and one Saturday evening we cycled to Dalrymple and found a vantage point. Sure enough we heard loud bangs at first light, and we spotted a green van parked by the river with "Fishmonger" painted on the side. We headed towards the sound of the explosions, and found five men using Samsonite and netting the dead fish. They scampered, we chased, and the Lawrie Bros fired their shotguns in the general direction of the poachers. But they escaped, and we reported the matter to the police. The fishmonger was fined and had his fish and van confiscated. The police told us that a miner had had his hand blown off, but they had no further details. It is possible that one of the shotgun pellets set off some explosive in the hand of one of them, possibly in his pocket. We never heard any more, but fish began to appear in good numbers and we caught our share.

One glorious Sunday morning we set off at 6 am as I had to be home at midday to go to a cocktail party. By 11 am I had caught nothing, and I set off to collect my bike, leaving my salmon rod, reel and line with one of the Lawrie brothers, as he had got his fly caught in a tree and in trying to free it he had broken his rod. As I approached a lovely pool just above the farm I saw a salmon moving. Up went my trout rod, and I tied on my strongest cast and a salmon fly. On my third cast the salmon was well and truly hooked. I could not apply much pressure with a trout rod, and it took me down to the backing. As there were trees on the bank I could not follow it, so I had to jump into the river, and got soaked from head to foot. After about half an hour I got the fish under control and duly tailed it onto the bank. It was a big one; I strung it over my back and set off for Prestwick, arriving late but full of pride. It weighed just over 28 lb.

CHAPTER 18

LIBERATOR AND OTHER INCIDENTS

When Poland fell, large numbers of Poles found their way to Britain and made a major contribution to the war effort, particularly in the RAF. Vladislav Sikorski was a great Polish patriot and was not only Commander-in-Chief of all Polish forces but was Prime Minister of the Polish Government in exile. He was flying back from North Africa in a Liberator converted by SAL, and stopped overnight at Gibraltar for a conference. The next morning the Liberator, with a very experienced Polish crew, ran all along the runway and straight into the sea; the aircraft never got airborne at all.

Sabotage was suspected and the Navy was able to recover the aircraft. Everyone on board had drowned. Bob Pasulovitch and I were flown out to examine the aircraft, which was not too badly damaged, and it soon became evident as to what had caused the crash. All Liberators had a lever on the throttle pedestal which, when pulled up, locked all the controls. When in the locked position it was kept up by a canvas strap which went round the throttle levers and hooked into the roof. This simple device prevented the throttles from being opened if the controls were locked. As it was a bit fiddly to fit, some crews had the habit of pulling up the lever and wedging it in position with a wooden box that stored the sextant; this was not considered dangerous as the flight manual demanded a full control check before take-off. This cannot have been done on this occasion, with the result that the controls were locked on take-off and the aircraft could do nothing but go straight into the sea. How an experienced crew could make this fatal error was never established; there was no trace of sabotage, or any other faults.

Another Liberator carrying Air Vice-Marshal Dawson back from India just disappeared and was never heard of again.

The third Liberator incident concerned one of a flight of five specially prepared at Prestwick to carry the massive 10-ton bomb; it was planned that they should fly non-stop to bomb the oil wells at Ploiesti in Rumania. They were all fitted with special long-range tanks, and the leader of the flight was Captain Joe Kennedy, elder brother of John F. Kennedy, later President of the USA. Somewhere over Europe Kennedy's plane was blown to smithereens, and no trace was ever found of any wreckage. The rest of the flight completed the mission and the oilfields were severely damaged. There was no sign of enemy action and our investigations led to the conclusion that a fault had developed in the fuel transfer system from the large auxiliary tank to the main tanks, causing an explosion that detonated the 10-ton bomb – hence the total deetruction of the aircraft.

I was involved in two other hairy incidents with Liberators. On one occasion I was doing a test flight to check modifications on one of the gun turrets, and the plane was being flown by a pilot from No. 1 AONS who, when the school closed, became a test pilot under Dick Ellison. As we roared down the runway I realised that the engines were not developing full power. I dashed up to the cockpit and noticed that the fuel booster switches were in the 'off' position. I reached over and switched them 'on,' but for one awful moment I thought that we were going to crash. We just made it safely over the trees although the undercarriage hit the top of one of them.

I shouted: "For God's sake don't retract the undercarriage; it may be damaged. Do a circuit and land."

We did land safely but a branch was stuck in the nosewheel mechanism, which could have caused problems if the gear had been retracted.

That particular pilot later emigrated to South Africa, eventually becoming Operations Director for South African Airways. He later hit the headlines for using a cane to discipline his stewardesses; it was alleged that there was a sexual motive, as he was into flagellation.

The second incident was also on a test flight, a prolonged one with two purposes: to evaluate and set up a better version of Anti-Submarine Vectoring (ASV), the latest radar system, and also to test out new sighting devices on the 22 mm cannon. Two submarines were exercising in the Irish Sea and we had to endeavour to locate them on the ASV, both on the surface and submerged. Also a number of 50-gallon oil drums had been cast adrift between Turnberry and Ailsa Craig and we had to try to sink them with the 20 mm cannon. Fortunately the new sighting mechanisms were excellent and we sank them all. We were firing tracer, and some of the shells ricocheted off the waves, passed over the lighthouse on Ailsa Craig and exploded on the rocks nearby. Eventually there was a complaint from Trinity House, but the explanation and apologies were fully accepted.

We then set off to find the submarines with a fully-trained RAF crew aboard to operate the radar. Dick had been causing the aircraft to pitch and yaw so that we could test the new sighting devices, and as we progressed north into cloud there was some heavy turbulence. We could not get any response from the radar operators on our intercom, and when I went back to see what was wrong I found them completely prostrated and semi-conscious due to airsickness, so we had to abort the test.

We were aware that the compass was faulty and of course we had been depending on the radar to navigate us home. We were completely lost above cloud and I was terrified. Dick kept his 'cool' and did some time & speed calculations, and decided that he would descend through the cloud over the sea; as he knew the area very well because of his sailing exploits, he was confident that he would recognise the coastline and we would then be able to return under the cloud back to Prestwick.

Remembering what had happened in Arran I was even more terrified and vowed that if we got back safely I would never fly again. With all those hills around I reckoned that with just one mistake we would all be dead. The descent began, my teeth were clenched, I felt sick, and I kept peering through the windscreen and looking out of the side windows; then I saw it, a gap in the clouds, and below the sea and green fields. We descended into the clear and there we were, west of Upper Loch Tarbert in the Western Isles.

I shouted with relief but Dick said: "We are not out of the woods yet; there are a lot of mountains between here and Prestwick."

But the cloud lifted somewhat and we had an uneventful flight home and a safe landing. Dick had a remarkable sense of direction and without his skill the results could have been tragic.

Stewart Kennedy had great personality and rugged good looks, and he always seemed to have a bevy of beautiful secretaries and personal assistants around him, all of whom were efficient, clever and lovely to look at, and who obviously enjoyed working for him. When I first became a consultant and had an office in the administration building, he allotted me a secretary called Anne; she was married but her husband was a Captain in the Highland Light Infantry and was in France. She was a most delightful girl, an excellent shorthand typist, hard-working, and could not do enough for me. As I said earlier these early days were frantic and we worked very hard. She was currently living with her mother in St. Quivox Road in Prestwick, but after Dunkirk her husband became a prisoner of war. Two people working together and being in close proximity for most of the day are bound to develop an attraction for each other, and that happened to us. Nevertheless we kept our feelings under control and there never was any physical contact between us.

The Ellisons went off on holiday for a few days and I was staying in Torver, looking after the house and driving Dick's car, a Triumph Gloria. I was working long hours and Anne was doing so too, so one evening I took her out for dinner to the Burns Monument Hotel in Alloway. Afterwards I asked her if she had ever driven over the hills from Drongan to Hollybush. It was a famous beauty spot, and the view across to Arran and the Campbeltown peninsula, with Ailsa Craig to the south, was spectacular. It was a glorious summer evening, so we went and enjoyed the view and talked about life in general and our ambitions for the future; she told me how much she was missing her husband, and inevitably a petting session developed, and she asked me to take her to bed. The circumstances were ideal, a nice car and an empty house at Torver awaiting us. It would have taken a very insensitive man to have refused such an offer, but fate had other ideas.

On the outskirts of Prestwick we had a flat tyre, and I could find neither the tools nor the jack. We could not afford, either of us, to have our reputations compromised and we were in a dilemma; it was after midnight and there were no other forms of transport, so we had to walk. St. Quivox Road was just within walking distance, but Torver was too far. I walked Anne to her mother's house and we both saw the funny side of it and had a good laugh. Her mother was still up, and after a cup of tea I rang Transport and asked them to come and change the tyre.

A short time afterwards I went off to Gourock, so there was no chance of further dalliance. Anne's husband died of wounds in a prisoner-of-war camp and she eventually married a very nice Major who was at Adampton House, and went off to America after the war.

All the many months I was at Gourock I never had a secretary, as life was too hectic to write letters. However, I had a loose-leaf leather-bound diary in which I recorded every single thing that happened each day. DPCA expressed amazement about my having such a good memory, but little did they know that I had everything written down. This habit was an excellent discipline as it taught me to write down, record and memorise, and this proved invaluable in later life.

When I returned to Prestwick and became assistant works manager I was allotted a secretary, Miss Jean McCallum, whose father had a licensed grocer's shop in Ayr. She was extremely efficient and mothered me more than previous ones. She was a tower of strength and helped me to stay sane and sensible when I was experiencing difficult times with the "Hate Campaign" and disloyal staff. As the war progressed and I became busier and busier, Jean needed some help and recruited a very young secretary called Winifred Allison, whose father was manager of the gasworks in Ayr. Jean stayed with me until after the war, when she left to marry a nice young fellow who worked in the cost office for Bruce Erskine. I met her again 40 years later when I attended the SAL 50th Anniversary celebrations in 1985.

Jean had trained Winifred Allison so well that she became my principal secretary and served me well until I left in 1949. She was not especially goodlooking but had a bright personality and was very efficient. She became a friend of the family and used to babysit for us, and our children Gill and Alastair called her Maylisson. Eventually she had an affair with a handsome fellow, Ian Reid, whose father was gamekeeper on an estate at Blairgowrie, and at one time had been champion of Scotland at clay pigeon shooting. Ian worked in AID and after the war I persuaded him to work for me as a salesman, when he proved a great success. He was married with two children, and Hugh Rowand and I used to go to Blairgowrie and stay with his family. We fished the rivers there and also the Lochs Kinloch and Lintrathen, the latter being the reservoir for Dundee. I was introduced to the art of clay pigeon shooting, and due to my early training in rifle shooting became quite proficient at it. This skill stood me in good stead when, many years later, I took part in shoots in America and at Hatfield. But at that time I was unaware of the liaison, which caused Winifred Allison much unhappiness.

Another of Stewart's ladies was a most charming girl whose husband was taken prisoner of war after Dunkirk, and she became a *chauffeuse* to the top management. She was an excellent driver, was always immaculate and always wore an elusive fragrant pine perfume. She used to drive me around a lot and Fred Hopkins particularly had a high regard for her. When the war ended she became redundant, but she became my personal assistant and statistician, and was very good at both. She had a liaison with a charming American, and one morning I found her in tears. When he had found that she was pregnant, he had denied responsibility and scampered back to America. I listened patiently to her very sad story and found that she did not want the baby and had tried to get rid of it by drinking gin and taking hot baths, followed by douching, but all that had failed. So I had a very confidential chat with our doctor. Abortions were illegal in these days, and I never enquired about the detail, but two weeks later she arrived all smiles – her periods had started again, and all was well. She was eternally grateful and thereafter could not do enough for me.

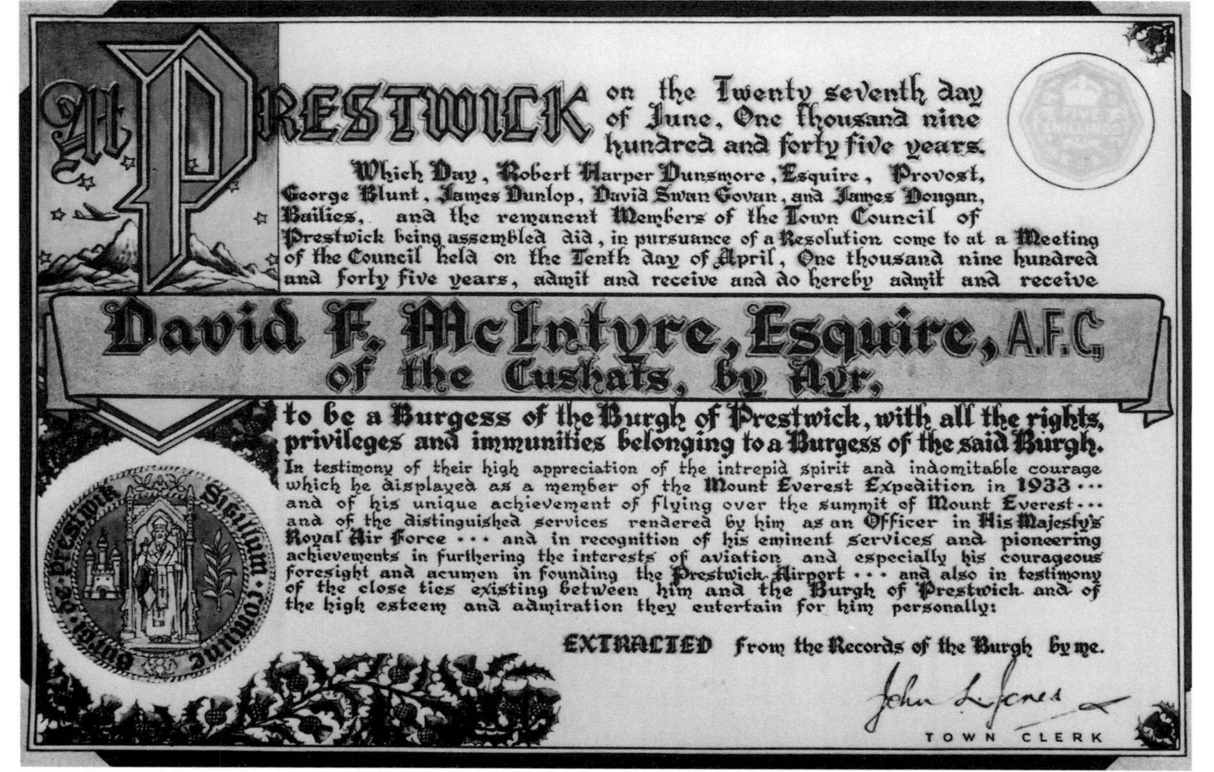

At PRESTWICK on the Twenty seventh day of June, One thousand nine hundred and forty five years.

Which Day, Robert Harper Dunsmore, Esquire, Provost, George Blunt, James Dunlop, David Swan Govan, and James Dougan, Bailies, and the remanent Members of the Town Council of Prestwick being assembled did, in pursuance of a Resolution come to at a Meeting of the Council held on the Tenth day of April, One thousand nine hundred and forty five years, admit and receive and do hereby admit and receive

David F. McIntyre, Esquire, A.F.C., of the Cushats, by Ayr,

to be a Burgess of the Burgh of Prestwick, with all the rights, privileges and immunities belonging to a Burgess of the said Burgh.

In testimony of their high appreciation of the intrepid spirit and indomitable courage which he displayed as a member of the Mount Everest Expedition in 1933 ··· and of his unique achievement of flying over the summit of Mount Everest ··· and of the distinguished services rendered by him as an Officer in His Majesty's Royal Air Force ··· and in recognition of his eminent services and pioneering achievements in furthering the interests of aviation and especially his courageous foresight and acumen in founding the Prestwick Airport ··· and also in testimony of the close ties existing between him and the Burgh of Prestwick and of the high esteem and admiration they entertain for him personally:

EXTRACTED from the Records of the Burgh by me.

John L. Jones

TOWN CLERK

A copy of the Certificate appointing David McIntyre as a Burgess of the Royal Burgh of Prestwick, dated 27th June 1945. Photo: author's collection.

Then let us pray that come it may,
As come it will for a' that,
That man to man THE WORLD O'ER
Shall brothers be for a' that.

(Robert Burns 1795)

6th ANNIVERSARY DINNER

Transatlantic Air Services to Prestwick Airport

29th November, 1946

*

An uninterrupted navigable ocean that reaches to the threshold of every man's door ought not to be neglected as a source of human gratification and advantage.

Sir George Cayley (1809)

TOP: The cover of the 1946 Programme for the 6th Anniversary Dinner of the Transatlantic Air Services, depicting a very busy airport immediately post-war.
BOTTOM: The first inside page of the Programme introduces the occasion. Both reproductions from the author's collection.

Menu

Melon Rafraîché

—

Petite Marmite

—

Dindonneau Rôti aux Chipolata

Pommes Croquettes Choux de Bruxelles

—

Poires Jeanne Granier

—

Café

Toast List

"THE KING"

Chairman: His Grace The Duke of Hamilton and Brandon, G.C.V.O., P.C., A.F.C.

"GUEST OF HONOUR"

Proposed by: The Rt. Hon. Joseph Westwood, P.C., M.P.

Reply: Livingstone Sattersthwaite, Esq., Civil Air Attache, American Embassy, London (Representing His Excellency The American Ambassador)

"CIVIL AVIATION"

Proposed by: The Rt. Hon. Thomas Johnston, P.C.

Reply: The Rt. Hon. Lord Nathan, P.C.

"AIRLINE OPERATORS"

Proposed by: The Rt. Hon. Lt.-Col. Walter Elliot, P.C., M.C.

Reply: A. Plesman, Esq., President-Director, K.L.M. Royal Dutch Airlines

"CITIES AND BURGHS OF SCOTLAND"

Proposed by: The Rt. Hon. Lord Selkirk, O.B.E., A.F.C.

Reply: The Rt. Hon. Lord Provost Sir Hector McNeill

"OUR HOSTS"

Proposed by: Air Chief Marshal Sir Frederick Bowhill, G.B.E., K.C.B., C.M.G., D.S.O.

Reply: D. F. McIntyre, Esq., A.F.C.

TOP: The Menu.
BOTTOM: The Toast List.
Both reproductions from the author's collection.

TOP: L4673, the first Westland Lysander built at Prestwick; the contract was then cancelled after the Dunkirk evacuation.
BOTTOM: Bob McIntyre (designer of the Prestwick Pioneer) and I relax during a caravan test run/fishing trip in 1947.
Photos: author's collection.

CHAPTER 19

DAVID MCINTYRE – A MAN OF VISION

Towards the end of 1943 David applied to Sir Arthur Street, Permanent Under-Secretary of State for Air, to Sir Stafford Cripps, Minister of Aircraft Production, and to the Air Ministry to visit the USA and Canada to investigate American air transport policy, to endeavour to arrange licences to convert American military aircraft for civilian use, and to study equipment and methods in force at the various airports used on the North Atlantic air routes. His application was supported by invitations from the Presidents of the Consolidated-Vultee Aircraft Corporation, Douglas Aircraft and TWA.

Permission was granted, and David left on Saturday the 15th January 1944 in a Douglas DC-4 operated by TWA. The route – a somewhat circuitous one as David also wanted to investigate the possibilities for post-war expansion in what he called "air tourist" traffic – was as follows: Prestwick–Marrakesh (Morocco)–Dakar (Senegal)–Fortaleza (Brazil)–Puerto Rico (West Indies)–Washington.

During this visit to the USA and Canada David covered thousands of flying miles and met practically every influential person in the world of aviation, both in manufacturing and operating. Even in those days aviation was being dominated by financial interests, particularly by Victor Emanuel in the States, and such interests were potentially harmful to the advances in research, development, manufacture and operation which should have followed the experience gained from war-time. There was great argument as to who should operate airlines, nationalised bodies or free enterprise. In Canada there was a bitter struggle between Canadian & Pacific Railways and Trans-Canada Airlines, which was Government-owned and dominated by a headstrong and stubborn man, the Hon. C.D. Howe.

David was seeking American support to break down the British single-instrument policy, namely a nationalised airline with no competition. The Americans thought that the BOAC Board under Lord Knollys and Critchley was a complete "circus" and would never succeed long-term. There was no doubt either that David McIntyre was determined to compete in air transport operation, particularly on North Atlantic routes, and to make Prestwick Airport the largest and finest airport in the world, with facilities for very large flying boats as well.

He signed letters of intent with Consolidated-Vultee and Douglas for conversion work, and also one with TWA on co-operation in airline operations with an airline owned and operated by SAL. This opened the door for this country to take an enormous step forward in post-war aviation.

I have been re-reading his report (which must be the only copy left in existence after all these years) and in view of what has happened and what is still happening in world aviation the contents are fascinating. So I have decided to include some sections of the report here, information that has never been made public before.

At the beginning David outlined one of the main reasons for his visit as follows:

On this occasion I wanted to be free to visit all interests in the States and Canada where information was likely to be obtained regarding American Air Transport Policy and which would be of assistance to the Company in formulating its post-war policy.

When the party finally reached Washington, he recorded the following:

In all we had flown 10,000 miles in 48:30 hours. Throughout the whole flight, which was made by the same aircraft with changes of crew, I was very impressed with the professional simplicity of the TWA organisation, by the enthusiasm of air and ground crews to keep the aircraft in the air and the cheerful team spirit and all-round efficiency of the crews. In fact, throughout I felt that there must be some tremendous incentive given to TWA staff in order to achieve the spirit and enthusiasm which I witnessed, and on arrival in Washington the first question I asked was about the form of incentive which they used, expecting to be told that a very high cash bonus was paid to staff on some basis of hours flown, and was pleasantly surprised to be told that the only incentive was the natural desire to see that TWA did a better job than its competitors. This was gauged from the hours flown per aircraft per day, the impossible ideal being that all their aircraft should fly 24 hours per day. I was told that on the trans-Atlantic service the DC-4 aircraft, including "hangar queens" (aircraft which are unserviceable for lengthy periods during repairs or modification) were averaging 9 hours per day every day of the year. On checking their figures over I discovered that they were in fact averaging 7¾ hours per day, which is much higher that I would have considered possible on such long-distance and difficult routes.

On the BOAC North Atlantic service from Prestwick, for instance, their Liberator aircraft, excluding "hangar queens," are averaging 1¼ hours per day. The use of air equipment is a very good yard-stick of the efficiency of an airline, and it is only when it is in the air that it is serving its purpose.

David had a productive meeting with TWA in Kansas, with whom he was attempting to build a strategy for the future, and then flew on to Los Angeles for a pre-arranged meeting with Mr Learman, the Managing Director of the Consolidated-Vultee Corporation:

Mr Learman reiterated his hope that our two Companies might be able to get together in airline operation and he again explained an old idea which he has had in his head for a long time that the best way to develop world aviation was for a suitable Company in each country to join together in an International Airline Company, each operating the portion of the route appropriate to their geographical position. . . .

I explained that we were ourselves trying to open the door to freer enterprise in overseas aviation and that if and when they were in a position to discuss co-operation on overseas airline routes we would be very interested to hear from them, especially as we were likely to be using similar equipment.

Mr Learman took me for a quick run round their Experimental Section where I saw the latest conversions of the Liberator for transport purposes, their latest bomber, the B-32, which looks very suitable for conversion as a pressurised commercial aircraft and also a new version of the Liberator which they were building without authority and which consisted of a new circular fuselage of great length replacing the present bomber fuselage. Drawings of this version I brought back to our Chief Designer.

I was aso shown a new project on the drawing board, a large passenger transport capable of carrying 350 passengers on a thousand-mile route. This aircraft had six large engines embodied in the wing with extension shafts through the trailing edge. An interesting feature of this new project, which had an all-up weight of 275,000 lbs, was that it adhered to the orthodox type of undercarriage as used on the Liberator. [This was later devleoped into the well-known B-36 bomber with its distinctive engine sound.]

Consolidated still have no faith in the future of flying boats but are becoming believers in our theory of long runways . . .

Later on in his visit David was able to meet the influential financier Victor Emanuel:

I was already aware of his wide holdings in the various airline and aircraft manufacturing companies which he has in the name of an Investment Company called The Aviation Corporation, and I had been informed at San Diego that he had already made some tentative steps towards selling Consair Lines to Pan American. I was very interested in his statement that he had endeavoured to arrange an amalgamation between American Airlines and Pan American but that so far he had been unable to do so on account of the wide divergence of views of the two Presidents, Juan Trippe of Pan American and C.R. Smith of Amercian Airlines.

This and the general tone of the conversation confirmed my fears that American Aviation was in danger of becoming a large private monopoly and that Victor Emanuel had hopes of creating an American 'I.C.I.' of Aviation. Such a monopoly would be even more undesirable than Government monopolies and could be really dangerous if it fell into the wrong hands.

Three days later David met with the top brass of TWA:

. . . it became quite clear . . . that TWA considered that our proposals were practicable and that they were prepared to back them and us up to the hilt.

I got the impression that they were in Aviation for aviation's sake and that the co-operation which had already been shown between the two companies was a very natural one and likely to grow in strength to the benefit of both.

A few days after that there was a meeting in Canada with CPR (Canadian Pacific Railways):

. . . there is obviously a strong determination amongst business people in Canada and within the CPR Co that CPR will operate North Atlantic air services. However at the moment they are completely stymied by the policy of the Hon. C.D. Howe, the present Minister of Munitions and Supply, and who was previously President of Trans Canada Airlines, the Canadian Government instrument for internal and external airlines.

One of the other responsibilities of the Hon. C.D. Howe was the operation of all airlines in Canada. David's report continues:

. . . CPR are a very determined Company with a great tradition of pioneer work in many forms of transportation and with the power of big business and a great deal of public opinion in their favour they will undoubtedly break into the North Atlantic air services in the fullness of time.

There is also a slight danger that if they are prevented by the Canadian Government from operating out of Canada to Britain they might use their British connections to operate out of Britain to Canada, and this might present an element of competition to ourselves at too early a stage to be helpful.

We can take it, however, that in the event of CPR operating to Great Britain and ourselves operating to Canada a similar measure of co-operation as we are proposing between ourselves and TWA will be welcomed by CPR. At present, of course, we are handling the ground organisation at Prestwick for the TCA's trans-Atlantic service, which uses converted Lancasters.

David then mentions meeting his old friend J.P. Bickell, who had been in charge of the ATFERO Department of the MAP under Lord Beaverbrook before coming to Canada two years earlier as Chairman of Victory Aircraft; this was the Crown Company which manufactured Lancaster bombers, and apparently they had also received an order for 200 York aircraft, the passenger version of the Lancaster. He and the Hon. C.D. Howe had recently had exchanges, and as David left Canada questions were being asked in the Commonwealth Parliament calling for a disclosure of the the correspondence between Howe and Bickell which, if it came out, would show a tendency for Crown Companies such as Victory Aircraft to be operated for political advantage rather than the advantage of the war effort and the output of bombers.

The next day David had a meeting at the Ministry of Information with the Hon C.D. Howe, Baron Silvercruys (Belgian Ambassador Extraordinary and

Plenipotentiary to Canada, Air Marshal Leckie (Chief of the Air Staff, Royal Canadian Air Force) and Lt Cdr. C.P. Edwards (Deputy Minister, Department of Transport).

David says:

It was quite obvious that the whole Canadian civil aviation policy is entirely controlled by Howe, who is very strong-willed and completely pig-headed on the subject. There were, however, one or two quite intelligent individuals in their civil aviation department who were most anxious to see that Canada adopted a broader attitude on this very important subject. . .

I was very pleased to meet Bob Leckie as he had been most helpful when we were getting Prestwick started, at which time he was Superintendent of RAF Reserve and Tedder was Director of Training, which job Leckie took over when Tedder was promoted . . .

The conversation at lunch naturally turned around to post-war air transport policy, and I endeavoured to persuade Howe that at least one inter-hemisphere airport in Canada with very long runways would be essential to world aviation, which would also be restricted and slow to develop unless Canada changed its policy and ceased to be such a determined example of the single chosen instrument.

This was especially dangerous as they were the nearest example to the United States which might be encouraged to follow suit. Fortunately everyone at lunch, except Edwards who had been a radio operator and was merely a "Yes" man to Howe, lined up on my side.

Baron Silvercruys was particularly outspoken even to the extent of accusing Howe of planning the future of air transport in terms of the past, and reminding him that at one time he was equally convinced that 3,000 ft should be the maximum length of runways as he now was in his statements that not a foot more than 8,000 ft would ever be required. The more Howe was pushed into a corner the more determined he became, and I should think there is little hope of Canada adopting a broader attitude towards aviation as long as Howe is in his present position of authority.

One of David's last meetings was with the Civil Aeronautics Board in Washington:

They were obviously most interested to obtain the views which I had assimilated from experience of Prestwick, and we had a long discussion on international airport planning on which I found them very open-minded . . .

I was also surprised to find how positively vindictive they were at the single chosen instrument policy of European countries which Pan American Airways was trying to copy in the States and that they were every bit as adamant that on no account would any other form of transportation be allowed to have a control over, or connection with, air transport.

When I quite frankly explained that the policy of our Company was to prize open the closed door of the single chosen instrument policy in Britain they became anxious to help us in any possible way. They appreciated that we were probably the only immediate alternative to BOAC . . .

David's report continued:

It struck me that a Company such as ours, in an endeavour to break down a single instrument policy in Britain, would as a private company receive endless support from America, even to the extent of obtaining the latest American equipment with which to initially equip an airline.

One gathered around the States that BOAC's portrayal of Britain's effectiveless in the air was making us the laughing stock of the world, but I was to receive the most cutting remark of all from the Civil Aeronautics Board. I was asked what Britain thought of the new board of BOAC and I attempted a non-committal reply to the effect that Lord Knollys was a very intelligent type, and that Critchley appeared to be very effective in all his previous activities. To this I received the remark: "Isn't it a pity that Lord George Sanger is dead?"

Shortly after this David finally returned to Prestwick via Stephenville (Newfoundland), and his general impressions of the visit to the States and Canada were summed up at the end of his report:

1) The American mentality and system of Government have not yet reached the same stage of responsible maturity as the British. This appears in their intense individualism and the difficulty which they find in any form of compromise.

2) Canadian sympathy is becoming more inclined towards co-operation with America than with the British Empire, apart from odd waves of Scottish Presbyterianism and such points of tradition in which they feel superior to the Americans.

3) It seems probable that Britain could eventually surpass American technique in aircraft production if required to meet a healthy and expanding British air transport system. It would be difficult to make up the years which we have lost in acquiring the art of airline operation. The professional technique of airline operation and the American attitude towards it, which have been built up in a spirit of keen competition between highly efficient US Airline Companies, would require to be copied by Britain in the first instance.

4) The struggle against apathy and disbelief with which Aviation Companies of all nations have had to contend appears to have engendered a brotherly attitude between these Companies and a willingness to co-operate in the advancement of world aviation, placing in most instances national ambitions in a position of secondary importance. I formed the impression that perhaps more would emanate from this factor than from the various International arrangements which in the fullness of time may be negotiated between Governments.

5) Canada looks at present as if it might be the stumbling block in Aviation development . . . .
6) In addition to our intention to operate North Atlantic Air Services and eventually around the Northern Hemisphere we should at least consider aiding this by taking some of the cream of the air tourist traffic market. Air cruises widely advertised covering many parts of the globe in the course of a two weeks' cruise, stopping perhaps a couple of days at four or five points, will have a greater appeal to present and future generations than playing deck quoits for a couple of weeks on a surface vessel.

The letters of intent which David concluded with the Consolidated-Vultee Corporation, Douglas and TWA during his visit proved of great value to the manufacturing establishment at Prestwick, and we became the biggest, the most successful and the most profitable unit in the world.

I have already referred to the driving ambition and success of David McIntyre and now, some 54 years later, I still ponder about what might have been. There can be no doubt that David was a man well ahead of his time. if he had not lost his life in a tragic accident in 1957 (see Chapter 28) the UK – and maybe even the world – aviation picture could have been vastly different and perhaps not have been dominated by the Americans for five decades. Richard Branson and Colin Marshall have shown what can be done in running efficient, competitive and world-class airlines, and gaining leads over the Americans.

Controversy still rages about the siting and size of national airports, and yet Prestwick lies unwanted and underused. It proved its worth during the war in terms of weather conditions, position, and having an Air Traffic Control system already in place.

David also envisaged a monorail system serving all the major cities in Britain; this had been invented and proved by a Scotsman before the war, and has been used with great success between Tokyo Airport and Tokyo City. It would have been cheaper than motorways and caused less congestion, but the 'Establishment' was too blind and too stubborn even to listen.

I eventually resigned in 1949 (see Chapter 28) and went to work for de Havilland; this was due to a major difference I had with David McIntyre over his profligate spending of all the substantial profits made by the manufacturing and conversion factories on trying to find ways to beat the Government's single instrument policy.

Yet I still wonder who was right. If he had succeeded, what a different Britain we might have had.

PART III: PEACE AT LAST

CHAPTER 20

AN UNEXPECTED AWARD

Even before we were married Joy and I had decided that the ideal family would be two boys and two girls. Indeed, when we chose the engagement ring it had four diamonds, one for each of our children – we hoped. But with no permanent residence and the uncertainties of wartime and a possible call-up we decided to delay having a family; after all, I was only 27 and Joy was 24, so we reckoned we had plenty of time. However, after our idyllic week at Weem, Joy discovered she was pregnant, and on the 17th of April 1944, at Greystones Nursing Home, Prestwick, we were blessed with a lovely baby daughter, Helen Gillian. In 1946 she was joined by our second child, Alastair William.

Accommodation at this time was quite a problem; for a year or two we had several short-term rentals, but eventually we moved into the top flat of the Old Manse at Monkton, which was just behind the main factory at Prestwick and owned by SAL. It was a beautiful old house and Robert Burn's nephew used to be the Minister there.

We celebrated VE-Day on the 9th May 1945, and this was soon followed by VJ-Day on the 15th August. I do not remember any massive celebrations on the latter occasion, more a sense of great relief, and those who had been in danger thanked God that they had survived.

I spent that day quietly with Hugh Rowand; we went off in his Bentley to Dungavel Loch on the Duke of Hamilton's estate for some trout fishing, and stopped at a pub near Loudon Hill to pick up some sandwiches and two flagons of scrumpy cider. I showed Hugh some of the rock climbs on Loudon Hill, and when we got to the loch it was time for lunch. It was a glorious hot day, and no fish were showing. We drank a little malt whisky to celebrate and then had our sandwiches, washed down with the scrumpy. But when we started to fish, we found our legs had 'gone'; we were not drunk and could converse coherently, but we had no sense of balance and felt dizzy. So we lay down and had a good sleep, and found on awakening that a rise had started and trout were plopping all over the loch. The trout were not large but fought well, and we had a good catch. We drove home safely in the late evening, but I have never drunk scrumpy since. The next few days I spent at Southbraes Drive with Joy, Gill and Joy's father & mother.

The next few months were sad ones workwise. How long would it take for the existing contracts to be cancelled? What would happen to and who would pay for all the work in progress, and who would pay the wages for all the work force? We sadly missed the experience and negotiating ability of Stewart Kennedy, who had gone to de Havilland's, and most of the responsibility fell on me. Fortunately there was a very energetic and able accountant, Bruce Erskine, who had been with us for a long time, but had not been in the mainstream of top management because of Stewart's great ability. Now he quickly blossomed and we got down to sorting things out, which meant having many long and tiresome meetings with DPCA at Millbank House, London and the CRO at Merton College, Oxford.

On the 3rd December 1945 I received a letter from 10 Downing Street. It said:

"Sir,

I am desired by the Prime Minister to inform you that it is his intention, on the occasion of the forthcoming list of New Year Honours, to submit your name to the King with a recommendation that he may be graciously pleased to approve that you be appointed a Member of the Order of the British Empire.

Before doing so, the Prime Minister would be glad to be assured that this mark of His Majesty's favour would be agreeable to you, and I am to ask that you will be so good as to communicate with me accordingly at your earliest convenience.

Yours faithfully,
ATTLEE,
Prime Minister."

Throughout the years the Honours system has become more and more debased and prostituted. John Major, in his genuine desire to make the system more democratic, abolished the British Empire Medal and lumped the MBEs and the BEMs together. The result had the opposite effect, and seriously upset those who received an MBE when it really meant something, which only goes to show the lack of judgement that exists in political life today. My award in 1945 made a terrific impact on me and all my friends and colleagues. It boosted my morale dramatically and more than adequately rewarded me for all the trials, tribulations and disappointments over the previous five years.

Strangely enough no one else at SAL was so honoured, and I was surprised that the efforts of David McIntyre, Dick Ellison and Stewart Kennedy had not been officially recognised in some way. I came to the conclusion that David McIntyre had upset the 'Establishment' so much that those close to him had been excluded, and that the politicians must have felt sorry for me because of the evil persecution against me during the "Hate Campaign." The award not only made me very happy but it was particularly pleasing for my family and friends.

CHAPTER 21

OF SWORDS AND PLOUGHSHARES

We had to face up to the problem of reducing a work force of some 7,500 people who had served us so loyally and efficiently during the war. There were no redundancy payments in these days but we wanted to treat everyone as kindly as possible. We had to make the best possible deals with the government, and after some tough negotiations they treated us fairly. DPCA procured work from Transport Command for the conversion of Liberators, Dakotas and Douglas C-54s, and CRO continued certain contracts for Spitfire and Hurricane repair & servicing.

The deal that David had made with Consolidated-Vultee and Douglas was a good one. We did not have to pay any royalties, but any improvements we made became the property of the principals. We were able to expand our engine overhaul activity with contracts from de Havilland for the overhaul of Gipsy engines, and negotiated a contract with Pratt & Whitney for the overhaul of their radial engines.

We also had to find commercial work for Prestwick and Greenock. There was a national shortage of low-priced houses and also buses & coaches. Some 'bright spark' had thought up pre-fabricated houses and so we explored that market. The most favoured design was the "Arcon"; this was a steel-framed structure with pre-fabricated plumbing, bathroom, kitchen and electrical units, and the main contractor was a large manufacturer of windows at Chester called Williams & Williams. We made contact through the Earl of Selkirk, who knew one of the Williams brothers, and we flew down to Chester in the SAL Consul piloted by the Earl. The Williams brothers, four of them, were all snobs and were very impressed to be doing business with a real Earl, and we came back with a contract for 20,000 Arcon houses complete with the units. The steel framework was made at Caird's Yard at Greenock and the units at Prestwick.

On the way back from Chester the weather closed in and we had to make a landing at Barrow-in-Furness and stay overnight. We had no overnight kit but nevertheless celebrated our success, and it was the only occasion I shared a bedroom with an Earl.

To meet the contract price, we needed a complete new layout at Gourock and very tight control of production times. Before the war ended I had taken on a very bright young graduate engineer from the Royal Technical College at Glasgow, and he and I went to Gourock and planned the layout. The job involved cutting to length various steel sections and arc-welding them together, then drilling & milling, and then dip-painting in a tank, with a whole array of conveyor equipment. I put the young engineer, James Eugenie Hunter, in charge and thought that all would go well, as most of the work force, including the girls, had previous shipyard experience. Yet two weeks later they were on strike, saying that they could not meet the times and make a decent wage as they were on a "payment by result" scheme.

I dashed up to Gourock and explained that we had only taken on this contract to keep them in work, and that if they were not prepared to make the effort, then we would have no alternative but to cancel the contract and close the place down. That shook them a bit, but they still said they could not make a decent wage. So I then offered to bring a management team up to Gourock, and explained that if we could not beat the times then we would talk again; grudgingly they agreed. We picked a team of foremen and managers, and on a Saturday morning at eight o'clock we started the plant. We allowed two shop stewards to act as observers, and by the Sunday afternoon had proved that all the times could be beaten and a very good wage earned. We retired in triumph to the Bay Hotel and had a good celebration.

Work resumed, we made a very handsome profit, and later received a repeat order. Hunter proved to be an excellent production manager, and remained with us till the end of the contract. But then we could not find any more work and the yard had to be closed down. James Hunter – he hated the name Eugenie – left and went to America; I kept in touch with him for many years and he eventually became Vice-President with Pratt & Whitney. George Fordyce, who I mentioned earlier, went into business with Sir John Colville to manufacture up-market kitchen units and made a lot of money. John Colville built a lovely house in Perthshire, which was completely round and became quite a showpiece. The units at Prestwick were successful too and made a good profit.

Bob McIntyre and his team designed a bus body and cab in duralumin with monocoque construction and glass wool insulation. It provided a light weight and strong assembly, and was not subject to corrosion as all parts were anodised. The light weight reduced running costs and soon there was a great demand. However there was a severe shortage of chassis, engines and transmissions. The first coaches were sold to Scottish Motor Traction, a bus monopoly run by the great entrepreneur John Sword, later Sir John. He became a millionaire and it was rumoured that he sold his buses when they were worn out at written-down book value to Millburn Motors, owned by another entrepreneur called James Sanderson, who revamped them and sold them to other bus companies at a high profit which they both then shared.

John Sword put me in touch with Sanderson, who said that he could get me chassis, engines and transmissions, so I went to see him; he was a great extrovert with loads of personality, and had a finger in many pies. He owned one of the best stores in Glasgow, and it was alleged to be run by his mistress. He arranged to take me to London and we went down by train first-class and booked in at the Mayfair Hotel. He then took me on a tour of drinking clubs by day and night clubs by night. When I asked him when we were going to do business he told me to shut up and learn patience. On the second evening we finished up in a sumptuous flat in Kensington, where there was champagne, music and girls, and in the centre of it all was Freddie Dawson, the famous dealer in War Surplus who eventually went to jail for selling contaminated orange juice.

When we eventually we got down to business Sanderson had negotiated the purchase of 250 Commer lorry bodies complete with engines for £280 a time. The next day when I pointed out that these were 2 ft 6 in too short for our buses he responded, did I think he was daft? He explained that he had it all fixed; the chassis and propeller shaft would be cut, the necessary extension pieces welded in, and there, lo & behold, a new bus chassis.

It was a great deal for Sanderson; he had cornered the market and controlled the supply of chassis, the sale of the finished product and the selling price. I was all for approaching Dawson but I was persuaded that that might be dangerous. I hated being outmanoeuvred, but I knew that Sanderson had laid out £70,000, as Dawson only did deals like that for cash, so I raised the price of our bodies. We sold two versions, a standard and a luxury coach and, fully equipped with seats, the price was £5,000 for a standard coach and £6,000 for the luxury version. When I learned that they were being sold on for £10,000 and £12,500 I was not at all pleased.

It seemed that we were doing all the work and Sanderson was making all the profit. As we had plenty of space at Prestwick, I arranged for a delivery of 50 chassis on the grounds that we were setting up a production line, and when these were delivered we stopped delivery of all the completed coaches. When Sanderson phoned, I told him that as he had not paid for any of them, my directors had instructed me to suspend delivery until all outstanding debts had been cleared. He was very angry indeed and phoned David McIntyre, who told him that he would have to deal with me. Eventually he invited me out, wined & dined me at one of the best restaurants in town, and then issued threats to sue for breach of contract. When I complained that he was taking an unfair advantage of me he told me that I had a lot to learn about business, and would have to understand how deals were arranged and fortunes made.

After a few more outbursts, I suggested we should each submit audited costs of the work we were each doing and then split the profit. Having heard that he was a bit short of cash, I offered him a cheque for £35,000 to finance half the chassis deal, provided that he paid for delivery of all the coaches within 30 days of delivery, subject to approval of my directors. He reluctantly agreed to this and my directors endorsed my plan. He was not then very pleased when I deducted all his outstanding debts from the £35,000 cheque. When he rang up I said that I thought that was fair.

He laughed and responded: “Laddie, you’re learning!”

Eventually we sold over 500 coaches. We also designed and built double-deckers, and most of these were sold to SMT and Alexander’s, but they were not as profitable as the coaches. Nearly 40 years later there was an article in the papers that some of them were still in service, one of them being in Arran.

We were then approached by an inventor from Greenock who had developed a folding caravan, but had no money to manufacture it. He was sure that it would sell in great numbers, as all the war veterans would want holidays and caravanning was becoming very popular. Bob McIntyre and his team redesigned it to be of monocoque construction with insulation. The roof could be jacked up and the sides unfolded, and it could sleep up to six. It had a small kitchen, a shower, a lavatory and Calor gas heating, and when it was all folded up it weighed just under 10 cwt, which meant that it could be towed easily behind a small car.

We built a prototype, which of course had to be road-tested, so McIntyre, Rowand and Neill, all being keen fishers, went off every other weekend into the Highlands of Scotland. We worked hard on the testing and kept records of the time taken to unfold it and have it ready for occupation, roadworthiness, comfort and whether it was leak-proof. This led to numerous modifications, and eventually we took many photographs and published a sales brochure. The caravan sold like the proverbial hot cakes and we could hardly make enough to fill the demand. It was price-sensitive and did not make a lot of money, but it gave us a lot of fun and made a good contribution to the overheads.

We also diversified into agriculture, as Dick Ellison had bought a farm at Trabboch Mains. The most popular tractor at that time was the Ferguson with hydraulic lift and numerous accessories, including a circular saw. However there was no cab, so drivers were fully exposed to the elements; Dick had suffered in this way and had the bright idea of that we could manufacture a suitable cab. So that's what we did; it was a huge success and sales rocketed, as it seemed that every farmer wanted one. It likewise had to be made to a price, but it always made a profit and, even more importantly, provided work for many loyal people who otherwise would have been made redundant. However the tractor makers soon caught on and began to make their own version. We tried to arrange a joint venture but Massey Ferguson, whose factory was at Gatehead near Kilmarnock, did not want to know.

Meanwhile David McIntyre made his own contribution to our diversification programme. He was intensely interested in the development of jet engines, and thought up the idea of a jet-propelled boat. A toy boat 9 in long was developed, made from aluminium and with a copper diaphragm inside the hull; this was connected to a jet pipe which protruded from the stern. Underneath the diaphragm was a little paraffin lamp; when the boat was put in the water the diaphragm filled, the water boiled, and away the little boat chugged: it was quite fascinating. We applied to the Board of Trade for a licence to make 50,000, but it was refused as aluminium was in very short supply, due to the need for peace-time kitchen utensils to replace those melted down during the war. But several hundred of these boats were made and gave great pleasure to many children.

Another great idea which came to nothing.

TOP: Dakota CS-TDF was the very first airliner to be delivered to Portugal for TAP after the war.
BOTTOM: Delivery of Dakota HB-IRL to Zurich; from L. to R., wireless operator (Tom), Dick Ellison, myself, Karl Meyer, Paul Westerman.
Photos: author's collection.

TOP: The first Dakota delivered to Fred Olsen Lines, probably LN-NAD. From L. to R., Olsen's chief pilot, radio operator (Bill), Olsen's MD, Fred Olsen, Dick Ellison, myself.
BOTTOM: Brian Powell and I sit in the comfort of Lord Beaverbrook's Dakota planning the route to fly "the Beaver" and Winston Churchill to Cannes. Photos: author's collection.

TOP: Fokker F.XXII G-AFZP of Scottish Airlines, c.1946.
BOTTOM: Scottish Airline's first Dakota, G-AGWS, c.1947.
Photos: via Prof. D. Cameron.

TOP: DH.86B G-ACZP seen during overhaul at Prestwick on the 10th April 1947.
BOTTOM: HB591, a Fairchild Argus for civilian conversion at Prestwick, c.1947. Photos: via Prof. D. Cameron.

CHAPTER 22

POST-WAR PLANS

Coping with the transition from a war-time to a peace-time economy was a challenge and a struggle. The fact that we achieved it at all, and always made a profit, was due to the dedication and understanding of all the people, and also to the initiative, innovation and determination of management. However aircraft conversions provided by far the greatest workload, and proved highly profitable. I found this work exciting and adventurous, and it gave me the opportunity to travel the world widely. David McIntyre's agreement with Douglas and Consolidated-Vultee provided us with an impressive lead; the world was awash with military aircraft most of them were on 'Lease-Lend.'

However, on 17th August 1945 'Lease-Lend' ended and ownership reverted to the US Government, who set up the Army Surplus Commission to sell at the best prices, some of which were ridiculously low. SAL had a stack of US dollars put aside, but exchange control made it difficult to obtain more of them. However we were able to buy three Liberators and five Dakotas. One Liberator and three Dakotas were converted for Scottish Airlines, and the others were used for demonstration.

David had his plans well laid. They included a night flight by Liberator to New York carrying 24 first-class sleeper passengers at £80 per head return, as well as mail and freight. He also had in mind a daily service to and from Canada and the USA, and direct connections from Prestwick to Paris, Amsterdam, Hamburg, Berlin, Oslo, Stockholm and Lisbon, using converted Dakotas. He also planned services to Moscow, Peking, Vladivostok, Alaska and Vancouver. Neither had he forgotten the Far East; he programmed flights to Vienna, Belgrade, Istanbul, Cairo, Karachi, Calcutta, Hong Kong and Tokyo. These were not just pipe-dreams but were carefully planned, including the logistics for passenger handling, fares, refuelling and servicing. He also planned to have converted Dakotas fitted out with a Customs & Immigration desk, so that foreign passengers landing at Prestwick could remain "in transit" and be cleared during their onward flights to London, Manchester, or wherever within the UK.

David made a formal application to the Americans for the purchase of 10 Liberators and 25 Dakotas. He offered $3,000 for each Liberator and $2,500 for each Dakota; all of these were lying at Prestwick unused, but were being maintained under a contract to SAL paid for by the Army Surplus Commission. The offer was accepted, and it would have been a good deal for everyone and provided further conversion work for the manufacturing side of SAL; however it was vetoed by the Labour Government, who were totally committed to a nationalised airline, and would not countenance any conflict of interest.

Nevertheless Scottish Airlines were allowed to accept a contract from BEA to fly from Prestwick to Belfast return. The first aircraft to fly this route was a *de luxe* converted Dakota, G-AGWS, carrying 21 passengers for 30 shillings single. It was so successful that the Government passed a bill nationalising all airliners registered in Britain.

But David McIntyre did not give up; he, his lawyers and American friends found a way – charter flights. Scottish Airlines contracted with foreign operators to supply aircraft & crews and run their airlines for them. They flew services for KLM, Air France, Sabena, Aer Lingus, Luxembourg Airlines, TAP (Portuguese) and Hellenic Airways – later Olympic. They flew regular services for Icelandic Airways using Dakotas and Catalina amphibians, and a Liberator flew a direct service twice weekly from London to Athens.

A long-term contract was signed between Scottish Aviation Ltd and the Greeks, David McIntyre being appointed to the Board of Hellenic Airways, and Tommy Hope, one of the original flying school instructors and a senior captain with Scottish Airlines, became the first managing director. Operationally this service and those run by other airlines using converted Dakotas were a tremendous success. Unfortunately, due to politics – and unscrupulous behaviour by the Greek directors – it finished up as a terrible financial disaster for Scottish Aviation, and eventually the company was taken over by Aristotle Onassis, the shipping tycoon. It was then renamed Olympic Airways, whose subsequent success added considerably to the fortune of the Onassis family. The saying "Never trust a Greek bearing gifts" proved only too true, and SAL got well and truly 'screwed.'

Scottish Airlines had another subsidiary, Scottish Air Express, with an office in Pall Mall, London, which specialised in air freight and travel agencies. In conjunction with the Anchor shipping line it ran a fortnightly "Fly-Cruise" to Portugal and the Spanish Riviera. David was also very friendly with the President of TWA, whose station manager at Prestwick was John Logan; John had operated from Prestwick Airport for some years, and had travelled with David on his tour of America in 1944. This resulted in further charter work to North & South Africa, and the Middle & Far East. At its peak Scottish Airlines had a fleet of 25 aircraft and over 100 aircrew. It played a major part in the Berlin Airlift and in the airlifting of refugees when Pakistan separated from India, with all the horror and massacres that that entailed.

But to us at SAL these were the years of plenty, adventure and fun, the years when SAL dominated the world in the art of converting and selling military aircraft dressed up as airliners. The first problem was to acquire ownership of aircraft to convert. As mentioned earlier, we purchased (with the help of MAP, CRO and our American friends) three Liberators and five Dakotas. Two of the Dakotas were overhauled and refurbished as demonstrators, one as a standard model and the other *de luxe*; the remaining aircraft were converted for Scottish Airlines. We designed and published glossy brochures highlighting all the advantages of the 'new' airliners, which were equipped with plush reclining seats, overhead luggage racks, attractive curtains, lighting, a lavatory, and a galley to serve light meals.

Throughout the years 1945 to 1950 Scottish Airlines was a major player in world aviation, and Prestwick was a major world-class airport, also responsible for weather and air traffic control over the Atlantic and continental Europe. David McIntyre was pressing his Board to sanction the purchase of three Constellations, which were Lockheed's very first of the new post-war airliners, and in the early 1950s he wanted to buy Comets, de Havilland's revolutionary jet-powered airliner, further examples of his forward thinking.

CHAPTER 23

A NORTHERN EUROPEAN SALES TOUR

Just after VE-day, on 12th May 1945, Dick Ellison and I, with a wireless operator, a flight engineer and a beautiful hostess took off on a sales tour of Northern Europe. We planned to visit Norway, Sweden, Denmark, Holland, Belgium and Switzerland. After a smooth flight we landed at Oslo, met our contacts and arranged demonstration flights for the next day. The interest was intense, and we were flying for most of the day showing the aircraft off to different people. The airfield was busy, and there was a holiday atmosphere all around.

We felt flattered, but soon learned that it was not our visit that had generated the enthusiasm: that day was traditionally "Freedom Day," a national holiday when everyone had a party. They were celebrating the secession of Norway from Sweden, but as this anniversary was the first since Germany's defeat the celebrations were all the more elaborate.

Our hosts entertained us royally; for the next 48 hours we went from party to party. There was dancing in the streets, firework displays, parades, bands & music of all descriptions, and much drinking of champagne and aquavit. Mindful of the strenuous programme ahead Dick and I stayed reasonably sober, but one evening we became separated from our engineer, wireless operator and hostess. We found our wireless operator out for the count in a bar near our hotel and had to carry him home. The next morning he was suffering from a terrible hangover, but the other two arrived for breakfast bright and smiling, and we made our departure to Stockholm on schedule.

Our welcome there was cordial and we were invited to dinner by some Swedish friends I had made during my war-time visit to rescue the "Air Grocer" B-17. The Swedes are not quite as extrovert as the Norwegians, but our visit was certainly a success. The highlight of that visit was the excitement of shopping where there were no shortages of any kind. Time was tight but one of our friends arranged for us to go to one of the most prestigious emporiums in the city; his father was a director there and we were given VIP treatment. We wanted to buy clothes, shoes and toys for our wives and children, so we were each given an assistant who could advise on size and quality. I bought Joy a beautiful bath robe which she wore for many years, together with a nightie and a dress, a dress and shoes for Gill, and a romper suit and little shoes for Alastair. I also bought some beautiful glassware, which we still have. And believe it or not all the clothes fitted! We stayed in the Grand Hotel, and I can remember standing at my bedroom window early the next morning watching fishermen throwing a huge weighted net into the water and then dragging it up with lots of fish in it.

We then proceeded to Copenhagen, which I remembered well from my *S.S. Neuralia* cruise. The Danes did not seem to have the same enthusiasm as the Norwegians or even the Swedes, and we gathered that a certain gentleman in Danish Airlines was alleged to be still pro-German and a little anti-British. The highlight of that visit was my ability to show the others the best sights of Copenhagen, particularly the Tivoli Gardens.

And so on to Schiphol, the home of KLM, where we were met by Dr Plesman and Curly Veenandahl, Vice-President (Engineering). Dick Ellison knew them both because of the original purchase of the Fokkers for No. 1 AONS. They were very impressed with our demonstration and were particularly interested, as the KLM DC-2 piloted by Parmentier and Moll had come second in the Mildenhall to Melbourne Air Race in 1934. What was even better, they owned several Dakotas all ready for conversion, so it was agreed that I would return soon after the current tour was over to discuss contract conditions and price.

The visit to Brussels was even more promising, and we were thrilled to learn that King Leopold of the Belgians wished to have a demonstration flight. At first I was not overly impressed, particularly about his surrender to the Germans against his Cabinet's wishes. However he was a keen aviator, spoke good English and was charming, and wanted to know if we would design and convert a personal aircraft for him. He said that he would provide the plane plus five others he wished to have converted for the Belgian Air Force. That certainly endeared him to me!

We then proceeded to Zurich, where we were met by Dr Brandt, the engineering director of Swissair. He was a taciturn Swiss gentleman and seldom smiled, but he was always courteous and correct. He asked if he could come to Prestwick and see our set-up, and of course we said we would be delighted. In due course he did so and a contract was signed. So we flew home very satisfied with our tour.

Some weeks later I went to Amsterdam to negotiate the contract. As KLM were supplying five Dakotas, and we did not know their condition, discussions were lengthy. I suggested two contracts, one for conversion and one for overhaul; the latter price would be quoted after a strip inspection at Prestwick, which if they so wished could be verified by their own engineers. After three days of tough negotiation the contract was signed. I was very impressed by Mr Veenandahl; he was very fair, commented that "you only get what you pay for," and prevented the Vice-President (Finance) from squeezing the prices too hard. He looked after me very well, showed me the sights of the City, took me out to dinner, and took me drinking in the *Flying Dutchman* hostelry which all the KLM crews and personnel frequented after work.

I was staying in the Central Hotel, previously the YMCA, complete with indoor swimming pool, badminton & squash courts and a gymnasium. It was arranged that a KLM car would pick me up at six o'clock the next morning to drive me to The Hague so that I could fly in one of the Dakotas back to Prestwick. I had an early dinner and, tired out with all the negotiations, I went to bed. But I was so excited at signing the first contract that I could not sleep, so I got up, dressed and went down to the bar. There I met Nick Campbell, an American who, I discovered, had been a Major with the Quartermaster Regiment of the US Army Air Force. He had been transferred to the Commission for Disposal of Surplus Equipment, and was in the process of negotiating a deal with KLM for aircraft and spares. He knew Amsterdam much better than I did and so we went out on the town and visited some of the bars. In those days the city was much more respectable than it is now and there was no noticeable drug scene. We walked through the 'red light' district and finished up at a night club called *Le Rossignol.* I was impressed by the kindness and friendship shown to us wherever we went because of the fact that British and Americans had liberated Holland, and everyone was very grateful. We met up with two pretty Dutch girls and danced a few dances with them, but mindful of my early start I walked back to the hotel, had a couple of hours sleep, and then was picked up and was soon on my way to The Hague.

It was a bitterly cold and frosty morning, and my fellow car passenger was the pilot of the Dakota, who had flown with the Dutch Navy and spoke little English. I found the landscape very flat, with many canals and bridges, but it didn't take long to reach the outskirts of The Hague; I found the city remarkable for the number of handsome buildings, churches and spires.

At that time the airfield surface was grass, reinforced with metal netting. There were 10 passengers for the flight, plus a crew of three. We took off and climbed over the city, and it was then that the port engine failed. The pilot dived to gain speed and we just missed the roofs of some high buildings, and then the starboard engine also failed and I knew we were going to crash. All the passengers were sitting on the long bench seats down each side of the fuselage; so I unbuckled my safety belt and lay down on the floor with my feet against the forward bulkhead, and kept in that position until we crash-landed on the sand dunes just short of the sea.

The next thing I can remember was that I was running like hell away from the aircraft. Dakotas had a habit of burning on crash landings, so my subconscious memories told me to get as far away as possible. Eventually I stopped and looked back. There was no fire, but neither was there any movement from the plane, which had split open – there were bodies everywhere. Fire engines and ambulances were soon on the scene, but I do not remember very clearly what happened next, except that I was told I had concussion and had to rest.

Some hours later Curly Veenandahl was at my bedside, very concerned. The aircraft was a write-off but fortunately no one had been killed. He said that he had laid on another aircraft to fly me back to Prestwick, but I told him that there was no way I would fly again and that I would go home by sea. However a doctor cleared me to travel and gave me an injection and some pills; they must have been heavy tranquillisers, because after an hour I was on top of the world and ready for anything, and so I flew back safely to Prestwick on a Lockheed 8-seater. Fortunately I had no lasting effects from the accident.

Shortly afterwards a replacement Dakota arrived at Prestwick for conversion. We were told that, when the previous one had crashed, the first engine failure was due to the pilot failing to run up his engines before take off, and the second was because the wrong propeller had been feathered and the healthy engine had been shut down. Fortunately, apart from broken limbs and some chest & head damage, no one had been seriously injured. What a lucky escape for us all! A similar crash happened in Denmark a few weeks later, which burned and killed all on board, including the Crown Prince of Sweden and Grace Moore, the famous singer. The reason the KLM Dakota did not burn was because the pilot had switched off all the electrics and the soft sand had not only smothered all the sparks but had also absorbed the fuel leakage.

The very first civil airliner to fly after the war in Europe, and perhaps in the whole world, was a converted KLM Dakota, PH-TBR. It was a SAL 21-seater standard model, and I had the joy of flying in it on its delivery flight to Schiphol in September 1945. It was piloted by Captain Parmentier, KLM's chief pilot, and a very special celebration took place when it landed. That week was the first anniversary of the battle of Arnhem, which was being celebrated all over Holland. PH-TBR flew over Arnhem at the height of the festivities, and I will always remember the sight that met our eyes as we flew slowly overhead – a huge firework display, cheering crowds, and military music from massed bands, which we could hear clearly despite the noise of the engines.

Dr Plesman had laid on a dinner party in the Amstel Hotel, to which I was invited; I was seated next to a beautiful girl, and on her other side was Nicky Campbell, who had just completed a big deal for the sale of spares as mentioned earlier. Of course we started competing for the girl's attention. Bols gin was the national drink; it had a faint oniony taste and was drunk neat, and this with the food and the wine made me feel a little queasy, so I retired to the cloakroom to bathe my face with cold water. The celebrations continued, but I do not remember much except that I awoke the next morning in a strange bed in a beautiful flat. It turned out that the girl had felt sorry for me and, as I had no hotel booked and nowhere to go, she had taken me home.

That day I spent with Curly Veenandahl, discussing the next conversion, which was going to be a *de luxe* model. I also asked about his deal on spares and emphasised that if he had any surplus I would like to buy some. He said he had made a very good deal with Campbell and had more than enough, so if I brought over a list of our requirements he would try to accommodate us.

We also discussed his wartime experiences; I did not realise the trauma of living in a country overrun by the Germans until I heard how the Veenandahl family had existed throughout the war. They were of Jewish extraction and the horror was absolute; the cold, the hunger and the deprivations were bad enough, but the threat of being arrested, interrogated and tortured was constantly with them. To see their friends disappearing and possibly being killed or sent to concentration camps was almost unbearable. He took me home to meet his family and showed me the hidden cellar where he had sheltered some of his friends for two years, and explained how difficult it had been to find food for them with the constant fear of discovery. After liberation the relief was so great that they wept tears of joy, but even after that the shortages of food and clothing were far greater than in Britain, and Curly asked if I could send him bolts of worsted cloth and bicycles for his family and friends; I promised to do what I could on the next delivery.

However such things were not only difficult to get, they required export licences. When I returned to Prestwick I phoned a contact of mine, Syd Harris, and he, being a Jew, was very sympathetic and promised to help. We had been very good customers of Tube Investments during the war and they undertook to get us priority deliveries of bicycles. The next problem was to arrange export licences, which proved very difficult. I went and talked to my friends in Customs & Immigration and told them of the sufferings in Holland. They discreetly turned a blind eye, and thereafter every aircraft delivered carried bicycles, bolts of cloth and knitwear. In return, incoming aircraft for conversion carried barrels of oysters, crates of Dutch gin & Advocaat, and a variety of Dutch cheeses, so every time we had a party, to which of course we invited our understanding friends.

I became quite friendly with the Veenandahls and on the next visit I did a deal for a large quantity of spares for Dakotas, C-54 Skymasters and Pratt & Whitney engines. He let me have them at cost, in spite of the fact that due to short supply prices were rising daily. Curly was a man of great kindness and integrity, highly thought of throughout the aviation industry. His word was his bond and once he had shaken hands that was as good as a guaranteed contract.

To illustrate: some months afterwards Bruce Erskine showed me invoices for spares which had been charged at three times the price agreed. When Bruce phoned the accounts department in Holland he was told that the prices were correct and reflected current increases. The next time I was in Amsterdam I somewhat diffidently raised the matter with Curly, whereupon he sent for the financial director, gave him a good bawling out, and warned him: “Never ever do that again; when I make an agreement I never break it.”

During that visit another amusing event occurred which showed me that one can never be too careful in a foreign country. One evening I took an American acquaintance to the night club *Le Rossignol*. They remembered me from previous visits and we had a very good time. As we left to walk back to the hotel the American said: “Oh! I’ve left my scarf, I’ll just nip back and get it.”

But the next morning he did not appear for breakfast, and neither did the KLM car come to collect us. When I phoned KLM I was informed that there had been a problem, and the car would call as soon as possible. Eventually I learned that when the American returned to the night club it was to keep an assignment with the girl to whom he had taken a fancy. In the morning he had awakened in a down-town flat, completely naked and minus all his possessions, including clothes, shoes, money, passport and airline tickets.

My friendship with Curly Veenandahl ended in very tragic circumstances. A year or two later KLM purchased one of the new Lockheed Constellations, and Curly was flying back on it from America, intending to stop over at Prestwick. The Constellation was being flown by Captain Parmentier, and as it was just about to land at Prestwick it touched the top of a hill; it recovered but then flew under some power lines and crashed, killing everyone on board with the exception of the Lockheed representative, who jumped out but died later in hospital. It was a terrible blow that such a good and kind man as Curly should survive all he had suffered during the war, and then should be killed so tragically.

The accident enquiry established that the primary cause had been a faulty map. The height shown on the map for the approach path was 380 ft lower than the true height. Parmentier, a very experienced and careful pilot, had been flying in cloud and had just touched the ground with the undercarriage, but had not been able to recover in time to miss the high tension wires strung on pylons.

The second civil airliner to fly in Europe was a *de luxe* 21-seater Dakota, G-AGZG, for Scottish Airlines. David McIntyre was pressing hard at the time for the completion of two other Dakotas and three Liberator 24-seat conversions, all for Scottish Airlines.

David's enthusiasm to get Scottish Airlines flying was well known, and caused us some embarrassment. Six aircraft being converted for the Ministry were not getting along very fast, and sure enough we had a visit one day from two high officials from MAP. They arrived just before lunch, chatted to us quite pleasantly, and congratulated us on the publicity covering the first civil airliner to fly in Europe for KLM. It was clear where this conversation was heading, so Fred Hopkins took them off to lunch at the Mess in the old Orangefield Hotel.

I excused myself, saying I would join them later, and dashed over to the hangar containing their aircraft. Little work was being done on them, so I sought out Frank Burnard and explained about our visitors. Some speedy reorganisation was done, and after a good lunch we took them on tour. They were complimentary about our factory layout, and said how marvellous it was to see an organisation which had obtained so much work so quickly and was such a hive of activity. They then asked if they could see their aircraft, and we said "of course," and off we went. They wanted to know why completion was taking so long, and Frank Burnard explained that the delays were because the aircraft were in poor condition, having stood around for so long without maintenance. He also explained that there was a spares shortage and the contract stated that MAP were responsible for supplying them. They looked a bit dumbfounded and promised to do something about it on their return.

But it turned out that they did not have any spares, as stocks had reverted to the US Army under 'Lease-Lend.' However they did have about 50 Dakotas lying at Silloth which they had bought as a job lot, and they asked if we could send a working party there to cannibalise some of the aircraft for spares. Of course we were delighted to oblige. We eventually received a contract to have a permanent working party at Silloth to service the aircraft there, and later still we bought some of them for a song.

Bob McIntyre's team designed a super-executive aircraft for King Leopold the Third. It was an 8-seater with lounge and dining accommodation, a galley & bar, and two settees which could be turned into sleeping quarters. The quality was of the highest, with wood veneers for all the furniture and luxurious reclining seats. The King and his new wife, created Princesse de Rethy after a morganatic marriage, were delighted, and an order for five *de luxe* conversions for the nationalised Belgian airline – which eventually became Sabena – was confirmed. Leopold became very unpopular later and eventually a regency was created under his brother Charles, but that was after all the aircraft had been paid for and delivered.

The Sabena chief pilot was a most charming and talented man, and had flown into Prestwick many times. Again tragedy struck one day as he was leading a flight of five aircraft into Prestwick for conversion. The weather was bad and he had instructed his other pilots to fly round the coast over the sea and head into Prestwick that way, whereas he knew well the direct route over the hills and planned to follow it. But he never arrived and there was no "May Day." An air search was mounted and sure enough a burnt out-aircraft was spotted on the hills above the infamous Rhinns of Kells just above Carsphairn. It was a notorious area for aircraft crashes, as the configuration of the hills caused heavy turbulence and severe downdraughts. The only Tiger Moth to be lost from No. 12 EFTS with pupil and instructor had crashed there, killing both.

I knew the district very well, had climbed most of the mountains and had fished – with Hugh Rowand – Lochs Harrow and Minnoch, which were just below North Garry Top – 3,210 ft high. Hugh and I set off in a Land Rover to Carsphairn and thence south to Earlston Loch, and drove up the track at the Pollharrow burn to Loch Harrow, from whence we had to proceed on foot. We guessed that the pilot had made his landfall at Wigton Bay and was navigating in a straight line for Prestwick. The aircraft must have just passed over the saddle between Millfire and North Garry when a downdraught pulled it into the side of North Garry Top. The bodies were so badly burned that they were unrecognisable. The two pilots, seconds before the crash, must have risen from their seats as they were clasped in each other's arms in what was left of the cockpit. We set off downhill and met the RAF Mountain Rescue team on their way up with stretchers and body bags. We were shocked and saddened and arranged for the village hall to be used as a mortuary. But the worst part was still to come when we took two of the pilots from the other aircraft to try to identify the bodies and attend the inquest. Rings, watches, and dentistry were the only means of identification. I wondered what had gone through the minds of the crew just before impact and had the dreadful thought that it might happen to me some day.

CHAPTER 24

MORE AIRLINER CONVERSIONS

The first Liberator to be turned into a 24-seater *de luxe* airliner was G-AHZR. Another two quickly followed, together with the second and third Dakota. The conversion business went on from strength to strength, and orders kept rolling in. The first aircraft for Swissair was Dakota HB-IRL. Typically for the Swiss, we had a Swissair engineer, Karl Meyer, to oversee the overhaul and conversion, and he was very thorough.

Dick Ellison and I had a bright idea and we suggested that we should take our wives over on the delivery flight so that they could enjoy a holiday in Switzerland. The suggestion was welcomed and *en route* to Zurich we flew down to Croydon to pick up some freight. By the time this was loaded there was hardly room for Joy and Beryl, and the weight was getting near the maximum allowed. Trust the Swiss to save the pennies on freight charges! We had to get the loaders to readjust the weight distribution because of the centre of gravity and, of course, to free two seats for our wives.

The journey was a good one but when we arrived over the airfield it was full of sheep. Karl, whose English was not very good, kept pointing out of the windows shouting: "Muttons, muttons, no good." Dick called the control tower, who apologised, said the sheep would be moved as soon as possible, and could we please fly a holding circuit. I was sitting in the second pilot's seat when suddenly the starboard engine cut out. I immediately shut down the engine and feathered the propeller; in view not only of our weight but also my memories of past crashes I was more than a little worried, but Dick kept his 'cool' and we landed safely.

We were met by a charming young man called Paul Westerman, who spoke impeccable English and took us for lunch in the airport restaurant. As Karl Meyer had signed out the engines he was left to diagnose the fault, but this turned out to be a simple fuel blockage. Paul drove us to our hotel and said that he and Dr Brandt would like us to have dinner with them that evening at the famous Bor au Lac on the side of the lake. We had excellent food and excellent Swiss wine, and a very pleasant evening was had by all. At night we had our first experience with a Swiss duvet on the bed: no sheets, no blankets, and the duvet kept falling off, so we were either too cold or too hot.

The next two days we spent sightseeing. We sailed on the lake, drove up into the mountains, had a trip on a funicular railway, and went by train to Berne. We were impressed by the cleanliness and the efficiency everywhere. We bought ourselves Omega watches and, of course, Swiss chocolate for our children. Then it was time for Dick and me to return home, while Joy and Beryl went off to Rapperswil, a beautiful Swiss village on the lake. They had a lovely holiday and enjoyed the peace and rest – and the shopping, as they had indulged in a little currency speculation. They discovered that they could cash their travellers' cheques for Swiss francs and then buy pounds and come home with more money than they had started with. It was illegal, of course, but they did not know that and it turned out that many others did it all the time. Swissair flew them home to Croydon and I met them at Kilmarnock station.

There were also many pilots from Czechoslovakia who knew Prestwick well, and it was not surprising that the National Airline CSA should come there for their Dakota conversions. The first of these was delivered to Prague by Dick and myself. The Labour Government was particularly interested in the political climate there after the war, and we were asked to take a delegation of 10 politicians with us. I expected Prague to be a dull and deprived city, considering what they had suffered during the war, but in fact it was just the reverse, full of gaiety, dancing and song, with loads of beautiful girls bent on having a good time. One of the politicians was a young and handsome man with a very enquiring mind, anxious to see everything and learn everything and who wanted to take part in all the festivities: his name was Harold Wilson.

We flew them all back to Croydon on an unconverted Dakota, and with memories of what had happened to me at The Hague, I spent a full morning giving the plane a stringent inspection before signing the flight certificate. We bought some beautiful cut crystal in Prague and I was particularly pleased with a salad bowl I had bought for Joy. I was not so pleased to have to pay £25 duty on it at Croydon when all the politicians were cleared without question.

One day Colonel Humberto Delgado, the President of the Portuguese airline TAP, arrived in my office. He was a charming man, spoke excellent English and had a suitcase full of money in case we wanted a deposit. We showed him around and before he left we had signed a contract for five Dakota conversions, three standard models and two *de luxe*. He would supply the aircraft and there would be a separate overhaul contract after strip inspection. I wondered why countries like Holland and Portugal could get surplus aircraft so easily while we found it so hard. In confidence he told me that ready cash and contacts were the answer, and gave me a telephone number. I discovered that there was a flourishing black market all over Europe and North Africa; certain people were becoming millionaires by dealing in surplus equipment, much of which was not even on record.

Freddie Dawson of bus body fame was an expert on US Army deals, including food and cigarettes, but he eventually went to jail as I explained earlier. Colonel Herb Johnson, who had been a car salesman in Chicago, was the USAF Surplus supremo. I got to know him well and liked him; he was clever, efficient and 'on the make,' but was very careful. He was a man who kept his word and he never broke his promise to me. In 1950, after I had left SAL and joined de Havilland, he enlisted my help in a court case he was having against certain of his associates who had swindled him out of a company called Global Aviation that he had set up.

The first aircraft to be delivered to TAP was a *de luxe* model, CS-TDF, and at the invitation of Colonel Delgado it was delivered by Dick Ellison, Tom Watson (the wireless operator) and myself. It was a glorious sunny day, and as we flew over the North Sea, down the French coast and across the Bay of Biscay, everything seemed so calm and peaceful. We could see the coast of Portugal when my eye caught the petrol gauge and I was alarmed to see that the needle was nearly on 'empty.' Neither Dick nor I could understand this as we had both checked the flight plan and ensured that we had adequate fuel for the journey. We were flying at 12,000 ft, so Dick throttled back the engines to conserve fuel. Just as we crossed the coastline both engines started to splutter, but we managed to landed safely, although even before we had finished taxying both engines stopped. We were safe, but rather humiliated, as the welcoming party was awaiting our arrival; Dick had to call up the control tower and ask for a tractor to tow us in. We discovered later that this aircraft, unbeknown to us, had been fitted with self-sealing tanks, which reduced the fuel load, but this had never been recorded in the log.

It was our first visit to Portugal and we were very hot. It was customary during summer to have a siesta of three hours in the middle of the day and then work till seven or even eight in the evening, so this meant of course that an evening meal did not start much before 10 pm. The arrival of the first Portuguese civil airliner since the war was a great event, and a suitable celebration had been organised for the following evening.

The next morning we were back at the airport at 6 am to familiarise the crew with their new aircraft, and then took all the dignitaries for courtesy flights along the beautiful Portuguese coastline. We then returned to our hotel for the siesta, but found we could not use the lift as there were firemen and ambulance men there; apparently a little boy had climbed onto the top of the lift and had been crushed to death.

At 7 pm we set off to the celebration dinner in Lisbon. It was a lavish affair and lasted for five hours – there were 12 courses with a different wine for each. Delgado was not only President of TAP but was an active politician and a member of the government, so there was a galaxy of VIPs attending, many speeches, and much hilarity – most of which, of course, we could not follow. About 1 am those still reasonably sober took off for a night club. A lasting memory was the number of balloons decorating the hall there, and when one burst it was quickly replaced by one of the hostesses; it took me some time to realise that all the 'balloons' were in fact condoms. Both the class system and social relationships were strict and well-defined, and we should have known that no respectable ladies would frequent a night club, indeed no respectable lady would go out alone without a chaperon. There was a vast gap between the rich and the poor, and no conversation would take place without a formal introduction first.

The following day Humberto Delgado took us on a tour of Lisbon and told us something of his life and future ambitions. In due course the other four aircraft were delivered and all were paid for promptly. I never heard from Delgado again, but many years later he was in the headlines of the national papers here when it was reported that his body had been found buried in a shallow grave. We never heard the outcome, but it was suspected that his murder had been politically motivated.

CHAPTER 25

A CHALLENGE I COULD NOT RESIST

I am fortunate in having been able to retain all the passports I have used over the years, and these have been of great help in recalling where I went and when. I was widely travelled in Europe and the African Continent negotiating contracts, and on special occasions delivering aircraft. The reason I mention this now will become apparent in a moment.

In 1946 I started having eye trouble. I had inflammation in the eyes and bouts of pain behind them, and the diagnosis was conjunctivitis. However the condition got worse and the bouts of pain became more severe. At times they would disappear and I would feel fine, and then they would return with increasing intensity; in fact they became so bad that on one occasion I was confined to bed and even strong painkillers did not alleviate the pain. Joy then called in a specialist, who was critical of the doctor and diagnosed iritis. He said that it had been left untreated for so long that I might lose my sight. I was terrified as Dad had a history of eye trouble and was slowly going blind. I was given drops to dilate the pupils, and had to stay in bed in a darkened room. Then the search began to find the cause. Dr Stevenson, the SAL doctor, was most attentive: I had blood tests, urine tests, X-rays of just about everything – including my teeth – and they all came up negative. Dr Stevenson and the specialist had a conference in my room and the latter asked Dr Stevenson why he had not checked for venereal disease, as this was one of the possible causes. Dr Stevenson explained that he knew me well enough to think that such a test was unnecessary, but he got well and truly told off for being unprofessional, and I was cross-examined too. So further blood tests were made, but all was well.

Eventually, after throat swabs were taken and sent to the pathology laboratory, it was discovered that I had a particularly virulent streptococcal infection, probably picked up abroad. I was given antibiotics, which got rid of the infection, but my eyes still gave trouble. That was a very worrying and frustrating time. The pain lessened but I could not focus my eyes and my sight was very blurred, so much so that I could not read or write. I spent four weeks in a darkened room and my main relaxation was playing Solitaire; I learned to move all the marbles by touch, so that it was easy to solve the puzzle. Every day I tried to beat my own record on the time it took from start to finish. Joy and the children were a great comfort and when finally I was allowed to get up and get out, it came as a marvellous relief to find that I could see again. I was desperate to get back to work as there was so much happening, but I was only allowed to go back for short periods.

During my convalescence I spent some time in the Mess chatting to the various pilots and aircrews. The subject of Passport & Custom Control came up, and the view was that officials were cracking down on passport and baggage examination. I was foolish enough to be talked into a bet that I could travel across Europe without a passport or Customs check. I was offered odds of five to one on a $200 bet, and a bonus of another $100 for every airport through which I passed. This bonus would be waived unless I could produce documentary proof of having entered and left each place. It seemed too good to turn down and, as soon as my doctors cleared me to travel, I planned the journey. Naturally I had to leave my passport behind with those taking the wager.

I started off by flying to Iceland with Scottish Airlines, and then continued to Oslo, Stockholm, Copenhagen, Hamburg, Schiphol, Brussels, Paris, Zurich, and Lisbon. It was ridiculously easy; I had hand luggage only, with a big ticket on it saying “Crew in Transit.” I knew all the airports well, and also how and where to go to hitch a lift to the next destination. I had my SAL lapel badge Ref. No. 1070 prominently displayed on my jacket, and in my pocket my Ministry of Aviation Aircraft Engineer’s Licence. Fred Hopkins had strongly recommended that I should apply for this as soon as the Air Registration Board reintroduced the exams after the war. I had to sit written examinations on Dakotas, Skymasters and Liberators, followed by rigorous oral and practical tests. I passed and thus had the authority to carry out inspections and certify aircraft as fit for flight. At each airport I made a purchase and asked for a dated receipt, as it had been agreed that this would provide evidence for my attendance at each airport. All went according to plan until I reached Zurich, where I was stopped and interrogated. The official spoke little English and I spoke no Swiss. He kept saying “Passport, passport,” and I shrugged and pretended that I did not understand.

When an interpreter arrived I explained that I was ‘in transit’ and was making my way to Lisbon to certify an aircraft as fit for flight, and in my hurry had forgotten to bring my passport. I was told that it was a criminal offence to try to enter Switzerland without a passport, and I was locked up. What a fool I had been even to try; the prospect of losing $200 when I was so near to success was hard to bear, but the thought of a prison sentence was even worse.

Then I had a brain wave. A working party from SAL was in Lisbon at TAP replacing the self-sealing tanks that had nearly caused our Dakota to crash into the sea some time earlier; if I could convince the Swiss that I was going there maybe they would agree that I could continue my journey. I asked for the use of a phone and rang Dr Brandt at Swissair. He was not there but I got Paul Westerman and explained my predicament. Paul roared with laughter and thought it was a huge joke, but within the hour he was with me, together with someone from Passport Control; I was given a stern lecture and then released. I took Paul and the passport man to dinner, paid the bill and got a receipt, and then Paul told me I could get a night flight to Lisbon, courtesy of Swissair. Once there I made contact with the SAL team in case someone checked, inspected the tanks and signed the flight certificate. The SAL team would be returning to Croydon, and I could have gone with them, but after

Zurich I was a little wary; I did not want to get caught at Croydon on the very last leg.

So I talked to the operations manager at TAP and found that they had a flight to Luxembourg the following morning. As I explained earlier, Scottish Airlines were running Luxembourg Airlines, and I knew that I would have no difficulty in getting a flight back to Prestwick. All went to plan and I arrived back safely at Prestwick, then as I was walking through the terminal two men in uniform approached and said: "Mr Neill, you have not passed through Immigration or cleared Customs yet. Please come this way."

I was completely shocked. Then they both burst out laughing: they were party to the bet. I had won!

TOP: Trans-Canada Lancastrian CF-CMW at Prestwick, c. 1946.
BOTTOM: Hellenic Airlines Liberator SX-DAA at Prestwick, c.1947.
Photos: via Prof. D. Cameron.

TOP: TWA Dakota NC54549 at Prestwick, c.1947.
BOTTOM: Scottish Airlines Dakota G-AIOF outside the Fokker hangar at Prestwick, 1947.
Photos: via Prof. D. Cameron.

TOP: KLM DC-4 PH-TCE with the Orangefield Hotel in the background, c.1947.
BOTTOM: Danish Airlines' converted B-17 OY-DFA at Prestwick, c.1947.
Photos: via Prof. D. Cameron.

TOP: KLM Dakota PH-TBN at Prestwick, c.1948.
BOTTOM: G-AHZR, the first Liberator converted for Scottish Airlines, c.1948.
Photos: via Prof. D. Cameron.

TOP: Passengers disembark from Scottish Airlines Dakota G-AGZF at Prestwick, c.1948.
BOTTOM: The Bristol Brabazon visits Prestwick, c.1950.
Photos: via Prof. D. Cameron.

TOP: This artist was flown all the way from Addis Ababa to paint the insignia on all the aircraft for Haile Selassie, the *Lion of Judah*. Photo: author's collection.
BOTTOM: VL515, the prototype Prestwick Pioneer (A.2/45) with its original Gipsy Queen engine. Photo: via Prof. D. Cameron.

TOP: G-AJIA, an early BEA Dakota conversion.
BOTTOM: G-ALYF, the prototype *Pionair* conversion for BEA, seen in one of the first liveries c.1950.
Photos: via Prof. D. Cameron.

TOP: Roll-out of G-ANTP, the prototype Twin Pioneer, in June 1955.
BOTTOM: The derelict Walrus G-AJNO, still at Prestwick in 1955.
Photos: via Prof. D. Cameron.

CHAPTER 26

THE *LION OF JUDAH*, CEYLON, INDIA & PAKISTAN

With my eye trouble and many weeks of worry, I had been very depressed. This successful adventure I've just related was a great boost to my ego and lifted my spirits tremendously. My friends were very complimentary, as they had been sure it could not be done, and very generously paid out in full – $3,000. At the time of the bet I think that they were feeling sorry for me, as I later learned that a rumour had been going around that I was going blind.

I was no sooner back to work than I was off again on a delivery flight to Oslo in the first Fred Olsen Line *de luxe* Dakota conversion. On my return the TWA Operations Manager wanted me to fly to Addis Ababa with him; he had negotiated a contract to run Ethiopian Airlines and had undertaken to supply five aircraft. Haile Selassie, the Emperor and the *Lion of Judah*, had taken refuge in Britain when his country had been conquered by the Italians, and had then been restored to power when we threw them out in 1941; he was therefore very pro-British. I wondered why the contract to run the airline had gone to TWA and not to Scottish Airlines, but it turned out that it was part of a deal by David McIntyre to enlist TWA's help in running Atlantic services by Scottish Airlines.

We flew in a TWA DC-4 with a refuelling stop at Tripoli, and then across Libya and the Sudan to Addis Ababa. After the vast desert wastes of the Sudan I was surprised how mountainous Ethiopia was, and how pleasantly cool it was when we stepped out of the plane. I was struck by the poverty and backwardness of the villages we flew over and the affluence in the capital itself. The palace was a building of grandeur, and the splendour of the uniforms and the protocol surrounding the Emperor was impressive. He was regarded more as a god than a human being, and we were instructed as how to behave in his presence. Talk about bowing and scraping: however we had to conform. Eventually we were ushered in to the throne room, and there he was in a splendid uniform, wafting a jewelled fly-switch. The major domo made a little speech, which we could not understand, the Emperor welcomed us in perfect English, and then we all departed.

Some time later we went to the Emperor's private quarters, and this time he was in civilian clothes, impeccably dressed and with a broad smile on his face. He was a tiny man but had both personality and presence. He had flown in the King of the Belgians' executive aircraft and wanted a better one. He showed us some sketches of what he wanted, and hinted that price was of no object, but it must be a plane fit for the *Lion of Judah*. We had supper with him and he behaved like a perfect English gentleman. Next morning we went into the contract side of the business with his advisors, and negotiated a satisfactory price for five aircraft. When I quoted a price of around £40,000 for the royal aircraft no one batted an eyelid. The sketches had been drawn by an Ethiopian artist who had been educated in England, and when the aircraft were nearing completion this young man came to Prestwick and painted all the insignia on the fuselage himself.

Shortly after I had returned home David McIntyre had a phone call from Lord Pakenham, Minister for Air, stating that he had been contacted by the Air Transport Minister of Ceylon about the purchase of civil airliners. Mr Kotelewala, the Minister, was expected in London the following week, and could David come and meet him? David had a permanent suite in the Savoy, so a meeting was arranged there and I was asked to go as well. David tried his best to persuade the Minister that he should not bother to buy aircraft but should let Scottish Airlines supply the aircraft and the crews, and also run the airline. David was at his most charming and convincing best, and I felt that he had persuaded the Minister; however for political reasons the suggestion was turned down although SAL did receive a contract for two aircraft. I made contact with Herb Johnson, who sold me two Dakotas for £1,000 each cash subject to inspection and no questions asked. The contract included supplying a crew and flying the first aircraft from Croydon to Colombo with some VIP passengers aboard.

When delivery was due a delegation of five Singhalese cabinet ministers, including John Kotelewala, happened to be in London and they wished to fly back in their own aircraft to Ceylon. Our chief accountant, Bruce Erskine, raised the question of insurance and contingent liability, which I had overlooked, and we had to get advice from SAL's lawyers. They advised that the ministers must take out comprehensive insurance cover for the aircraft, the crew and all passengers and should pay for it. This was agreed but took a day or two to organise.

We had done no business in India so far, so David asked if I would go and study possibilities. I was not very keen as troubles were just beginning over the separation of Pakistan from India, and I did not fancy flying with the airlines there. David said that he had been talking to John Kotelewala and apparently they had now acquired a third aircraft and wanted that converted too. He had arranged that the Scottish Airlines crew could use this aircraft to fly me around India and then come home. As he was a great persuader I agreed.

First I had to arrange all my inoculations for yellow fever, typhoid & paratyphoid and cholera, then came some hurried shopping for tropical gear. I kissed my family goodbye and we took off for Croydon. I acted as flight engineer and general factotum, while Captain Robert Smith was first pilot. On the way to Croydon the VHF radio packed up; neither the radio operator nor I could fix it, and we debated whether or not to return to Prestwick. One thing was certain; we were not going to embark on a long flight without it. I knew that there was a high-level VIP send-off for the Singhalese ministers, so I suggested we carry on until the delegation was safely on board, and once we had taken off I would tell them that we were going to return to Prestwick for a replacement radio.

They were indeed given a great send-off, with Lord Pakenham and his colleagues waving them away. I then got through to Prestwick tower on the HF set and asked them to get a message to David McIntyre to come to the tower and radio me back; in fact he was quite pleased to have the opportunity of being asked to entertain half the Singhalese Cabinet. I found Mr Kotelewala easy to talk to and very understanding, and asked him if he and his colleagues would like a tour of the factory, and if they minded staying overnight. They did not mind at all, thoroughly enjoyed the tour and were impressed by the size and amount of work being done. In the evening they were entertained to dinner by David McIntyre, the Duke of Hamilton and the Earl of Selkirk who happened to be at Prestwick that day. John Lionel Kotelewala became Prime Minister of Ceylon in 1952 and was knighted in 1956.

When I walked through the door that evening my wife and children were surprised and delighted to see me, and wanted to know how I had been to India and back so quickly.

The next morning we took off once more. When flying over the Massif Centrale in France we ran into a heavy thunderstorm; the trailing aerial was struck by lightning and disappeared, and the strike travelled up the wire and blew up the VHF radio. Talk about having a jinx! We landed at Marseille, but there were no facilities there, so we proceeded to Malta where there was an RAF station at Luqa. They were terrific, provided accommodation in their Mess, and had a new VHF set and trailing aerial fitted ready for take-off the following morning. We made a refuelling stop at Tobruk and then flew on to Heliapolis Airport near Cairo. Tobruk was baking hot but Cairo was beautiful and cool, like an English summer's day. We stayed in the Airport Hotel, which was of 5-star quality, and bought handbags and other leatherwear locally, of excellent quality and very cheap. Next stop was Al Basra for more fuel and thence to Bahrain where we stopped for lunch. We flew over the Gulf of Oman and then over the Arabian sea to Karachi, where we stopped overnight in the British Forces Club, a typical example of colonial splendour. However our passengers were not allowed entrance there as they were classed as 'coloured,' and they had to stay at the Central Hotel.

The next day we made Bombay, refuelled and then flew direct to Colombo. We arrived there about six in the evening and found the airport seething with people – it was a kaleidoscope of colour. Everyone had turned out to welcome the first Singhalese civil airliner, and in particular the most popular politician John Kotelewala. Even the crew had garlands of flowers placed round their necks.

We were then all invited to the Kotelewala bungalow for a party, but when we arrived we found it was not a bungalow at all, more of a palace, and the party was in full swing. Our host was still a bachelor and had the reputation of being very much a ladies' man. The food was good, the drink was flowing and the feminine company was terrific – Singhalese girls are very beautiful. This was the first time I had ever seen tall glasses with lovely girls engraved on the sides; as one drank the contents the girls disrobed. In the wee sma' hours we got back to the Gaulface Hotel, the best on the island, right on the beach with golden sands and lovely rolling waves.

The next day we were taken to the race-course, but I began to feel unwell, so much so that I had to return to the hotel and go to bed. In the evening Mr Kotelewala arrived with his personal doctor, who gave me a thorough examination. He diagnosed that I was suffering from the after-effects of all the inoculations, gave me some pills, and told me to rest in bed.

The following day Robert Smith came in and showed me a telegram he had received from Prestwick; Scottish Airlines had been given a contract to fly refugees between India and Pakistan and *vice versa*. Every crew and every aircraft was urgently needed and so off they flew to Calcutta.

This neither improved my health nor my state of mind; I could not sleep well, could not eat and felt lonely, abandoned and depressed. But by the third day I felt a little better, so I had a bath and went down to the bar, where I ordered a large malt and sat wondering what to do next.

Then a very Scottish voice said: "Why are you looking so sad, laddie?"

A large middle-aged Scot had moved onto the next stool; I was so pleased to have someone to talk to that I poured out all my woes. He was a tea planter, was born in Kilmarnock, had gone to Kilmarnock Academy, had been an apprentice engineer with Glenfield & Kennedy, and in the depression had emigrated to Ceylon. His plantation was up in the hills of Kandy and he was having a few days' leave. There was a strong Scottish presence in Ceylon, and he took me to a party at the Royal Yacht Club where he had many Scottish friends. He was a bit lonely too as his wife had gone back to Scotland with his sons, who were returning to school in Edinburgh. He took me to the races, to the zoo, to the Silver Falcon night club, and successfully cured my bout of depression.

I then had to face up to and plan my tour of India and Pakistan. Ceylon Airways' officials were most helpful and flew me to Bangalore, the home of the Hindustani Aircraft Company, who had been writing to us with a suggestion that they should do conversions in Asia on a sub-contract basis from SAL. This made sense to me as the cost of delivery would be saved, and wages were much lower in India.

They had acquired a number of Dakotas, Skymasters and spares for a ridiculously low price. The general manager, Iain McIntosh, had a Scottish father and an Indian mother and had been to school in Dundee. Bangalore was the 'Garden City' of India and the surrounding country was fabulously beautiful. I was entertained right royally and even went on a tiger shoot. Sitting in a *howdah* on a very large elephant was quite a thrill, and although we saw tigers, none were shot, which pleased me as I would not have liked to see such a beautiful animal killed. The staff at Hindustani were of great help to me; I had no language difficulty as Iain McIntosh interpreted, told me of all the airlines operating or hoping to operate, and the names of the people I should see. They made appointments for me by telephone, booked hotel accommodation, and even offered me the services of a beautiful secretary who was fluent in the languages of India as well as good English. I was very tempted but declined as I thought that her presence might be misinterpreted.

I flew to Madras, but there did not seem to be much business there so I continued to Hyderabad, which was a state within a state with its own government, laws and customs. The Prime Minister had a heart condition and could not fly as altitude caused him breathing difficulties, so the Nizam wanted to know if we could supply a pressurised executive aircraft. I said I thought it could be done but it would be very expensive. He was reputed to be one of the wealthiest men in India and said that the cost was not important but early delivery was.

I tried to phone Prestwick but could not get through; however I was able to contact the British air attaché in New Delhi, so I asked him to send a message to Group Captain McIntyre about this very special aircraft, and to ask him to arrange for a design and a quotation.

Then I continued to Bombay, then to Baroda where the Maharaja was very pro-English, had a famous racing stable in England, and was a well-known and very wealthy playboy. He had met the Duke of Hamilton when, as the Marquis of Clydesdale, the Duke had flown over Everest. I never expected to meet a Maharaja, but I was summoned to his palace and served a very English afternoon tea. He ordered an executive aircraft on the spot, asked me to convey his regards to His Grace, and to see that the plane was ready for the next racing season. My first firm order from India – I was really thrilled!

I flew on to New Delhi and booked into the Imperial Hotel there. I had a pleasant room with private bath, and was just unpacking when an Indian walked in and started doing likewise. As he could not speak a word of English, I went to reception to complain but was informed that accommodation was so scarce that sharing was essential. So we nodded politely to each other for the next four days and there was no problem.

I should have gone from Baroda to Karachi, but there was so much fighting, rioting and massacres because of religious and political hatred that I needed some advice from the Embassy. To be frank I had not enjoyed any of my flights so far in India; some of the aircraft I would not have signed for as "safe to fly," and the quality of airmanship left a lot to be desired. Also the airfields were poorly controlled, and many of the aircraft were badly overloaded. But Group Captain Tudor, the air attaché, reckoned that the worst was over and that Karachi was safe if I could get there.

In the hotel I met Wing Commander John Corby, who was doing a tour of India and Pakistan for de Havilland's. He had been a pilot with SOE (Special Operations Executive) during the war and had received an OBE for clandestine service in occupied France and Holland. We compared notes and he had been just as frightened as I had been. I borrowed his typewriter to write my reports, and when I returned it the following morning he was still asleep and I could not wake him; so I phoned the embassy and a doctor arrived, who diagnosed severe heat stroke and heat exhaustion, after which John was taken to hospital. If he had not been found he could well have been dead by evening. Little did I know that John and I would become close colleagues and lifelong friends.

I was lucky to then get a lift on a Scottish Airlines Dakota flying refugees from New Delhi to Karachi. Over 30 passengers were crammed into an aircraft with only 21 seats. I sat on the jump-seat on the flight deck and happily we arrived safely. My contact there was the operations manager of Orient Airlines, a famous pilot called Nevil Stack who had pioneered the original flights from London to India. Orient Airways was owned by Nagin Ispahani who had made a fortune out of cotton, and being a Parsee had many contacts. Nevil told me that if I played my cards right there was a chance of an order for 25 conversions.

When I met Ispanhani I gave my best sales 'spiel,' and it seemed to go down well. He said he had 25 Dakotas, all owned by him personally, and he wanted them converted to civil airliners, but he only wanted 12 of them returned to Karachi and the other part of the contract must cover delivery to others of his customers outside Pakistan. When I asked whom these customers might be, he would not tell me, but from hints I suspected that they were from the new state of Israel, and perhaps Egypt. This made me a little suspicious as there was great tension in the Middle East and plans were afoot to partition Palestine into Arab and Jewish states.

However he took me out for dinner the following evening, and entertained me with tales of how, starting as a very poor boy begging for food, he had become seriously rich. It was a fascinating story and he explained how it was essential to exploit every opportunity in life; indeed he planned to make Orient Airlines the most powerful airline in Asia. When we talked about the conversion contract, I asked if what he was doing was legal; he said that all the obstacles had been overcome and there was no problem. He went on to state that if I cooperated with him there would be something in it for me. When I asked what he meant, he said that one of the aircraft would be mine, and when it was sold the proceeds would be paid into a numbered account in my name in Switzerland.

When I thought about picking up over £30,000 my mind reeled and I was sorely tempted. I said I would think about it, but when we met the next day I said no, I could not agree, and I would have to consult my directors.

Ispahani responded: "There is no time for that, and if you do not agree the deal is off."

I was in a difficult position; to lose a contract for 25 aircraft was unbearable, and I dithered. He noticed this and then asked whether, if he made it *two* aircraft, I would agree. That clinched it as I had always sensed a bad smell about the deal, so I tried to be diplomatic and said I would try to work out an arrangement once I returned home. But he said pointedly that this conversation had never taken place and ushered me out. I was so upset that I went back to my hotel and cried. I felt even worse when I could not get a flight out of Karachi, and suspected that Ispahani had put the word out. The only hope was Scottish Airlines, but after two frustrating days I managed to get a lift to Calcutta via Bhopal and Jabalpur.

My reason for going to Calcutta was not only to sell aircraft but buses. India and Pakistan had the greatest collection of ramshackle buses one could imagine, and I had heard that a bus operator and garage owner in Calcutta might be interested. Calcutta was one of the most depressing cities I have ever visited; it was dirty, humid and hot, and even the best hotel was a slum by comparison with others I had stayed at in India. There were beggars everywhere, and at night doorways and even pavements were dormitories for the vagrants, and it was sad to see how many of them were children.

The garage owner and bus operator was a Scot from Glasgow who had been a pupil at Hillhead Academy. Was I pleased to see him! But he was very pessimistic about his future there and his business was up for sale, as he saw no future for ex-patriots in a country determined to gain its independence from British rule. He was distressed to see Rajagopalachari taking over as Governor General from Earl Mountbatten, and all he wanted was to get his money – and himself – out of the country. So there was no prospect of any orders.

His garage was full of gleaming new Rovers, and I expressed my envy as it was nearly impossible to get a new Rover in Britain.

He said: "Go and choose one." So I picked out a beautiful silver-grey 70 Series saloon.

He said: "Would you like it?"

I replied: "Yes, but how much?"

"Seven hundred and fifty pounds."

"But what about Export Licences, Purchase Tax and Deliveries?"

"Forget them," he said; "just sign here and a car like this will be delivered in Prestwick on any date you choose."

I thought I must be dreaming but I signed.

After that I flew back to New Delhi, where I saw John Corby again. He had fully recovered and was very grateful for my intercession, which he said had saved his life. I told him about the Orient Airways negotiations and John's view was that I was well out of that one.

I flew back to London on an Avro York, a noisy, hot and tiring journey via Bahrain and Casablanca. Many people think that sales tours like this one are glamorous, exciting and enjoyable, but after a lifetime of world travel on business trips I can assure you that the most lasting memories are fatigue, frustration, boredom, and loneliness. No wonder many businessmen away from their wives and family for weeks on end seek solace in feminine company.

There are of course moments of euphoria, excitement and joy, particularly when one has succeeded in negotiating a lucrative contract. The net result of this trip after four weeks away from my family was one firm contract for the Maharaja of Baroda and the prospects of a new Rover motor car for £750. However long-term it certainly paid dividends. The pressurised aircraft ordered by the Nizam of Hyderabad was a great success, and was the only pressurised Dakota ever to fly. This led to further orders from Bharat Airways, the Hyderabad airline. Also the arrangement with the Hindustani Aircraft Company was a huge success; they sent a team over for training, and when they went back we sent a team to supervise the work in-house. They sold over 50 Dakotas and 12 Skymasters in India and Pakistan, and our share of the profits was substantial. I formed a lasting friendship in Bangalore which led to further cooperation when I was at de Havillands and, even later, Hawker Siddeley.

The sequel to the Orient Airways saga was a very tragic one. When I had been in Bombay I had met Adam Smith, a Scot from Darvel. He was nearly ten years older than me, had been educated at Kilmarnock Academy, and had become Director of Civil Aviation in India. He had been very helpful to me over the Ceylon transactions, and to Scottish Airlines when they were negotiating the contract for the repatriation of the refugees.

Then the scandal hit the national press; he and Nevil Stack had been arrested for fraud and for breaking the international agreement on the movement of aircraft. It emerged that this was the Ispahani scam in which I had so nearly become involved. The law was that any aircraft exported for modification or conversion must be returned to the country of origin, and could only be sold on after an export licence had been granted. This law was to prevent exploitation of the sale of military surplus from country to country. For example India and Pakistan had large stocks of aircraft, as these countries had been major staging posts for aircraft traffic to the Middle and Far East. If they had gained ownership after 'Lease-Lend' finished they would have had a monopoly and could have held other less fortunate countries to ransom. Ispahani had had the bright idea that, if he exported his aircraft to his nominees in Bombay, they could get a legitimate export licence to send them to Prestwick for conversion, after which they could be returned to Bombay. Then as civil aircraft they could be sold to Orient Airways for 'peanuts'; Orient could then sell them to Israel and Egypt or indeed to anyone else at huge profits. The scam nearly worked, but the civil servant in Karachi who had signed the export licences was a Hindu and he got transferred to Bombay. When he was asked to grant an export licence for the same aircraft to go to Prestwick, he smelt a rat and the whole thing was exposed.

So Adam Smith and Nevil Stack were arrested. Ispahani denied all knowledge, and Smith and Stack went to jail for five years. Stack was a devout

Catholic; one day he asked to be allowed to go to Mass, and on the way committed suicide by throwing himself under a truck. Adam Smith's wife came to visit us in the Old Manse at Monkton; she had just had a child, and was completely devastated.

I was furious that Ispahani had got off scot-free. I wanted to go back to Bombay and try to get Adam Smith out of jail on appeal, but I was told by SAL lawyers that I had no proof and that I would be wasting my time, so that was that.

CHAPTER 27

WESTMINSTER AIRLINES

This top-class and rather exclusive private airline was started by Max Aitken, Lord Beaverbrook's son. It was financed and owned by the newspaper group and we supplied the first aircraft, G-AJVY. The chief pilot was Brian Powell, whose wife Brenda was the daughter of one of the Ferranti brothers and, although she was only about five foot two she was the English ladies' squash champion. Joy and I became quite friendly with them, especially later on when they moved to Chester when Brian became a test pilot at de Havilland's Broughton factory during the time when I was in charge of production there.

During the war a very wealthy Canadian, J.P. Bickell, was in charge of ATFERO under Beaverbrook. When he went back to Canada he had a Dakota converted by Canadair into a super-duper executive aircraft. Beaverbrook was envious and decided he must have an even better one, so an order was placed with SAL by Beaverbrook Newspapers. We were sent photographs of the Bickell aircraft, and Brian Powell was seconded to Prestwick to ensure that we produced an aircraft to put Canadair's efforts to shame. All the furniture had to be veneered in bird's-eye maple, the chairs and couches had to be upholstered in leather hide, and there had to be a hot shower and a lavish bar.

All the stops were pulled out, we thought that we had produced the finest executive aircraft ever, and Brian Powell flew it down to Blackbushe Airport for Lord Beaverbrook's approval. But he rejected it: he did not like the seats, he thought the leather was too plebeian, the curtains should be Chinese silk, and the carpets were not plush enough. He also wanted an office desk and a phone to the flight deck. In addition all the chairs were to be replaced with the same design that he had in his Club, the Athenaeum.

So we had no alternative but to revamp all of these furnishings, and finally our efforts were approved. Beaverbrook then wanted to know if the aircraft had the range to fly him to Canada so that he could show that he had a much more plush aircraft than Bickell. We had to find a place for the long-range tanks, but as he was travelling with a staff of only four we could take some of the furniture out, fly it to Dorval and replace it before he did his "show-off" tour in Canada and America.

Before the tanks were fitted Brian Powell and I flew the aircraft down to Blackbushe, so that "the Beaver" could show off his latest toy to his friends. The passengers included his secretary and his butler, and he wanted to fly over his house in the country. It was a hot summer's day, there was a lot of turbulence and many of the passengers were airsick, but "the Beaver" did not bat an eye. In fact he was so pleased with himself that he threw a lavish party at the Hyde Park Hotel, where he complimented me for SAL' s efforts and said: "So you were that brash young lad who was so rude to me when you were at Gourock."

I took that as a compliment. We chatted together and he asked me what my ambitions were, to which I replied that I wanted to be successful and happy.

He replied: "Whatever you do, never try to get rich. Riches can be a curse and bring unhappiness."

Lord Beaverbrook was not handsome, but he had tremendous charm, personality and drive, and could be very generous. He was attractive to women and on the flight he had a beautiful lady as his secretary and hostess. She was the estranged wife of a shipping magnate, and had a luxurious flat in Mayfair. After the party I had nowhere to stay, and so she took me home with her. We had an interesting conversation and I learned a lot that night.

Beaverbrook's tour of Canada and America showing off his aircraft was a great success, but we had still not been paid for the aircraft. The managing director of the Beaverbrook Newspaper Group considered the modifications sheer extravagance and, despite the further alterations we had been asked to make, tried to hold us to the original price. When the aircraft returned from North America to have the long-range tanks removed and the furniture fitted again, Brian Powell told me that the next trip was to take Churchill to the Beaverbrook villa in Cannes. Bruce Erskine was getting nowhere over the payment and found the MD of the Newspaper Group very intransigent. So I rang Lord Beaverbrook and told him that until the bill was paid in full his aircraft would be staying at Prestwick. He was furious, not with me but with his MD, and the cheque for the full amount was received the following week.

He then rang to confirm that all was well and invited me to go to Cannes with Brian Powell. We had a wonderful three days there, and it was a thrill to meet Sir Winston Churchill. We did not stay in the villa but were booked into a classy hotel with the crew, and "the Beaver" gave Brian a handful of money and told him to have a good time. That was the only time I have ever been to Cannes. We went to the casino and placed some modest bets, but the most exciting thing of all was to watch the "high rollers" gambling, particularly at the *chemin de fer* tables.

CHAPTER 28

TIME TO MOVE ON

Mrs Constance Yuille had run the Neill family business very efficiently and profitably throughout the war, but she had become pregnant and now had a son. We never learned who the father was but it was certainly not her husband. This, together with the recession at the end of the war, resulted in a turndown of business, and for the first time there was a loss of £540 for the year ending 30th November 1945.

That was the year of decision. Should I leave Scottish Aviation and concentrate on the family business? With all the excitement that I had had and the thrills of being in the aviation business, it was not a hard choice to make, but as the business was still being conducted under my name I had to take steps to safeguard my interests, and so a limited company, Modern Engineering Supplies, was formed with a share capital of £5,000. £3,500 was issued capital, I held £3,340 and Mrs Helen Constance Yuille held £160.

Mrs Yuille at that time lived at East Lodge, Corraith, near Symington. She needed some help and I engaged a young man, Alan Hunter, to do the selling, but he was not a success and the next year's loss was £875. Dad was still in the business, but failing health prevented him from making a great contribution and I thought it unlikely that it would ever make enough profit to support three families.

I decided to keep the company in case I wanted to start it up again in later years, but when I discussed the future with Mrs Yuille, she was relieved because she had been plucking up her courage to tell me that she wanted to leave anyway as she was going to Canada to remarry. I therefore negotiated the sale of all the stock to an engineering supplies company in Glasgow. The price for an outright sale was so low that I agreed to sell it on a sale or return basis. I made a list of stock and had it audited by our new accountants, Rogerson & Goldie of King Street, Kilmarnock. That turned out to be a bad deal. I was supposed to receive a monthly statement of sales and a cheque, but nothing happened and when I went to see the new owner he claimed that the stock was a load of junk and unsaleable, so I had to sue him. The lawyers I engaged were McCosh & Gardiner of 163 Main Street, Prestwick.

A meeting was held in Glasgow to see if an out-of-court settlement could be reached. It was my first experience of a rough tough Glasgow solicitor. He said his client would not pay a penny, and that Modern Engineering Supplies was a 'bucket-shop' company and had not even sent in annual returns to the Companies Registration Office in Edinburgh in accordance with the Companies Act.

I turned to Mr Gardiner and said: "Would you please record what this gentleman has said. He has uttered a slander and I want you to sue him for defamation of character."

A portrait of the author; this was taken in 1958 when I left de Havilland's. Photo: author's collection.

David McIntyre as he was in 1953, still with many ambitions in aviation. Sadly these were never fulfilled as he lost his life in a crash in 1956.
Photo: courtesy of Douglas McIntyre, David's son.

The other lawyer said: “It is not slander; I am claiming ‘veritas’; I have carefully checked the records, and there is no record of any returns for this company.”

So I produced copies of the returns which I had in my briefcase, and retorted: “Well, what are these then?”

There was some confusion now his bluff had been called, so I said: “We are leaving now and Mr Gardiner will serve a writ on you as soon as he gets back to his office.”

The climate immediately changed dramatically, and I left with a promise of a certified cheque for £5,000 within seven days and the return of all the unsold stock within 30 days. These conditions were met in full.

I have not said a lot about the conversion of C-54 Skymasters to civilian DC-4s, but nevertheless we did our share at Prestwick. The first one was done for SAS, a consortium of Swedish, Danish and Norwegian airlines. There were not nearly as many of them around as there were Dakotas; they cost more to buy and the profit on their conversion was not so lucrative.

Later we did a deal and acquired all the remaining Dakotas at Silloth for virtually nothing, so we were able to offer complete aircraft at very competitive prices. I have before me the price list published at the end of 1948 when we were offering complete aircraft, fully overhauled, for the following prices:

Freighters	£10,500 to £13,500
Standard Models	£15,500 to £17,500
De Luxe Models	£18,000 to £20,000
Executive Models	£30,000 to £40,000

The profits were fabulous, and SAL should have been the wealthiest manufacturing company in Europe, but unfortunately the airlines were losing money as fast as the manufacturing side was earning it. David McIntyre was convinced that if he hung on long enough all would come right and the airlines would prove very profitable. However this time he would be proved wrong.

However David did argue correctly in that conversion profits were short-term and would not last, and he was determined to get into the manufacture of new aircraft. He heard that the Ministry were asking for tenders for a design study for an Air Observer and Artillery Spotting Aircraft with short take-off and landing characteristics (STOL). Bob McIntyre did such a good job that the design was accepted and we were asked to tender for 100 aircraft. This was a vitally important contract as it could well establish SAL as a prominent plane-maker. We burned the midnight oil and put in a presentation and a price that we hoped would secure the order. Costs had been pared to the bone, but there was still great jubilation when David came back and announced that we had won the contract. What he did not tell us was that he had dropped the price by 10% to get it.

As I said earlier we were currently living in the Old Manse at Monkton, just by the factory; it was a marvellous place for a family – secluded, lovely gardens carefully tended by SAL gardeners, I could walk to work, and we had a very happy family life. My business life was exciting and satisfying too, and we had an excellent social life and lots of friends. I was still young, in my early thirties, but I was beginning to have doubts about the financial viability of the company.

Here two amusing stories must be related. A retired diplomat had been engaged by the Nizam of Hyderabad to do a report on SAL. He showed it to me as it was highly complimentary. However in the opening paragraphs it mentioned "Mr Neill, a man in early middle age." I had never thought that I was middle-aged, and that comment made me think even harder about my future. The second story is about a meeting I was having in my office with Ministry cost officials trying to find ways of claiming price increases on the STOL contract because of specification changes instigated by them. The door suddenly opened and in walked two very young children hand in hand; they were, of course, Gill and Alastair. Gill piped up: "We have come to see what you do all day, Daddy," whereupon there were gales of laughter. They had walked through the gardens at the Old Manse, right through the factory and so to my office. Shortly afterwards a somewhat flustered mother in her apron arrived with a security guard to escort the children home. Thereafter the mood of the meeting lightened and we secured our price increases.

Old Manse was the very first house that we had to furnish, and here my $3,000 win came in handy. Afflecks in Ayr was a fashionable store with manufacturing facilities. I knew Tom Affleck well as we had given him a lot of business on our conversion work. They were also funeral undertakers, and had provided coffins and other services for the Belgians and the other Liberator fatalities at Heathfield. All furniture and furnishings were in very short supply, but Tom made a beautiful oak double bed for us and also a very handsome three-piece suite. The bed followed us all round the country and we still sleep in it. The three-piece suite is still in the family and my younger daughter Fran treasures it. They were all made out of coffin boards – or so the story goes. There was an antique shop at the cross at Prestwick and we made some excellent purchases there, all of which are still with us and are now quite valuable. The sideboard and 6-drawer tallboy in our dining room, the oak chest on the landing, the antique 7-drawer desk in our lounge, plus three chest of drawers in our bedrooms were all acquired for less than £100. They must be worth a thousand or two today. Our other purchases from Afflecks were: 4 kitchen chairs and a table, a steel kitchen cabinet, 8 dining room chairs, 2 oak single beds, 1 metal single bed, 1 coffee table, 1 sewing box and 1 set of bedroom furniture comprising 1 dressing table, 1 wardrobe, 1 tallboy and 1 bedside table. The bedroom furniture was solid oak, imported from Poland in a knocked-down condition, which Joy and I reassembled *in situ*. We also bought five carpets and a stair carpet, and a dressing room mirror.

The total cost, including the specially-made bed and three-piece suite, was exactly £600. With the exception of the two single beds – which were stolen – and the carpets, everything else is still in use, having followed us to each of the seven houses we have owned over a period of 50 years. What value and what quality!

A decision to give up everything we enjoyed and seek pastures new was not easily made. I was earning £1,000 per annum, and when I considered the vast sums of money that we were making I began to wonder. After all I was only an assistant works manager but it was me who appeared to be doing most of the work, as Fred Hopkins liked a quiet life and Dick Ellison was becoming more and more involved with his farm. Dick too was worried about the financial future. I had enjoyed the glamour of travel and all my bosses were very appreciative of my efforts, and gave me every support. I confess that I was impressed with being in close contact – indeed friendly contact – with the premier Duke of Scotland, the Duke of Hamilton, and his brother the Earl of Selkirk. I can well remember being invited to dinner with them and David McIntyre, so that they could listen to the accounts of all my adventures in Ceylon, India and Pakistan. I was also thrilled to be invited to a ball he was giving for charity in Ayr. But the financial position steadily deteriorated, and every time Dick, Fred Hopkins and I went to see David expressing our distress, he told us there was no cause for worry, and out would come the drinks and the charm.

Eventually on 7th December 1948 I wrote and tendered my resignation. Dad had died on 28th September of that year and I was a little depressed anyway. I had no job to go to, but when I had spoken to Stewart Kennedy (who was now working for de Havilland's) he had told me that David McIntyre would never change his ways, and that there would always be a job for me in the de Havilland empire. However David would not accept my resignation, and suggested that I should write a report of what changes were necessary, and he would see that they were implemented.

At this time there was one item of light relief. Alex Holland, who ran the production control office, and Charlie Reid, who was in charge of progress, were quite incompatible as there was a personality clash. Both in their own way were good managers and efficient, but I knew that I would have to get rid of one of them; the question was which and how? Charlie kept disappearing from time to time, and rumour had it that he went to all the race meetings. When the next meeting was held at Ayr, we had him followed and sure enough he was there, with his billboard, clerk and tic-tac man. The board was headed: "Charlie L. (Lucky) Reid. Don't be greedy, bet with Reidy, put your money down, get the best odds in town."

When I had him in my office to ask for his resignation, he was not in the least concerned; he said: "Bill, I can earn more money at the races in three months than you pay me in one year."

He then told me he had been a bookmaker all his life, and had only come to SAL to avoid military service. He had an amazing memory and could remember a huge list of part numbers, and that was why he was such a good progress chief. We parted on the best of terms and I promoted one of his people, Jimmy McIntyre, to be head of the department. Jimmy was Bob McIntyre's brother; he did a reasonable job but was never in the same class as Charlie. Then Jimmy had an affair with one of his staff, a charming girl called Mary Capperall, and eventually had to leave.

I have previously mentioned Frank Broughton, superintendent of Liberator modifications and conversions. Frank was a large jovial man, a real extrovert, great personality and fun to be with, and it was rumoured that he had slept with most of the good-looking girls in his section. One evening Frank Burnard and I were having a drink in the *Red Lion* and there was Frank, with his latest conquest. As we watched another young lady walked over to his table with two foaming pints of beer, poured them over their heads and walked out of the bar. Frank took it in good part and commented: "So that is what you get for being nice to someone." His lady friend was none too pleased.

Frank was a bit of a rebel and there had been a running feud with the head of AID, Mr McKeown, for some time. Frank had made a number of toolboxes from old packing cases and had given them to his friends – I still have mine. He also built himself a super luxury caravan, and McKeown suspected that a lot of the material had been obtained out of the Ministry bonded store. We were all shocked when Frank was arrested and charged with theft, and his caravan was impounded by the police. He was given bail and AID pressed for his dismissal, but we refused this on the grounds that anyone is innocent until proved guilty. However AID had done their detective work well and had proof that the caravan wheels were Spitfire undercarriage wheels, which with their serial numbers could only have come from the bonded store. All the high-quality plyboard also carried serial numbers tying it to the Ministry bonded store. The case was duly tried in the Sheriff's Court in Ayr, and the only convincing evidence was the serial numbers referred to above. The night before these exhibits were due to be shown in court, the police compound was broken into and the evidence mysteriously disappeared. So the verdict against Frank Broughton was "Not Proven," which meant that the Sheriff considered him guilty but the prosecution could not prove it. The case got a lot of publicity; we could not sack him as he had not been found guilty, but neither could we afford to lose the co-operation of AID, so we were in a bit of a dilemma. I had always got on well with AID, particularly with McKeown, and after a reasonable period I persuaded Frank to hand in his resignation.

Sometime later Frank's name was in the papers; he had become quite a successful dirt track rider and, later still, we heard that he was living in luxury with a wealthy widow. Little did I know that a year or so after I had joined de Havilland's our paths would cross again.

When I was sitting in the York aircraft on my return to England from India, I noticed that I had come out in a bright red rash and I was itching all over. The first thing I did on arriving at Prestwick was to go and see Dr Stephenson, as I feared some awful contagious disease which I dared not pass on to my family. The 'doc' gave me a thorough examination, and when he drew his fingernail across any part of my body, it left a red weal. He diagnosed urticaria, and told me it was due to an allergy to something I had eaten, or more likely due to stress, but it was not contagious or infectious. He advised me to watch what I ate, relax and get plenty of fresh air and exercise. The rash disappeared, but every time I became stressed (such as when conducting a meeting) the rash returned. The problem lasted for many months but Dr Stephenson, being an old-fashioned doctor, did not want to prescribe tranquillisers.

So I fished, golfed and played squash. One day when I was teaching Ian Reid to play squash, he made a wild swing at the ball and his racket struck my left eye. I was in agony and he was extremely sorry and upset. It was feared that I had a detached retina and I had to stay in bed with sandbags on either side of my head for some days. I lay there, depressed and itchy, and gave a lot of thought to my future. I decided that the time had come to move, and phoned Stewart Kennedy. Apparently two jobs were available, one at Airspeed's at Portsmouth and the other at the DH Propeller Company at Lostock near Bolton.

One weekend I caught a train to Portsmouth and stayed in the Westfield Hotel. It was a nice old-fashioned hotel, but most of the residents were elderly. It was very hot and I was not very impressed by Portsmouth or Southsea. They did not compare at all well with Prestwick and were busy and 'trippery.' But I was well received at Airspeed and was offered the job of production manager at a salary £250 higher than I was getting at SAL. The general manager was William Denny, who took me on a tour of the works, but I was not impressed with them either.

The following weekend I went to Bolton and stayed in the Halliwell Lodge Hotel. I liked the town and the surrounding country, and was most impressed with the factory at Lostock; I had never seen such a huge machine shop in my life. There I met H.J. "Nick" Nixon, the production manager, Phil Whit (contracts) and a fellow Scot, Dougie Simpson, a friend of Stewart Kennedy. I was offered a job as assistant production manager at a salary of £1,500 per annum, which I was pleased about, and returned home to discuss it with Joy.

To leave my beloved Prestwick and go to England was a momentous decision. I worried about housing and about leaving my mother on her own in Kilmarnock. What made it worse was that the 8th Anniversary Dinner (to commemorate the landing of the first aircraft at Prestwick) was due. There was a scintillating guest list, the menu and wine list were sumptuous and the speakers were all very distinguished. I asked myself: "Are you really prepared to give all this up?"

However the report that I had written had been largely ignored and nothing had changed, so the next weekend I went to see Stewart Kennedy and stayed with him at his lovely house *The Belt* in Gustard Wood. He was quite sure that I should make the move and the next day he took me to see W.E. Nixon, the de Havilland chairman. He too thought that SAL was heading for serious financial trouble, and recommended me to leave. So I accepted the job at Lostock.

When I broke the news to David McIntyre he was very gracious and threw a fantastic farewell party. He also very generously said that Joy and the family could stay on in the Old Manse until I had settled in at Bolton and had found a house for the family. It was agreed that I would terminate my employment in June 1949 and would take up my duties at Lostock on 4th July 1949. I thought that was quite an auspicious date.

The last contract that I negotiated for SAL was with British European Airways for the supply of 10 Dakotas. For these the seat configuration, normally 21 seats, was designed with floor attachments so that the seating could be adjusted to take 24 or even 27 for short flights. The seats were removable and floor fixings were provided so that the aircraft could also be used as a freighter.

The contracts manager at BEA was Pitt C.F. Morgan, and I had a big argument with him because BEA intended to call this aircraft the "Pioneer." Now I knew that David McIntyre intended to call his new STOL aircraft the Prestwick Pioneer and I thought there could be a clash over the registered name, so I eventually persuaded Pitt Morgan to call the BEA aircraft the "Pionair," which I thought was a more suitable name – fortunately he agreed. Little did I know that when I eventually returned to Hawker Siddeley in 1973 he would be working there as spares manager.

It gave me great satisfaction to see the prototype Prestwick Pioneer receiving its airworthiness certificate, and to have overseen the completion of the first six production aircraft. The short take-off and landing characteristics of these aircraft were spectacular, and Dick ably demonstrated this by landing on the fairway of the first hole at Gleneagles, and then taking off again with the crowds cheering. The Pioneer did sterling work in Malaysia and other places and was a sensation for several years, but unfortunately it never made any money.

Several years later it was followed by the Twin Pioneer, which again turned out to be a splendid aircraft. However, after the findings on the Comet crashes in the early fifties were made public, it was discovered that the Twin Pioneer wing spar required strengthening as its life could be reduced due to metal fatigue; fortunately this was easily remedied. In the meantime David got a contract to fly out urgent spares to an oil company in Libya; the only Twin Pioneer available, G-AOEO, was an unmodified one, but David was prepared to take that risk. But over the Libyan desert on the 8th December 1957 the port wing failed and the aircraft crashed, killing all on board including David McIntyre and also Robert Smith, the pilot who had captained the Air Ceylon Dakota on my flight to Colombia with the Singhalese ministers.

David's son Dougal tells the true story of how, a year before the crash, he built a flying model of a Twin Pioneer, and during the first flight the port wing broke off while he and his father were watching.

And so ended the distinguished career of a great man. I still wonder to this day if he had not been killed what would have happened to SAL and Scottish Airlines. I am sure that he would have been every bit as famous and more successful even than all the others put together, including Freddie Laker and Richard Branson, because of his vision, determination and courage. In spite of our differences I could not have worked for a better or kinder man. SAL survived and eventually became part of British Aerospace.

In the middle 1960s Handley Page were developing a new airliner to serve the short-to-medium range market, with 25/30 seats, turboprop engines and a cabin with plenty of headroom. Indeed it was intended to be the logical replacement for the Dakota/DC-3, many of which were still flying worldwide.

In 1966 I had become MD of Kearney & Trecker and we were looking for a replacement for one of the company's aircraft, a Vickers Viscount. Fran Trecker, the K & T president, had been studying the Handley Page design and thought that it had a great future, and asked me if I could fix a test flight. Stewart Kennedy, who was by then chairman of Hawker Siddeley International, arranged it and we were very impressed. But Handley Page were in financial trouble and went into liquidation. Hawker Siddeley then bought Handley Page from the liquidators and sold the rights for the new aircraft to SAL, where it became known as the Jetstream. The 31 and 41 versions were very successful and for some years had a good share of the market. David McIntyre's dream had been realised at last and SAL was a successful aircraft manufacturer.

SAL had also acquired the full design and manufacturing rights for the Bulldog trainer, which proved very successful with the RAF and a number of foreign buyers including the Swedish, Botswanian, Ghanaian, Kenyan and Malaysian air forces.

Regrettably there was a huge recession in the late 1980s and Prestwick was allowed to go into decline – but that is another story entirely.

PART IV: THE DE HAVILLAND GROUP

CHAPTER 29

AN INTRODUCTION TO LOSTOCK

On 24th June 1949 we loaded up the Rover and set off for our new life in England. We had just finished an idyllic week's holiday in the Lakes, where we stayed at the Langdale Chase Hotel on the shores of Lake Windermere. By our standards it was a "posh" hotel; the food was excellent, the weather was beautiful and I began to relax again.

There was no motorway in those days, so the journey was first to Kendal where we joined the A6 to Milnthorpe, Carnforth, Lancaster, Scorton, Garstang, through Preston, then we rejoined the A6 past Houghton Towers, to Abbey Village, Belmont and so to Bolton. We found the scenery in the area beautiful and so our fears about a dirty, smoky, industrial town were alleviated to some extent. However it was Bolton Wakes Week, so the town was empty, all the shops were closed and the streets seemed dirty and untidy. We were booked into the Halliwell Lodge Hotel and were given a very nice family room with private bath, but they were not serving food of any kind during that week, and when we went in search of a food shop we found that they were all closed. Eventually we went to a farm off Chorley New Road and bought a dozen eggs. Back at the hotel, the girl behind the bar gave us a stale brown loaf and we asked her to slice it and toast the slices; then we boiled the eggs in the electric kettle in our room and consumed them along with the toast and some tea. The next day was a Sunday so we drove to Southport, where we were able to buy food. We spent the day on the beach but the sea was so far away we could hardly see it.

On Monday I started work at Lostock, where I was made most welcome and was shown my office; it was quite large but had no natural light and the only windows looked out over the vast machine shop. I spent the first day being shown around and meeting the various heads of department, had lunch in the management dining room, and returned to the hotel to hear the family news. Joy and the children had gone shopping and exploring, and seemed to be reasonably happy with what they had seen. We found time to go house hunting and decided the area in which we would like to live, but the prices frightened us a bit and we did not see a single house that we liked within our price range.

It was now time for Joy and the family to return to Prestwick. De Havilland's had undertaken to pay me both a subsistence allowance and the cost of my accommodation for three months. However I did not like hotel life and moved into Melrose, a family-run boarding house at 183 Chorley New Road. It was owned by the Ruaux family who had been evacuated from the Channel Islands during the war and had settled in Bolton. They had five daughters, so did not need to hire outside help, with the result that the service and food was excellent and the prices were very reasonable.

Living away from one's family can be stressful and lonely, so I was very lucky in my choice of digs, and found my fellow lodgers very compatible indeed.

Alan Dawtry was the Deputy Town Clerk of Bolton and a bachelor; later he became Town Clerk of the City of Westminster and was knighted.

Tom Hughes was married and worked for Production Engineers Ltd, a consultancy firm heavily engaged with the cotton industry; he was a 6 ft 3 in handsome extrovert, a great ladies' man and a Major with the 5th Loyals Territorials. Later he became Director of the World Health Organisation.

Peter Thomson was deputy head brewer with McGhee Marshalls and single.

Ian Smith was the son of a wealthy family who had a cotton business in India; he was studying textiles at Salford University and was also single.

An occasional guest, David Nicolson, was the head man at Production Engineers Ltd; later he had a distinguished career as a 'non-executive director' of many famous companies. Indeed he was the role model and did a great deal to publicise this relatively new kind of directorship – at one time he held some 30 such positions. He masterminded Heseltine's entry to Parliament and was rewarded by being asked to put together BOAC and BEA, which did not prove a great successs, but he got a knighthood nevertheless.

All of these had established an active social life in Bolton, in which I was quickly involved. Alan Dawtry had entrée to all the town hall functions, Tom was active in the sporting and social activities of the Loyals, and Peter had the run of the pubs and brewery parties, and when David was around we met the wealthy cotton families in the district.

I was of course also working very hard at Lostock and thoroughly enjoyed doing so. Harry (Nick) Nixon, Phil Witt, and Dougie Simpson, known as the "terrible trio," were all on the same level, and of course split responsibility never works, so when there were differences efficient management suffered. What was even worse was that each head of department was under the control of his relevant boss at Hatfield, which only added to the problem. After my first month I was invited to visit Hatfield with a young man called Ross White, who worked at Lostock under Phil Witt but also had a responsibility to the contracts manager at Hatfield; he had a public school background, educated at Rossal near Blackpool. Ross and I were both invited to stay with the Group Chairman, W.E. Nixon, and his family at their country home; this I thought a signal honour, but it turned out that Ross had been the girl friend of the Nixon daughter, and had been sent to Lostock to try to find out what was wrong there as the directors were not very pleased with the results.

I met all the department heads at Hatfield, and in due course was summoned to W.E. Nixon's office, where my erstwhile friend and colleague Stewart Kennedy was present. I was asked to give my impressions of Lostock, and I explained that, while it was very early days for me, I felt that split responsibility could never work and so to my mind there should be a "boss." I said that it seemed wrong that departmental heads at Hatfield should have authority over their opposite numbers at Lostock, and should interfere in the day-to-day running of the factory. I had the impression that there was a shortage of work, and that with such an excellent machine shop that should not be so; I also pointed out that a lot of the machine tools were out of date and should be replaced.

They then told me that I was only confirming what they already knew, but that it was difficult to make changes because of the personalities involved, particularly when Lostock was doing work for the Propeller Company, the Aircraft Company and the Engine Company, causing clashes of priority. They were very glad that I had joined de Havilland's and asked me to make return visits from time to time.

In fact I got on very well with the "terrible trio"; I had their complete support and became friends with all three. They took a keen interest in my social life and always went out of their way to see that I was never neglected or lonely.

Nick Nixon was married with a daughter and a son; the daughter had a career and led her own life, but the son Freddie was spoilt by his mother, who was a bit domineering. Nick had lost his right arm just above the elbow when he was working in Canada operating a milling machine; his overall sleeve had got caught up on the shaft and the cutter chopped off his arm. However he never had any artificial aids, and managed very well, although understandably he did not drive. His wife took him around most of the time until I arrived, after which he loved being driven in my Rover. He had been in machine shops all his life and must have worked almost every machine tool made. His practical and technical knowledge was of the highest order and I learned a great deal from him, and he was generous in passing on all this experience.

Phil Witt had been in the business all his life too, knew all about production times and rate-fixing, and was a superb estimator. He could look at a drawing and estimate the cost of making the part within a shilling or two without having to do all the calculations.

Dougie Simpson was a chartered accountant; he had a strong personality and was very extrovert and ambitious, but he was not as experienced as the other two. I travelled a lot with Dougie and he was the fastest eater I ever saw; he would finish his dinner before the rest of us had got to the second course. He was very tight-fisted and would never spend a penny if a halfpenny would do – he would rather eat at a transport café than a good restaurant. He was a great ladies' man, and fixed me up with a beautiful young girl as my secretary, Joyce Cavanagh. It was rumoured that he had ulterior motives, but if so he never achieved them.

After the war the huge factory was only two-thirds occupied, and the third at the west end was all vacant space. I tried to spend most of my time on the shop floor, getting to know the foremen, chargehands, shop stewards and the operators too. Labour relations were good, thanks to Nick, who was respected as he had made his own way from shop floor to top management. Several times I got lost and had to ask the way back to my own office, which always caused some amusement. A bonus system was in operation and all work cards had a time for each operation. I did not think it was a good system and it was subject to grave abuse. There was resistance to rate-fixers using stop watches, and lots of argument about time studies.

On one occasion I saw a serious argument between a shop steward, an operator and a rate-fixer about an item being machined on a centre lathe. So I walked over and listened, and it was obvious to me that the time being offered was a fair one – indeed it was generous. I said to the operator that I thought the time was generous, and then asked the steward: "Will you accept the time it takes me to do it?" He looked amazed, so I took off my jacket and machined the piece in less than half the time proposed. My reputation immediately soared!

Nick was very good to me in other ways. He was well known in production engineering circles, proposed me for membership of the Institute of Production Engineers and invited me to the annual dinners at the Grosvenor Hotel in London. He took me to steel works to see steel being made, and I still have a handsome stainless poker presented to me during a visit to Firth Brown. He introduced me to a host of engineering techniques: the "lost wax" casting process, electron beam welding, spark erosion machining, thread-rolling and thread-grinding machines, state-of-the-art heat treatment and plating processes, vapour blasting, metal spraying, the manufacture of printed circuit boards, the principles of air gauging and computerised measuring equipment. On one occasion we went on the Brighton Belle to visit CVA Jigs, Tools & Moulds in Brighton – run by Eric Aron – to purchase single spindle automatics. We were very well entertained and I admired Eric Aron's magnificent office at Portland Road, Hove. Little did I know that 16 years later I would be sitting in it as managing director of Kearney & Trecker.

I revamped the DH Sports and Social Club, campaigned for more active membership, started a rugby union football section, and persuaded management to take part in all kinds of sporting activities. We had management teams at cricket, football, hockey (playing against the ladies' team), badminton, table tennis, basketball, snooker and darts, and even had a good tug-of-war team. We played against the 5th Loyals, and had a good relationship with Bolton Wanderers. We played against the foremen and workers and all this improved the morale of everyone more than somewhat. In my spare time (what there was of it) I looked for a suitable house.

We wanted a family house in a good residential district, near parkland where the children could play, and reasonably adjacent to a suitable school, and at a price we could afford. With all the contacts I had made I was inundated with brochures and offers, but the ones that met the specifications were all beyond my resources and I did not wish to be lumbered with a large mortgage. I was amazed at the variety on offer and came to the conclusion that Bolton was a pretty good place in which to live and bring up a family. With smoke from all the factory chimneys it was not a clean town, but there were many scenic walks, playgrounds & parks, museums, libraries, and a whole variety of suitable schools. We found the people outgoing and friendly, even although some of the dialects were difficult to understand – indeed in the factory I found that often I could not follow half of what was being said.

After many disappointments I finally found a house at 6 Sefton Road, semi-detached in a cul-de-sac with a tennis and bowling club across the road. Moss Bank park was within walking distance, there were a few shops in the area and Church Road School was quite near. The house had a wooden garage in the lane, a large cellar for storage purposes, a useful attic room, a tall flagpole in the back garden, and a lifesize stone statue of a lady at the front door. In September Joy and the family came down to view it, and we decided to put in an offer. After a little bargaining the price was agreed at £1,850. To raise the money I had to sell my beloved Rover, but that was not difficult as cars of that type were in great demand; it went to a man from Farnworth for £2,250, and he came to my office at Lostock with a brown paper parcel and counted out the money. As I was travelling to Prestwick by train that evening, I had no alternative but to stuff all the money about my person, not something that one would dare to do today. The cash was paid into my bank in Prestwick and I immediately sent off a cheque to the house agent to secure the purchase of our very first house. It was super to see the family again, but sad to realise that soon they would be leaving the lovely Old Manse for good.

I then went to the SAL factory to see my old Riley, which seemed to have been well looked after in my absence. On the Sunday afternoon I set off for Bolton, but by the time I reached Lancaster the engine was spluttering – and then it stopped altogether. These Rileys did not have petrol pumps but were fitted with Autovacs, which operated by suction from the engine air intake, and the diaphragm was perished. All the garages were closed, but I got directed to the house of a proprietor and he very kindly opened up his garage and found a new diaphragm for me; fortunately he was a Riley fan himself. I eventually arrived back at Bolton safely and gave Joy a ring to tell her that all was well.

When I took possession of Trevalyn, 6 Sefton Road, the interior decorations were not very good, and there was quite a lot of work to be done. My friends at Melrose and at Lostock were most helpful and we all set about the work enthusiastically, but it took much longer than planned, as we had to fit it in between work and the various and many social events we attended.

The two main social events in Bolton were the Assembly Ball held in the town hall and the 5th Loyals' Ball held at the barracks in Fletcher Street. An invitation to either or both was highly prized, and the etiquette was very formal. Full evening dress and white gloves were the order of the day, and filling in one's dance programme to secure dances with the most beautiful girls was a major exercise. There was also a strong and well-supported Caledonian Society; most of the doctors and dentists in Bolton seemed to be Scottish, and I was amazed at the number of Scots from all walks of life who supported the Society and seemed to have great empathy with the Lancastrians. The Nurses' Ball was another great social event, and dinners held by the Law Society and the Medical Faculty attracted distinguished guests, while the speeches were usually witty and well worth hearing.

Over the years we lived at Trevalyn, de Havilland's played their part in the social calendar. The factory Open Day was a sparkling event with air displays, parachute jumps, all kinds of sporting events for the children, and a factory tour with exhibits from the training school. We hosted international table tennis, badminton and amateur boxing, and put on an annual pantomime and children's party, the proceeds from which were donated to charity. We also put on the biggest bonfire and firework display in the district.

Nick had established good relationships with the shop stewards, and this led to a unique tradition which continued for many years. Once a year the shop stewards' committee invited certain members of the management and staff to their shop stewards' picnic, the practice being to hire a coach and go off to Blackpool. In the morning we had a crown green bowling match on the famous "Waterloo Green," then we had lunch, the first course being oysters or whelks and chips paid for by Nick; after that we toured the Golden Mile, paid a visit to the Fun Fair, and then had dinner followed by a show. All this was paid for by the stewards. Eventually one coach became two, and by the time I left de Havilland's in 1958 it had become three.

Once a year the company held an annual dance at the Plaza Ballroom or at the Town Hall, and this dance was open to all employees. It was organised by the shop stewards' committee, and the profit went to the stewards – hence the picnic. However to keep it respectable the stewards always made a donation to a local charity. The shop steward convenor was Norman Vickers, a man of great integrity and experience, hence respected by men and management alike. As a result we enjoyed excellent industrial relations.

No. 6, Sefton Road, Bolton, the first house we purchased when I moved to de Havilland's in 1949; it cost £1,800 but the sale of my beloved Rover 70 more than paid for it! Photo: author's collection.

Joy and family at Balgowan, the Bolton house we built in 1956 in eight months without the help of conventional builders. Our four children are Alastair (rear L.), Peter (rear R.), Gill (front L.) and Fran (front R.).
Photo: author's collection.

The very first undercarriage built at Lostock for the Comet 2.
Photo: author's collection.

Taken at The Spinney in 1950: L. to R., Air Vice Marshal Sir Ralph Sorley (MD of DH Propellers), Harry Pover (one of the best-ever Production Directors in the industry), W.E. Nixon (Chairman of the DH Group) and Stewart Kennedy (Financial Director of the DH Group). Photo: author's collection.

Taken at The Spinney on 2nd May 1950: the group includes Stewart Kennedy (1), C.C. Walker, a founding Director and distinguished engineer (2), Harry Povey (3), W.E. Nixon (4), John Corby (5), the author (6), AVM Sir Ralph Sorley (7), Dougie Simpson (8) and H.J. Nixon, the finest machine shop production engineer in the business (9). Photo: author's collection.

Taken at the London Hilton Hotel in 1982 to prove that the Hon. Harold Wilson and I (then president of the Aircraft Golfing Society) were not really look-alikes even though we both smoked pipes! Photo: author's collection.

CHAPTER 30

THE DE HAVILLAND GROUP OF COMPANIES

The history of Sir Geoffrey de Havilland and his enormous contribution to the growth of many different aspects of the aviation industry is so well documented since its humble beginnings prior to the first World War that I will attempt only to briefly summarise aspects of it here. Subsequently he assembled a team of inspirational, innovative engineers, all of whom were dedicated to the continuing development of airframes and engines, and who for many years dominated the world in the design and production of a whole range of famous aircraft and engines.

During the inter-war years he perhaps became best known for the Moth and Gipsy range of airframes and engines, while in 1934 the DH.88 Comet racer G-ACSS won the Mildenhall-to-Melbourne Air Race piloted by Campbell and Black, with the Mollisons a good third in another Comet after the Douglas DC-2 piloted by Parmentier and Moll of KLM.

During the second World War de Havilland were also ahead in propeller design, and in conjunction with Hamilton Standard, an American company at Hartford, Connecticut, developed the first variable pitch, constant speed propellers. There can be little doubt that these and their variants gave an edge to the fighters and bombers which were so successful in dominating the air war, and winning it. The all-wooden Mosquito, a work of pure genius, became famous for its ubiquitous service during the war.

Post-war research on high-speed aircraft, an exciting but dangerous field, led to the experimental DH.108, which killed Sir Geoffrey's eldest son who was test-flying it over the Thames Estuary, and the DH.110, which killed John Derry and his observer during a demonstration at the Farnborough Air Show. But the Vampires, Venoms and Sea Vixens for the RAF and the Navy were all successful designs. In the civil field, the best-known of his passenger transports over the decades were probably the Dragon Rapide (a pre-war design), the Dove, the Comet – the world's first jet-powered airliner – and the Trident.

But to return to the pre-war years: propellers were so vital to the war effort that the Ministry decided to build a shadow factory for the sole purpose of manufacturing propellers, as the factories in the south were more vulnerable to air attack. Two sites were shortlisted, one at Prestwick and the other at Lostock; the favoured one was Prestwick, as de Havilland were part owners of SAL.

However, Bolton Town Council showed remarkable foresight and offered the Ministry a package deal that was difficult to refuse: free land and a moratorium on rates and rents for several years. They also stressed that there was an excellent pool of engineers locally, as well as Lancashire lasses who had dextrous skills by virtue of their experience in textiles, an industry already in decline. During the war Lostock and four other dispersal factories employed over 12,000 people, and produced over a million propellers for over 100 different types of aircraft. Lostock was so important strategically that the Germans tried to bomb it, and after one of the bombers was shot down on the hills above Rivington Pike, a map was found in the wreckage showing the Lostock factory; this was then framed and decorated the wall on the front entrance for many years.

In the south de Havilland's main design and production factories were at Hatfield, in a beautiful complex with its own airfield. On the other side at Manor Road was the headquarters of the Propeller Company, with its own design and development team. The Engine Company had its own separate establishments at Stag Lane and Leavesden comprising design, development, production and engine testing. They produced not only the Gipsy range of engines, but designed and produced the Ghost and Goblin engines for Comet airliners and fighters. De Havilland's had also acquired Airspeed's factories at Portsmouth and Christchurch.

All of these companies had their own Chairmen, Chief Executives and Directors, but the Group Chairman, W.E. Nixon, was a financial genius. In the early days when times were hard it was rumoured that he would not hand out a sheet of emery cloth, a new drill or even a light bulb until the worn out ones were returned. His vision and forward planning were formidable: he negotiated the purchase from the MOD at a very keen price of the shadow factory at Lostock and its equipment, as he also did the massive factory at Broughton near Chester. When the war ended there was a substantial reduction in the work load and Lostock in particular was very short of work. However the Aircraft Company and the Engine Company were quite busy, and it was decided that most of the machining work would be done at Lostock. The only other factory in the south that had a decent machine shop was the Engine Company at Leavesden, but they were very busy with a worldwide demand for Gipsy piston engines and the development of the Ghost and Goblin jet engines.

Lostock therefore had an ever-increasing workload, in addition to their indigenous propeller production. Hamilton Standard, who were part of the United Aircraft Group in America, were using Lostock as a manufacturing unit to fill their growing demand for advanced propellers worldwide, and Woodward Governors at Rockford, Illinois, had a close relationship with de Havilland on the manufacture of constant speed units for propellers and engine controls.

The Lostock machine shop was divided into three units. The propeller machine shop made blades and hubs for propellers, and demanded highly specialised machinery such as a Berliners (which machined the duralumin blade forgings), Potter & Johnson semi-automatics (which machined barrels), and a scurfing shop (which finished the blades to highly-polished fine limits). The aircraft machine shop manufactured a whole range of aircraft parts, from complete undercarriages to flying control unit pedestals and air conditioning equipment. The third unit was the constant speed and engine controls shop which produced a whole variety of parts for the Engine Company.

Such complexity and variety demanded the most efficient management team, whose abilities were tested to the fullest extent. As I said earlier, the "terrible trio" or, as they were known elsewhere, the "Holy Trinity," were very experienced and efficient in their own disciplines, however there was not one "boss" among them. The Propeller Company's Chairman and Chief Executive was Air Vice Marshal Sir Ralph Sorley, the Engine Company's boss was Aubrey Burke, and the Aircraft Company's production director was Harry Povey; all had strong personalities, all were efficient and successful, and all were prepared to fight their own corner for priority at Lostock. To compound the problem all the department heads at Lostock were responsible to their opposite numbers in the south.

Added to all of this was the work being done for Chester on machining assemblies for Doves, Vampires, newer marks of Comet and – later – the DH.125 executive jet project. It was impossible to balance the work load for these three machine shops; they were all either too busy or too short of work, and if aircraft work was placed in either of the other two shops it naturally took second priority to the indigenous work there, and vice versa. No wonder Lostock was subject to criticism. With hindsight it was amazing that the "Holy Trinity" coped as well as they did, and the solutions attempted from the main de Havilland board were the wrong ones.

The wage system at Lostock did not help the problem. It was a premium bonus system where the time for each operation was estimated, to which a bonus factor was added to provide an incentive to the operator to beat the time and earn a bonus in addition to his/her standard wage. The original idea was a good one, but eventually the system got corrupted and it became a battle between the rate fixer and the work force. If the time was tight then workers avoided that operation, while if it was generous then it was sought after; the result was that management could not control the programme, and work in progress was unbalanced.

Aubrey Burke came up with the solution to this problem; he decided that the Engine Company should take over a third of the factory at Lostock, install plant and run it as a separate machine shop. This was opposed by Sorley and Povey. The main de Havilland Board decided to appoint a general manager at Lostock, and without consultation with anyone already at Lostock they appointed Donald McConnell, who had been production manager at Wellworthy Lymington. Wellworthy were leaders in the production of pistons and piston rings and other automobile parts; however theirs was a mass production factory, and McConnell had no experience with a 'short batch,' 'high variety' production machine shop. So this appointment caused more than a little concern at all levels of management at Lostock.

McConnell took up his duties on 1st November 1950. He was highly intelligent and was prepared to listen and learn, but his first battle was to resist the Engine Company's desire to have their machine shop at Lostock with its own management. Sorley and McConnell pointed out all the drawbacks, such as competition for labour, shared services, division of overheads etc., and suggested another site at Squires Gate, Blackpool. However they lost the battle due to the urgency of Ghost engine production, which was vital to the Comet 1.

The Propeller Company's Board had been giving serious thought to the future. They foresaw the reduction in propeller sales due to the advent of jet engines, and had been seeking a major diversification into other fields, so decided to go into the missile business. They had submitted a design study for a specification for an air-to-air guided missile and it had been accepted. The prototype missile was code-named "Blue Jay," which eventually became the famous Firestreak. This was excellent news for Lostock, as we had visions of becoming merely a sub-contract machine shop for other companies. The demands of the contract necessitated a new philosophy and the recruitment of new people with different skills and engineering disciplines. We needed physicists, electronics designers, aerodynamicists, guidance & propulsion engineers and mathematicians.

Having lost out to the Engine Company, we needed space too. The man to whom I had sold my Rover some time before owned a multi-storey mill at Farnworth; when I heard that it was up for sale, Donald McConnell and I went to see it. The owner had been buying up cars during the war and had made a fortune selling them at inflated prices. He had built ramps leading to each of the floors so that cars could be driven up and down. Donald decided the mill was ideal and Albert Mill became the first production unit for electronics for the missile programme. Donald took on the responsibility for the recruitment of all the new staff and in October 1951 appointed three new managers, Cyril Hayes, A.E. Heath and E. Shaw, all to be stationed at Albert Mill. The mill had to be completely refurbished, and Donald McConnell planned and executed all this work, which of course added to the load on the maintenance staff at Lostock.

By this time the Korean War had started and there was growing pressure to have Firestreak operational. In March 1952 Guy Gardiner (chief engineer at Hatfield), and Donald McConnell held a symposium and stressed the magnitude of the task in getting Firestreak into production and into service, and how this was so vitally important to the future of the Propeller Company. At the same time there was equal pressure from the Aircraft Company to produce all the parts, including the complete undercarriage, for the Comet 1 which was going into service, and of course the presence of the Engine Company within the factory, competing for labour, services and parts, did not make life any easier.

Then, to crown it all, Nick Nixon resigned. He had been feeling upset for some time and with McConnell's appointment he felt that he was being left out of things. He had been offered the job of production director with Alvis, whose MD was J.J. Parkes, an old friend and ex-employee of the Engine Company at Stag Lane. This was a great loss to de Havilland's as Nick was undoubtedly the best machine shop production engineer in the Group. On 1st April 1952 I was appointed production manager; I wondered then if the date was significant.

When I was offered the job I was delighted. I thought: "I am my own man at last, and I will be able to take the decisions and put all the problems to rights." Little did I know the pitfalls ahead, and the frustrations I would suffer because of clashing personalities and in-fighting between the three companies.

Long before Donald McConnell arrived I had suggested that something should be done to enable the managements to meet regularly, get to know each other and thus promote better relationships. Subsequently the main Board had purchased a fine house in Knutsford called The Spinney, which had once belonged to George Formby and boasted a beautiful garden running down to the Mere. Its purpose was to provide accommodation for directors and VIPs travelling between the South, Lostock and Chester. The directors decided to hold a get-together for directors and management of the three companies and the first one was a great success, so it was decided to continue them annually. In this way everyone got to know each other, and competitive party games were very popular.

However nobody ever attended from the Engine Company, and I think that they felt that the Aircraft Company and the Propeller Company dominated the scene and that they were the odd one out. As I said earlier, the Engine Company took over the empty space at Lostock, the only logical reason for such a decision being an attempt to bring about closer relationships between the Engine Company and the major machine shop in the group at Lostock. Hydro-tels and other highly specialised machine tools were moved in towards the end of 1951, new test beds were built on land across the road from West Block for the testing of Ghost and Goblin jet engines, and the unit went into full production in May 1952. But the project had not been thought through carefully enough. A manager, John Stiles, was appointed, reporting directly to Leavesden; if he had been responsible to the general manager at Lostock then the scheme might have worked, but in practice the set-up exacerbated the tensions and reduced the efficiency of the whole site.

Meanwhile I tackled my new responsibilities with vigour. Donald McConnell was fully occupied with all the planning for the new venture into the missile field, and I was left to run the rest. I completely revamped the machine shop, did away with the three separate units, and turned them into a composite whole with machines grouped by type. The only exception was the propeller blade shop, which was highly specialised and run very efficiently by a Scot, Jock Gordon. I appointed Harry Billington as Superintendent over all the machine shops; he originally came from the Engine Company at Stag Lane where he had served his apprenticeship, had eventually married a Lancashire lass and then asked for a transfer to Bolton. I reorganised the assembly shops and appointed Teddy Jones, who had previously been in charge of the aircraft machine shop, as Superintendent.

All the stores had been at one end of the factory, causing delays for operators who had to go to stores to draw their equipment, but we resited the stores and cutter grinding down the centre of the factory to provide better access. We set up a work loading team, which agreed a programme one month ahead. Previously the work was done at the whim of the foreman and the chargehand, or even the operator, and a lot of time was wasted by the operator having to collect his work card from the time office and his tools, jigs, fixtures and material from the stores. This time was paid for by the Company separately from the machining time and encouraged fiddling, as operators would claim that they were waiting in a queue at stores when they were actually at their machine, thus earning an inflated bonus. We set up a team of expediters who collected all the necessaries and delivered them in a bin to the operators, who did not therefore need to leave their machines apart from answering calls of nature. We formed teams of tooling engineers, who patrolled the shops and provided help and advice. We endeavoured to establish a manufacturing schedule of the work load three months ahead, so that all machined parts for each assembly would be completed at the same time. Some parts would have a manufacturing time of months, others hours or even just minutes.

The current procedure was for the planning engineers to study a drawing and issue work cards for all the parts on it at the same time, irrespective of the manufacturing time cycle. This resulted in 'short cycle' items getting to stores too early and 'long cycle' items too late. In turn this caused unbalanced and unprogrammed production causing a high level of 'work in progress' and serious shortages. It was an enormous task to try to keep track of millions of parts. Production was not programmed but was 'shortage driven,' leading to an army of progress chasers expediting the parts on the shortage list, thus leading to still greater shortage lists. This problem was not just peculiar to Lostock, it was universal in all manufacturing units engaged in small batch production.

The introduction of a manufacturing schedule programming each operation on each part did help, but the manpower to do it properly would have been enormous. I was sure that a bonus system was quite unsuited to this type of production, and began to think about alternatives. I was convinced that clocking on and off at the beginning and end of each shift, and the need to clock again at the beginning and end of each operation, was a complete waste of time. I wanted to go to America and study the methods there, but I was told that my time could not be spared when there was so much to do at Lostock.

Having the Engine Company within the same factory did not ease our problems. There was competition for labour and a great deal of antagonism developed, especially when it was discovered that all the workers, staff and management who had been brought up from the South were being paid higher rates. We did all we could to make the Southerners feel at home; we tried to involve them into the culture at Lostock and invited them to all the social functions, but life was still very difficult. So I phoned Aubrey Burke, the managing director of the Engine Company, told him of all the problems and invited him to Lostock.

He had the reputation of being tough and ruthless, but I found him understanding and charming. We toured the factory and I explained all the problems. He was well aware of most of them and had never been in favour of the move to Lostock, but he had been overruled by the financial directors who could not see the sense of spending money to expand the factory space at Leavesden when there was plenty of floor space at Lostock. In the end it proved a grievous waste of money; within a year the Engine Company had to move again when the space was needed for the production of Firestreak. Once again the accountants were wrong and, if they had listened to the engineers, a great deal of hassle and money could have been saved. I became quite friendly with Aubrey Burke and kept in touch even after I had left the Group.

To celebrate the departure of the Engine Company we had a cricket match where every member of each eleven had to bowl four overs each. I am no cricketer, but when it was my turn to bowl I got a 'hat trick'! The first ball was a full toss which hit the wicket. The next trickled along the ground and did not even reach the wicket; the batsman run out of his crease, missed and was stumped by the wicketkeeper. The third resulted in a straight drive right over my head, but I put up my hand and the ball stuck to it. I was later presented with a beautiful chrome-plated Top Hat trophy mounted on a mahogany plaque and suitably engraved; it still enjoys pride of place on my trophy shelf.

In August 1950 we had received a notice that a new general manager had been appointed to the Chester factory; it was John Corby whose life I had helped to save in New Delhi. I invited him over to Lostock, where we reminisced and talked about the future.

Chester was one of our biggest customers, but all the work for them was placed by the Aircraft Company at Hatfield, which added another link in the chain and caused further confusion. Much of the work we did depended on 'free issue' material from Hatfield. The theory was that central buying would provide cost savings, and indeed this was true. However, when certain materials were in short supply, Hatfield would put their own requirements first, whereupon Chester and then Lostock would have to wait. The scheduling would originate from Hatfield, go to Chester, and thence to Lostock, but with thousands & thousands of parts keeping a track as to the whereabouts of the 'free issue' material and the tooling was a major task. Hatfield would say that it had been sent to Chester, who would deny it, but at the end of the day Lostock were blamed for holding up the programme. With the arrival of John Corby, the relationship between Chester and Lostock improved immensely and we were able to expose the shortcomings of Hatfield.

The chief production engineer at Hatfield was Stan Rudge and the production controller was Wilfred Ward, and they both arrived one day, together with Sir Ralph Sorley, armed with a huge schedule listing all the parts being made at Lostock which were behind programme and were holding up production both at Hatfield and Chester. Donald McConnell got a good old roasting, but fortunately, thanks to John Corby, I had been given a copy of the schedule beforehand and had done my homework rather better than Rudge or Ward. I was able to prove conclusively that in 90% of the cases the delays were caused by Hatfield's late ordering, and late deliveries of materials and tooling. Indeed I was able to show that in many cases these had not even arrived before the delivery was overdue. I've never again seen two people arrive so full of complaints and depart so completely nonplussed.

Comet production was going well and on April 8th 1953, my 38th birthday, we had one of the Comet test crews visiting Lostock to see where all the machined parts were made and assembled into undercarriages, control assemblies, air conditioning and wing assembly brackets, to name but a few. The next week they set off for India to do hot weather take-offs and landings under various loading conditions. On the 2nd May this aircraft, G-ALYV, crashed near Jalalogori in West Bengal killing all on board.

On the 25th July Comet G-ALYR was involved in a take-off incident at Calcutta when it ran off the side of the runway, damaging the starboard undercarriage and wing; fortunately on this occasion no one was injured. Rumour had it that the nosewheel had collapsed due to buffeting from heavy puddles on the runway, and we were horrified as the nosewheel had been machined, assembled and tested at Lostock. Geoffrey de Havilland was a brilliant intuitive engineer and it was also rumoured that his eye and natural talent had led him to believe that the nosewheel mechanism did not look right to him; apparently it did not look man enough for the job, but when he requested that the design figures should be rechecked he was assured that they were OK. The cause of the crash was never clearly established, but the nosewheel was modified nevertheless.

On 1st September 1953 Dougie Simpson resigned. His ambitions were not being achieved at Lostock, and he felt that many of the negotiations he had done in the past were being taken over by Donald McConnell. He was a big loss as he was very capable and a very hard and dedicated worker. He became financial director of the de Havilland Company of Canada at Toronto. Shan Wheate, one of Stewart Kennedy's 'bright young men,' was transferred from the Aircraft Company and became secretary of the Propeller Company with responsibility for financial affairs at Lostock. He was a chartered accountant from Glasgow, had lived in Southbrae Drive near Joy's parents, and had been a boy friend of Joy's younger sister Monie.

So now I had another friend 'at court.' I had never given up pressing for my sabbatical in the USA and Canada, and at last the visit was authorised.

CHAPTER 31

ACROSS THE ATLANTIC – MY EYES ARE OPENED

Con Williams was chief engineer on propellers and ancilliary equipment, and had been to Hamilton Standard and Woodward Governors at Rockford several times. It was decided that I would travel with him so that he could show me the ropes, and on 18th September 1953 we took off for New York in a DC-6. We arrived on a Friday and spent our weekend sightseeing in New York; I had never been there before and I found the City fascinating. We visited the Empire State Building and made records on its top which we mailed back home to our families. We explored Times Square, had drinks in Jack Dempsey's Bar, had lunch at the 21 Club and saw all the celebrities, and in the evening went to the Rainbow Room for the cocktail hour, where for one hour two drinks were served for the price of one. We had a swim in the roof garden swimming pool, and thus refreshed went for a tour of the topless bars, which were the latest novelty in the City. We finished by going to an all-night cinema where we saw *From Here to Eternity*. Next morning we went to one of the fashionable diners and breakfasted on grits with maple syrup, followed by two eggs (sunny side up), bacon and a steak, coffee and a Danish. After going for a stroll in Central Park, we checked out of our hotel, took a taxi to Central Station and boarded a train for Hartford, Connecticut.

Con Williams was very concerned as he had some highly-classified papers in his briefcase and somewhere on the journey he had lost his keys. The case was supposed to have a security lock, but on the journey I applied the skills learned from my Dad and picked the lock with a paper clip. We were made very welcome at Hamilton Standard and met all the 'top brass.' I was very interested in their manufacturing facilities, which were not as comprehensive or sophisticated as we had at Lostock, but some of their tooling was better, and I made copious notes. They had not solved the problem of shop loading and programming either, but had abandoned any bonus scheme and paid each operator a standard wage, to which was added an efficiency payment based on assessment by supervision. I did not think that this worked fairly or provided adequate incentives.

Con and I stayed in an old-fashioned hotel in Hartford. We were both keen bridge players and one evening took two of the secretaries out for dinner. It turned out that they were keen players too, so we all returned to the hotel, went up to our room and got the cards out. We were just getting down to the first rubber when a security guard arrived and told us we were contravening the law: no ladies could be entertained in guests' rooms. We protested that we were only playing bridge but they still had to leave.

The following day I flew off from the airfield at Windsor Locks for de Havillands in Toronto, where I was made most welcome by Dougie Simpson. He had hardly had time to settle in as yet and was living in the Royal Hotel, where I joined him. He told me about the strange drinking laws in Toronto;

you could not buy liquor without a permit, and in bars you were only allowed to drink if you were sitting down.

The management at de Havilland had planned an itinerary of all the places they thought I should visit in the States, where I should stay and who I should see. I was a little embarrassed as I had my own ideas as to where I wanted to go, and I thought they might be upset. Not a bit! They allowed me to use their telephone to confirm my visits to all the people to whom I had previously written, and helped me with my hotel bookings. I wanted to learn all I could about production methods, management style, training, inventory, work in progress, programming work loads, incentives, selection methods, aptitude & intelligence testing, and methods of payment of wages and salaries; and I wanted to visit Harvard Business School.

In the end I visited the following Companies: Chrysler Corporation (Detroit), United Aircraft, Pratt & Whitney, Curtiss-Wright, Thompson Inc. (Euclid Avenue, Cleveland), Kearney & Trecker (Milwaukee), Woodward Governors (Rockford), and Canadair (Montreal). There was a subtle difference in the way I was received at some of them. With the larger companies it was difficult to get past the public relations departments. Although the reception was cordial enough, the tours extensive and the guides well briefed, the information was stereotyped and slanted to enhance the reputation of the company image; to obtain information about the scenarios I wanted to study, and to find out the problems, was nearly impossible. The exceptions were Thompson Inc., Kearney & Trecker, Woodward Governors and Curtiss-Wright.

At Curtiss-Wright, when the tour was over, I thanked the young man but said that I had not seen what I wanted to see and had not been able to speak to the people who had the experience to answer my questions. I asked if I could meet someone in authority, and he called up the Vice-President of Production Engineering on the internal telephone system and explained who I was and what I wanted. A broad Glaswegian voice answered, more or less telling the caller to show me the door, and complaining that when he had visited the de Havilland Engine Company he had not even been allowed into the factory.

At this point I butted in and said: “That’s not a very nice reception to give to a fellow Scot from Glasgow.”

He was so surprised that I was invited to his office. It transpired that he had gone to Allan Glen’s school and we had played rugby against each other. We had a very productive discussion, and he insisted that I went home with him and stayed overnight.

Curtiss-Wright had a set-up very similar to de Havilland. They had Aircraft, Engine and Propeller Divisions, with one large multi-purpose machine shop. Their problems were exactly the same as ours, and so we were both looking for the “Holy Grail” which of course no one had found. How does one find a proper and fair method of payment which will motivate the work force and provide an incentive, and how does one find a method of programming the work load which will keep the inventory low and ensure that all the parts are available when needed, particularly when the batches are small and the number of parts in work are well over one million?

Curtiss-Wright had tried all different methods of payment, piecework, shared bonus schemes, assessment, grading, and aptitude testing, and had finally settled on a basic wage plus an annual bonus paid on overall results. All attempts at detailed shop loading had been abandoned and, like de Havilland's, production was 'shortage driven.' There was no evidence that Curtiss-Wright was any more skilled or efficient than de Havilland's; they had no apprentice scheme nor, indeed, any formal training, and the operators learned on the job.

My welcome at Kearney & Trecker, Milwaukee, was warm and friendly. I think that was because the de Havilland Group were customers and had bought many milling machines from K & T over the years. Francis Trecker had just been appointed President; he had been the playboy of the family and had travelled the world. As a big game hunter and a keen fisherman, he had got to know many influential people. The company had been through a bad patch, and Fran Trecker had done a lot to pull it round and was now searching for new products and new methods of machining. They had some very bright young engineers who were looking for ways and means of applying some kind of automation for small batch production. Mass production, particularly for the automobile industry, had produced all kinds of automatic machines which reduced the need for labour. K & T had entered this field and had become market leaders in the supply of production lines for making cylinder blocks, heads and crankshafts on flow-line principles.

They showed me their development plans to construct a machine which would read a drawing and reproduce the part on an automated machine tool. I did not think much of this idea as it depended on very accurate drawings being read by photoelectric cells. Their thinking was certainly on the right lines, but numerically-controlled machine tools had not been invented at that time. I got on very well with Fran Trecker, who was married but had no children; little did I know then that he would offer me a job many years later.

My next visit was to the Chrysler Corporation. I had never seen a mass production car factory and was astounded at the size and the amount of automated production taking place. There were many conveyor belts and overhead gantries and it was amazing to see how all the various parts arrived in the right place and at the right time. The speed at which the operators worked was also impressive.

My most lasting memory was the number of cabins dotted along the production lines, all occupied by men who were either reading, talking or playing cards. When I asked what they were doing, I was told that they were the highest-paid operators in the plant, the tooling engineers or "trouble-shooters." If a line stopped, hooters sounded, red lights flashed, and they immediately leapt into action, as their pay was substantially reduced until the line was back in action again. I thought that it was a superbly logical idea, and it started me thinking of ways and means of keeping the operators at Lostock continuously operating at their machines rather than strolling off to clock their work cards at the time office and collecting tools etc. from stores. Payment at all levels at Chrysler was directly related to numbers of cars produced per shift, with a bonus if the planned number was exceeded. It was not surprising to find that an American car was selling for about 55% of the equivalent price in Britain.

I particularly noticed that there were few grey heads on the production lines, and it was admitted that the pace of work demanded young fit men and women. Anyone over 45 either had been promoted to supervision or management, or had lost their job. There was no such thing as apprenticeships, and all the line operators were classed as unskilled.

The Thompson Corporation Inc. had a large factory organisation in Euclid Avenue, Cleveland, Ohio. Euclid Avenue was the longest avenue I have ever seen, it seemed to stretch for miles and miles. The President was regarded as one of the leaders in management techniques in America; he had written a number of textbooks on management, which were considered to be at the leading edge of liberal management and were used as standard works at Harvard Business School where he was a peripatetic tutor. Thompson were the leading makers of pistons, piston rings, connecting rods and big end & little end bearings for the automobile industry, all of this being highly automated. In addition they had a huge machine shop which catered for a massive number of miscellaneous parts for many industries.

I was fortunate in being shown around by a young graduate who had a master's degree at MIT in production engineering and a Master's in business studies at Harvard. I spent three days with him and was most impressed with the friendliness and enthusiasm of everyone, from top management to shop floor personnel. Everyone wore baseball caps with the slogan "I love my work at Thompson's." The theme was "leadership & motivation," and the staff were obviously convinced of the tenet "The more you enjoy your work, the more efficient you will be and the more you will earn." Everyone was on first-name terms and there was no clocking on and off. Trust and honesty were of major importance. There were notices posted everywhere such as "If you break the rules you are robbing your friends and colleagues." Medical and dental care was provided on site free of charge. Anyone could get hair care, eye tests, chiropody or physiotherapy in the company time free of charge, and the self-service canteen provided superb meals, all highly subsidised. Everyone belonged to the company pension fund; contributions were paid by the company, and to get a pension cost the employee nothing. Anyone could make voluntary contributions to enhance their own pension and, as these were tax-deductible, this scheme was very popular.

Thompson's approach to wage payments was common sense and simplicity itself. When they quoted for a contract, the price was made up of material costs, labour costs and overheads. The labour cost was broken down for each operation. If each worker did the work in less time, there would be a profit, if not there would be a loss. If each worker checked his own work, then it did not need an inspector and the overheads would come down. This may be an oversimplification of the system, but it worked. Work study teams with ciné-cameras roamed the works, and where times were being exceeded the film would help to show why the time had not been met, in which case the methods would have to be re-engineered. A bonus was paid out once a year at Christmas-time, based on the savings made. There was a competition every month, and prizes were awarded to the section who had made the biggest savings and hence the better output. Thompson's were exploring all kinds of psychological management aids for selection and training including intell-igence testing, graphology, aptitude testing and even hypnosis. I was fascinated to find that the James Mackie papers and textbooks were in the library and had been studied (see Chapter 2). We had an interesting discussion about them, and I was able to confirm how accurately some of his forecasts had turned out. The consensus of opinion was that all these aids had to be interpreted very carefully, and that the best results could only be obtained from interviews carried out by skilled and experienced staff.

Thomson had a very rigid rule to which I gave my full support. When they were assessing employees for supervisory or management positions, all candidates, no matter how good their academic qualifications, had to do a spell on the shop floor, and they were assessed at every stage of their development.

When I expressed my desire to visit Harvard and see how the Business School worked, arrangements where made for me to spend a week there. In the meantime I was invited to spend a weekend with my cousin and childhood friend Andrew Turnbull, the chief engineer with the Cleveland Light & Power Company, who lived with his wife Nacelle in a pleasant bungalow in a good residential district on the shores of Lake Eyre. September & October (the fall) were beautiful, sunny and warm, and all the foliage on the trees was a riot of colour. It was most enjoyable for me to sit quietly with the Turnbulls and their little son Drew, talk about times gone by, and relate my experiences in America – and at Prestwick during the war years. We went sightseeing in Andrew's lovely Buick Sedan, and went for a tour of Lake Eyre in his powerboat. We even tried some fishing but didn't catch anything.

One evening we phoned Andrew's brother Jim, who lived in New York. He worked as a motor mechanic and was married but had no children. I arranged to visit them when I passed through New York on my way to Harvard. I was fascinated by Andrew's account of how he had felt when he couldn't get a job back home, and how lonely he had been when he emigrated to the States. He found a job in Cleveland as a fitter with Cleveland Light & Power, and his loneliness was alleviated when he met Nacelle. He was ambitious and steadily climbed the ladder until he became chief engineer. With the liberal pension arrangements in America he was able to retire at 60. He was a great lover of Arran and had come to visit us when we were renting a cottage there.

It is interesting to speculate why Andrew, the eldest of three brothers, should have achieved a prominent position in the competitive world of power generation, while Jim never progressed beyond becoming a humble motor mechanic and Bertie never achieved anything better than being a clerk with Kilmarnock Council. I am not in any way denigrating their relative positions; they were probably happy doing their own thing and they were all brought up with the same opportunities, but I cannot help wondering how to define 'success.' I think that it must be judged by achievement and happiness. The lower the goal the better the chance of achievement; striving for a goal that is never achieved leads to frustration and unhappiness.

Andrew died of a heart attack at the relatively early age of 69. Nacelle died a few years later, we completely lost touch with Drew, and after my visit to Jim we never heard anything more of him.

Next to my visit to Thompson Inc., my time spent with the Woodward Governor Company, Rockford, Illinois was the most rewarding. They had very close links with Hamilton Standard and provided all the control equipment associated with constant speed variable pitch propellers. Woodward's President was Irl Martin, and Hamilton Standard's president was Earl Martin – quite a coincidence I thought. Woodward had been started in 1880 by a brilliant young engineer called Amos Woodward. He invented and developed speed governors for steam engines, and when petrol and diesel arrived he entered that field too, and it was he that supplied the speed control for the engine on the famous Wright Brothers' aeroplane. He had a Quaker upbringing, developed socialist ideas and believed that wealth should be shared by all those who contributed to its creation. He had no sons, but his daughter married Irl Martin, who inherited the company and continued and added to Amos's ideals.

His theme was that all men and women are equal and should have equal opportunities. Wealth creation was a desirable objective but should be shared to a fair degree by all. Everyone should have the opportunity to develop different skills and the best way to do this was by job rotation. Everyone after two years' probation became a member of the Company, and were allotted shares in it. Everyone was given the opportunity to buy further shares at a discount, but they were not allowed to sell these in the market, and Company members had to be given first option to buy at the middle market price. There was an assessment procedure for all employees up to the President, carried out yearly, and this was done by immediate colleagues. In each department there was an assessment panel that studied the various assessments, adjudicated on the results, and made recommendations concerning promotion and job rotation. Everyone had to do their stint on the shop floor, so that they understood what it was like at the sharp end. Accountants had to learn engineering and *vice versa*. Managers had to be proficient in all disciplines and had to do their share of selling so that they understood the customers' point of view. Every Company member had access to all company information, including wages, salaries, costing, sales figures and profits, and every quarter this information was disclosed at symposia where it was shown on film with pie charts and graphs.

Everyone ate in the same self-service restaurants – not called 'canteens' as it was considered that this name conjured up visions of inferior mass-cooked meals – and the quality of the food was excellent. Social activities were encouraged, and there were teams at every conceivable sport, such as softball, volleyball and ten-pin bowling. There were discipline and counselling panels too. Anyone not making the grade was interviewed and helped. Personality clashes, marriage and family difficulties – even affairs – were subject to counselling. It all sounded highly idealistic, but throughout the many years that I dealt with the Company, I never knew a happier or more successful place in which to work. There was a comprehensive medical and dental service, and every employee contributed to health care such as Blue Cross or others; premiums were paid by Woodward.

The product range was varied with many small batches, and I was anxious to see if Woodward had solved the problems that we had at Lostock. They had certainly experienced them though not solved them, but I found that we were in agreement on many principles; for example, clocking on and off either to monitor attendance or to control times on work cards was not cost-effective.

Individual or group bonus schemes always led to unfairness and abuse, but it was desirable to have some form of incentive to promote efficient effort. What mattered most was how much saleable work an employee produced during his/her attendance hours. In theory employees at Woodward's could work as many hours as they wished, negotiate their own starting and stopping times and be free to leave when they had achieved their set target. But it was essential to have a detailed manufacturing schedule so that each part was programmed for completion only when needed, thereby reducing work in progress and inventory.

In principle each operator would be responsible for the accuracy of his/her own work, thus reducing inspection time. Bad work should be heavily penalised. Every efficient and skilled operator should spend all his/her time producing at the machine or work station, and all fetching and carrying tools, parts, and paperwork should be done by other less skilled personnel. Machine shops should be laid out in such a way that parts travelled the shortest possible distance during their machining life until completion, and should not spend too much time queuing between operations, thus adding to high work in progress, delays, and ultimately the shortage list at assembly stages.

It was easy to define the problems but it was not easy to find solutions. To plan and control the programming of millions of parts was beyond the ability of manual control, as the number of people required to keep an accurate track of them all was not cost-productive. It was not until the advent of computer-aided design/computer-aided manufacture (CAD/CAM), powerful mainframe computers and CNC flexible manufacturing systems that the problems became solvable.

It was distressing to all those of us who had spent a lifetime of effort addressing these problems that their solution should have been attributed to the Japanese, who coined the slogans "Just-In-Time Manufacture (JIT)," "Flexible Manufacturing Systems (FMS)" and the "Kanban Theory." All of these in fact originated in Great Britain, but were not widely enough accepted because of conservative management and the short-term outlook of financial directors to spend the capital necessary. I spent some time in Japan in 1970/73 and they were further adrift in solving the problems than we were in the West.

Woodward had however arrived at a culture where clocking on or off was unnecessary. Like Thompson Inc., 'trust' was the byword; all employees were assumed to be honest and to perform to the best of their ability. As everyone was a member of the Company, incentives were there by virtue of the annual bonuses, share options and steady growth in profits. Woodward had tried 'group technology,' or the 'cell' system as it was known later, but had abandoned it as the cost of regrouping machine tools for every product change was prohibitive. They had laid out their machine shop, as we had ours, by type of machining, but between each line of machines was a conveyor belt. At the end of the shop was a large warehouse which was the central intelligence centre for the manufacturing programme. Bins containing the work to be done and all tooling was loaded onto the conveyor together with a tag indicating the operator's number. The operator picked it up, did the work and put it back on the conveyor. If the bin did not return to the warehouse on time it was chased by the expediters, and if they could not chase it, then the trouble-shooters investigated the reasons. The system was not perfect but it was the best that I had yet seen; every operator was responsible for his own quality, and random checks were made in the warehouse.

At the time of my visit the Vice-President of Production Engineering was Bill Whitehead. He looked after me very well and we became close friends, and when he switched to World Sales he visited us regularly in Bolton. I was also invited to Irl Martin's house, a beautiful home on the banks of the Red River. Irl was very democratic and regularly invited his employees home for a party or a poker session. It was the first time that I had ever seen an automatic bar in a private house. Stocks of every conceivable drink were stored in the cellar, complete with glassware, supplies of ice and mixtures. One dialled in the drink of one's choice, pressed a number of buttons and, lo and behold, it would arrive on the little conveyor complete to taste and in the correct type of glassware, usually the best crystal – or for the beer drinkers, silver goblets. Irl Martin had no sons but his daughter Mary Barbara was married to Billy Biddle who, in spite of the democratic ideas, was being groomed to take over when Irl retired. I liked Mary Barb and Billy, and over the years we became friends. During the next five years I paid many visits to Woodward's. Irl was also a great poetry lover and was delighted when I gave him the complete works of Robert Burns. In return he presented me with a copy of the collected poems of Robert Service.

I then flew from O'Hare Airport, Chicago, to La Guardia, New York, and took a yellow cab to visit James Turnbull and his wife in their Manhattan flat; this was on the sixth floor and was a comfortable home, but I thought that Jim, with all his talents, deserved better. However he seemed happy enough, and we spent the evening chatting about years gone by and I tried to pass on all the family news. Jim's wife was a most charming lady and obviously was the stronger personality. I got the impression that she thought that Jim was lacking in ambition and did not push himself enough. On the other hand he loved cars and car engines, and his hobby was restoring them; he did not seem to have any other interests. They both seemed a little sad that they had no children, and Jim recounted how much he had enjoyed his Sunday visits to Charles Street. I left for Harvard the next morning, and never heard from them again.

Harvard is the oldest College in the USA, founded in 1636 at New Towne (now Cambridge), Massachusetts. It was named after the English clergyman John Harvard, was originally a training college for Puritan ministers, and became a University under Charles W. Elliot (1869-1909). Six American Presidents were educated there, including John Adams, Franklin D. Roosevelt and John F. Kennedy. Other graduates included Emerson, Thoreau, Henry James and T.S. Eliot. John Harvard died at the early age of 31 from consumption, and left all his worldly possessions (including $779) to the College together with a valuable collection of his books and writings which, allegedly, formed the basis of the world-famous Harvard Library.

The University had an ambience all of its own. Amid the hustle and bustle of American life, the atmosphere was one of peace and tranquillity. The buildings were old, steeped in history, impressive and thought-provoking, and provided a marked contrast to the huge concrete and glass buildings of modern American cities. I walked through the cloisters and thought of all the famous people who had walked the same paths. The arrangements made for me by my friends at Thompson Inc. could not have been bettered. I was welcomed by the Vice-President of the Business School, who had arranged for me to have a room in the college and dine with the students attending business courses. He told me I was welcome to sit in at any of the lectures, and he hoped that at the end of my visit I would pass on my impressions to him and his colleagues.

I was completely flabbergasted by such unexpected kindness and interest. Here I was, an unknown and humble young man, being welcomed into a world-famous seat of learning without even having to pay for my board and lodgings, let alone the expensive fees pertaining for MBA courses. As time progressed I realized how much influence the President and Directors at Thompson had at Harvard, and how interested they had been in my accounts of the problems yet to be solved in Production Engineering technology, particularly when there was a massive number of parts to be manufactured to a time scale involving a huge variety of small batches. Such problems were well-known at Harvard and many ingenious schemes had been thought up, but none of them were cost-effective.

One theory was that large multi-purpose machine shops should be disbanded and replaced by a variety of small machine shops with low overheads where the work would be sub-contracted. However no one could come up with a solution as to how these could be integrated and controlled to meet the overall programme.

I was impressed by the degree of effort applied by the students at Harvard, by the intensity of the competition, and by the hard work and dedication required to get a degree there. There is no doubt that the academic standards were of the highest, the problems were thoroughly researched and understood, and many solutions were reached. However my major criticism was that both the students and lecturers did not have enough experience to understand the difficulties of putting theory into practice.

The Vice-President and his colleagues agreed with this but confessed that they had so far failed to get co-operation. They explained that industry in general was suspicious of Business Schools and were not only reluctant to send their staff there, but staff were reluctant to go, as they felt that time spent away at College might deny them their place in the promotion queue. Moreover, graduates returning to work were subject to jealousy and even ridicule. This was widespread throughout the engineering industry worldwide with the possible exception of Japan, and led to the domination of top management by accountants and lawyers who were usually articulate and had proficient degrees in business and legal matters. It was not until the early 1960s when the Management Degree Course was established at Churchill College, Cambridge, that things began to change; this course was a joint effort between the engineering industry and academics, and one with which I was closely associated when I was the managing director of Platt Brothers from 1958-1966.

United Aircraft were a large conglomerate with interests in machine tools, engines, and aircraft and general engineering; they owned Pratt & Whitney and Hamilton Standard. I have already related my visit to Hamilton Standard and the only other factory I now had time to visit was Pratt & Whitney. I already knew some of the people there as we had set up an overhaul unit at SAL for Pratt & Whitney radial air-cooled engines. I was made very welcome but did not learn anything new concerning production engineering nor how to overcome the problems of organising large machine shops. P & W management were more anxious to talk to me about the future of jet engine development, particularly the Ghost engine for the Comet. They thought that DH had done a wonderful job in developing the first jet airliner.

The real highlight of this visit was that they took me to see Niagara Falls. I found the tour a bit 'trippery' but was amazed at the massive volume of water flowing over the falls. The noise was thunderous and we could hardly hear ourselves speak. We got dressed up in oilskins and walked through the tunnels behind the waterfall; the scenery was dramatic and the spray was very wetting. The guide recounted all the people who had gone over the falls in various devices, and reminded us in particular of the famous wire-walker (Blondin) who in 1859 had crossed over on a wire rope pushing a man in a wheelbarrow.

The following day I flew back to de Havilland's at Toronto. Here I was entertained to dinner by the directors and their wives, who were all agog to find out what I had learned during my travels.

Russ Banner, the chief test pilot, was a keen fly fisherman and invited me to go for a day's fishing with him in the Northern Lakes. So at 6 am the following morning I flew north in a de Havilland Moth floatplane piloted by Russ to land on one of the small lakes, where we taxied over to a log cabin which served as the fishing lodge. We had a huge breakfast of steak, bacon and eggs with all the trimmings served by the keeper's wife and then set up our tackle. As often happens the keeper was not very optimistic and warned us that the lake was not fishing well; but undeterred, off we went in a motorboat, fished for two hours and did not see a fish or even a rise. Russ was just thinking of packing up and flying to another lake when he hooked a rainbow and netted it, and it must have been all of 6 lb. As often happens this seemed to have stirred up the fish, and in the next 30 minutes we were getting takes every other cast, but the fish were not hooking. In fisherman's parlance this is known as 'taking short.' There was then another long spell of nothing, but just before lunch-time we hooked and netted three each, the largest being over 10 lb.

It was a beautifully warm and sunny October day and the patina of colours on the trees was magnificent. We landed on a small island to have our lunch, and I pondered on how lucky I was to experience such peaceful and beautiful countryside, and particularly to have landed three trout. We fished again in the afternoon, but there was absolutely no sign of anything. Then when we were wending our way back a rise started. A slight breeze had blown up and we could see a hatch of flies being blown from the bushes along one bank. In next to no time we had caught over a dozen trout, and then the rise stopped as quickly as it had started.

We took off in daylight and arrived back over Toronto just as dusk was falling and the city lights were coming on. As we circled the city Russ pointed out all the important buildings and the numerous golf courses. Later on he took me to his favourite eating-place, an old converted Canadian & Pacific Railway dining car whose speciality was T-bone steaks.

The next morning I took an airliner to Montreal to visit Canadair. We flew along the shores of Lake Ontario and circled the city. The view from the air was quite different from the skyline over Toronto. The latter was a large city on a flat plain with modern skyscraper buildings, spreading north from the shores of the lake, whereas Montreal was a much more compact city with many of the old buildings reminiscent – not surprisingly – of the cities of France. The streets were narrower and the shops were smaller and more cosmopolitan.

My welcome to Canadair could not have been more gracious, and of course they had heard all about me from my years at SAL. They had been competitors of ours as they had had a licence from Douglas for the conversion of Dakotas and Skymasters in Canada and had converted the executive Dakota for J.P. Bickell (see Chapter 27). Apparently, when Lord Beaverbrook had arrived in his specially converted Dakota he had taken it to Canadair to show it off and brag about how much better it was than Bickell's. We had some very interesting conversations about conversions, including how profitable they had been and how clever David McIntyre had been in exploiting the market. We compared notes and discussed the future and what would follow to replace the highly profitable market we had been enjoying. They were anxious to know why I had left SAL, and asked how much money SAL was losing on their airline operations and in the production of the Pioneers. I was very careful not to make any critical comments, and told them what a wonderful life I had had at Prestwick, and how lucky I was to be now working for such a progressive company as de Havilland's. Their factory was not in any way as large as SAL and there was little that they could teach me; they were well aware of the hard row that they would have to furrow to prosper in the future. However they were most complimentary about the Comet and wished me well at de Havilland's.

This was my last port of call before my return to England. I had never sailed across the Atlantic before, and before I left I had received approval to sail home rather than fly, particularly as travelling by sea on the CPR line was cheaper than flying. CPR had three ships, the *Empress of Scotland*, the *Empress of Canada* and the *Empress of France*. Naturally I would have preferred to sail on the *Empress of Scotland*, but had to settle for a first class berth on the *Empress of France*.

I was very excited at the prospect: I had had a wonderful tour, I had stayed in all the best hotels and I had met many influential people. But I was missing my wife and family very much and we were expecting our fourth child. I had time to go on a shopping spree, so I bought all kinds of presents for Joy and the family. As many of the best shops only spoke French, my friends at Canadair helped with the shopping, and when I asked what I should do on my last night in Canada I was told about a super restaurant and night club run by a Scottish lady, but they reckoned it was unlikely that I would be admitted as it was most exclusive, and they could not help. All they knew was that her name was Jackie and that she came from Paisley.

I said goodbye to all my friends, went back to my hotel, did all my packing, and wondered how to spend the rest of the evening. Should I go night-clubbing or should I retire to bed? I put on my dinner jacket, called a taxi and gave the driver the address of the club that had been mentioned to me earlier, which turned out to be on the outskirts of the city in what looked like a country house. The large oak door had a spy hole in it, and when I pressed the bell, a speaker phone asked if I was a member and what my name and membership number was. When I explained that I was a visitor and not a member I was told that I could not get admittance.

I responded: "Tell Jackie that a friend of hers has come all the way from Paisley to see her."

Jackie came to the door, a little suspicious at first because of the licensing laws, but when I mentioned one or two places in Glasgow and SAL at Prestwick, these, together with my accent, worked the oracle and I was in. Like many people living abroad she was lonely and wanted to hear news from home. It turned out that her brother had worked at SAL and now lived in Toronto, and we finished up having drinks and dinner together. She was not actually the owner but was hostess and general manager; nevertheless I was given freedom of the house, and I soon discovered that it was a high-class casino and brothel. I played roulette and blackjack and tried to understand the poker games, *chemin de fer* and crap. I chatted up the girls and had a wonderful time, but resisted their advances even when they told me that Jackie had told them that everything was free; going back to my wife and family I was not taking any chances.

I got back to the hotel sometime after 3 am and slept like a log. When I reached the docks the next morning, there moored in all her glory was the *Empress of France*. I cleared customs and emigration and was shown to my cabin by my very own steward, who said he would look after me for the rest of the voyage. He brought down all my luggage, did my unpacking, repacked everything that I did not need on the voyage and then took it off to the storerooms. He then offered me morning coffee or a drink. I opted for both and he fetched coffee in a silver pot, neat little sandwiches and a large malt whisky. He gave me a programme for the voyage and a plan of the ship, and then took me on a conducted tour. There were only 40 first class passengers and he gave me a list of their names. The only one I recognised was a famous Glasgow building contractor who had recently been knighted. I went on deck and found that the quay was crowded with people seeing off their friends. The second class accommodation was not full either but there were certainly hundreds of people. Soon the ship's hooter sounded and there was an announcement that all non-passengers should leave the ship. Streamers were being thrown, the band was playing on deck, everyone was waving; then the gangways were withdrawn and the tugs started easing the liner out into the river – we were on our way.

That evening the Captain held a cocktail party at which all the passengers were introduced to one another. There were five tables seating eight each, and I found myself at the Captain's table with the Glasgow building contractor and his wife, together with a glamorous young lady who was introduced as his secretary. The two other couples were a Canadian banker and a carpet manufacturer from Huddersfield. The food was superlative, the wine was flowing and the service was of the best. I must admit to thinking: "Why would anyone wish to fly when they can travel in luxury like this?"

We sailed through the Hongueda Passage into the Gulf of St Lawrence, through the Cabot Strait past Cape Breton to starboard and Newfoundland to port, and so out into the Atlantic. The weather deteriorated and soon we were sailing through gale force 8 storms. The ship had no stabilisers and soon many of the passengers were seasick. I kept very active, took plenty of exercise and fresh air and drank whisky, as I thought that was the best way to avoid sickness; however after a day and a night of heavy weather we finally sailed into comparative calm. The entertainments officer then tried to get a party spirit going in 'first class'; he organised charades and fancy dress parties but found it hard going – bingo and prizes for the best guesses as to how far the ship travelled in 12 hours was about the height of excitement. Nevertheless it was a great experience for me and I thoroughly enjoyed the voyage. Even although the ship was old-fashioned the decor and the wood panelling was magnificent, and the standard of service could not have been bettered.

Many years later, when I was fishing on the Spey, Joy and I visited the Glerfarclas Distillery with friends. The showroom was beautifully panelled; I thought it looked familiar and sure enough a brass panel above the bar stated: 'This room has been constructed from the original panelling and wood carvings taken from the *Empress of France*.'

On the last night of the voyage the Captain held a farewell champagne party followed by a five-course dinner. He made a farewell speech, which was replied to by the Canadian banker, who from what he said must have been a shareholder in CPR and was probably having a free passage. Next morning I was up bright and early in time to see the coast of Ireland coming up, and a few hours later we were docking in Liverpool. Joy was there to meet me with a company car driven by our faithful chauffeur, Josh; she was looking absolutely ravishing in a dark green coat with a jaunty little hat, the most beautiful sight to meet my eyes for eight weeks. This was the 1st December 1953; Joy was nearly five months pregnant so we had the thrill of looking forward to our fourth child.

CHAPTER 32

IMPLEMENTATION OF NEW WORKING PRACTICES AT LOSTOCK

One advantage of sailing home was the avoidance of what is now known as jet lag; I was rested and full of energy. The second advantage was that I had time on board to write comprehensive notes of all that I had seen and done.

My first few days were spent in editing these and writing a full report with strong recommendations as to what I wished to do. I was sure that the method of paying wages and bonuses had to be completely changed, and that we had to concentrate in producing a detailed and workable manufacturing schedule. Donald McConnell and my engineering colleagues gave me full support in these aims, but some of the financial staff, particularly at headquarters, were less than enthusiastic. My arguments were convincing ones: amongst other things I said that there was no point in sending me away for eight weeks if I was not allowed to put into practice what I had learned. James McGregor Smith, the cost & works accountant, a fellow Scot from Edinburgh and educated at Herriot's School, was a vociferous and strong supporter. The other problem was to convince the shop stewards' committee that a change was not only essential but could be to their benefit financially.

We spent the next two months writing a new 'wage code.' The premium individual bonus scheme would be scrapped, and all operators would be paid a standard wage based on their skills, which would be assessed annually. For example a skilled toolmaker would be paid more than a capstan operator. The standard wage would be slightly above the average earnings of each group. The times for each operation would be the times contained in the estimate to establish the sales price. As each part was completed the actual time taken would be recorded, and each month the total would be published. If this total was below the estimated time it would be credited to a bonus pool, and once a year it would be shared by all the operators according to their status.

Service departments would be established on the shop floor, and operators would not have to leave their machines as everything would be brought to them. Tea breaks as such were not abolished, but tea trolleys carrying sandwiches, biscuits and sweets would be taken round the shops by the catering staff; tea and coffee were free but the rest had to be paid for. Each operator was provided with two sets of overalls free of charge, and one set was laundered by the Company each week free of charge; these had logos for each department for easy recognition.

Any scrap or faulty work was debited against the bonus pool. The management would have the right to retrain, demote or finally dismiss anyone not making a positive contribution to the scheme.

The theory was to encourage everyone to produce at maximum efficiency, and for them to be adequately rewarded for so doing. Each operator would have a vested interest in seeing that his workmates performed at their best, and all the 'fiddles' endemic to the old bonus system would disappear. Equally quality would improve as bad work or scrap would cost money. Under the old scheme operators would try to hoodwink the inspectors and get faulty work passed. Even when faulty work was found it was difficult and time-consuming to pinpoint the actual operator responsible.

We were fortunate in having intelligent and co-operative stewards and after some hard bargaining the wage code was accepted for a trial period of six months, subject to two shop stewards' representatives having access to the figures for verification purposes. We engaged in a strong propaganda programme, and plastered the factory with leaflets and notices emphasising what a major breakthrough this could be in wage negotiations, and how everyone could benefit. Every department had a large notice board showing the monthly targets and results. As I said earlier the old bonus scheme encouraged operators to concentrate on the good-paying jobs and neglect the bad-paying ones, leading to unbalanced production and high 'work in progress.'

A workable manufacturing schedule was vital to the success of the wage code, as the service departments needed to know well ahead what to programme. It was essential for the planning department to put a completion date on each route card, and working back from that to put a completion date on each operation. That was the easy part; keeping track thereafter was a mammoth task. Mac Smith was having some success in transferring the cost records to Power Samus. This was a system whereby information was stored on punched cards, and retrieval was done via an interrogation method of the holes. When tried on the manufacturing schedule, it worked and reduced the manual effort to some extent; it was far from perfect but we were progressing in the right direction. We tried to keep the time scales simple, and worked on week numbers rather than days or hours. There were many teething problems both with the wage code and the schedule, and we were unable to get rid of the shortage lists, although they were not as long or extensive as before.

As an added incentive we promised that for every part completed within the week number on the card we would add 10% to the bonus pool for that part. This worked a treat as every operator had a vested interest in working to programme, and the improvement was dramatic. Everyone began to have faith and even the operators started to believe that there could be a sizeable bonus at the end of the six months' trial period. Little did I know that I would not be at Lostock to see that happen.

CHAPTER 33

THE COMET CRASHES AND THEIR IMPLICATIONS

I briefly related the circumstances of the first two Comet incidents in India in Chapter 30. On the 10th January 1954 G-ALYP, a Comet in service with BOAC, crashed off the coast of Italy near Elba, killing all on board, 29 passengers and six crew. Shortly afterwards, on the 8th April, another Comet, G-ALYY, crashed in the sea near Stromboli, Italy, again killing everyone on board.

At the time I had been in particularly good spirits. We were expecting our fourth child imminently (Frances, born four days later) and on the day of the crash I was celebrating my 39th birthday. The Management Club was holding its annual dinner and W.E. Nixon was the guest of honour. Right in the middle of his speech he was handed a note telling him of the crash. Everyone was devastated and needless to say the festivities came to a quick end. The Air Registration Board immediately grounded all Comets and announced that until the cause of these crashes was discovered no more Comets would fly. This was desperate news: so much money was tied up in Comet and engine production it could mean bankruptcy.

The Comet G-ALYP was in quite shallow water and most of the wreckage was recovered by the Royal Navy. A most urgent and extensive effort was launched to lay out all the bits and pieces and try to work out what had happened. A brilliant young engineer from Farnborough, Arnold Hall, carried out the investigation in conjunction with all the boffins at Hatfield, and they eventually unearthed the most likely cause as being due to the little-understood phenomenon called metal fatigue.

Every schoolboy now knows that if a piece of metal is bent back and forth it will eventually break at the bend line, but at the time no one knew that if a fuselage was pressurised and depressurised many times the molecular structure would change to give a higher resistance to stress, this effect giving misleading information in the forecasting of safety factors. I will not enlarge on the technical details as they have all been related in *The Comet Story* which is available on film and video; but it is one of the most remarkable stories on detection ever written in the history of aviation. The reconstruction of what happened was brilliantly executed and I found viewing of the film heart-stopping.

It was a tragic and desperately worrying time for de Havilland's. Amongst the general public there was already a natural resistance to flying in airliners powered by jet engines, and these three crashes just made things worse. What was going to happen to all the Comets in production, all the engines and all the work in progress? De Havilland was facing ruin, the loss of jobs would be horrendous and the blow to the future of British aviation would be devastating.

And so a deal was agreed. All the Comets in work would be completed and sold to Transport Command. The fuselages would be reskinned with thicker gauge metal, which of course would reduce the payload, but that was not so important for the RAF. Meanwhile a new version of the Comet, the Mk. 2, would be introduced, incorporating all the necessary modifications to overcome the metal fatigue problem.

Time was of the essence. Comets had to be flying again as soon as possible so that they could be seen to be safe and that jet transport was viable. BOAC also wanted the Comet 2 as soon as possible, and their flying staff were full of confidence as they thought that the Comet was essentially a marvellous aircraft. Its speed, range, handling qualities and quietness were just what was needed for the rapid growth of air transport which the experts were forecasting; they were sure that jet airliners were here to stay. Of course I had a personal stake in all of this, and considered that those attempting to detract from the value of the advances already made were probably just jealous of de Havilland's brilliant innovations – probably not far from the mark.

It was decided to transfer all Comet 1 production from Hatfield to Chester, thus freeing Hatfield to concentrate on the production of the Comet 2. I was asked to go to Chester and take charge of all the production there, while Bob Wilde, the Deputy Chief Inspector at Hatfield, would be going there to take charge of quality.

I was completely flabbergasted and asked: "What about all my work at Lostock?"

I was told: "If the Comet problem is not sorted out there will not *be* a Lostock."

I was in a dilemma; I was enjoying Lostock and was just getting on top of the problems there. On the other hand I was very flattered to be chosen for such a critical and responsible position. William Denny was going to Chester too to carry some of the administration load. He had been general manager at Portsmouth and had interviewed me for a job there several years earlier. Ernie Middleditch, who was Harry Povey's assistant at Hatfield, was already at Chester. There was no way that I could refuse the job, but it seemed to me that there might be "too many cooks." I was determined to establish clear terms of reference before I said yes. I knew Bob Wilde and admired his ability and bluntness, and we got on well together, so I said that I would only take the job if I had complete authority over all production and Bob Wilde had complete authority for quality. Everyone connected with production at Chester would answer to me and the habit of departmental heads at Chester being responsible to their chiefs at Hatfield must cease. I wanted it made clear that neither John Corby, William Denny nor Ernie Middleditch could give me any instructions, and I would report directly to Harry Povey and no one else.

That caused more than a little rumpus, and some people thought that I was getting a little too big for my boots just because I had been to America. Harry Povey was more than a little irate and told me I would have to work as part of a team. I retorted that I would form my own team, I would be the boss, and then if it did not work out he could fire me.

I was not the most popular person in de Havillands, but Harry agreed and gave me full backing; John Corby also gave me his full support, Ernie Middleditch took early retirement and William Denny was helpful in his own quiet way. All the production staff at Chester were delighted as they had suffered too much already from Hatfield's interference and conflicting instructions.

Everyone was well aware that if the Comet programme did not survive, de Havillands would not survive, so the climate was favourable for maximum effort. At Chester we had not only the desperate need to get the modified Comet 1 back into service as soon as possible, we had also to maintain output on the Vampire, Venom, Dove, and DH.125 project to ensure a decent cash flow to pay the wages.

The first priority was to pick a management team to drive the Comet programme in the most dynamic way possible. John Corby knew the Chester personnel much better than I did, and I knew he was a good judge of character. We held a meeting in the concert hall for management, supervision and representatives of the shop stewards, where I emphasised the seriousness of the situation, stressed that we all had to make efforts well beyond the normal call of duty, and asked for volunteers. I pointed out that all our jobs were at risk, and we would need to cut out all unnecessary paperwork, forego meetings and discussions, and concentrate on the job of putting Comets back in service as soon as possible. I explained that Mr Wilde and I had complete authority over all quality and production and that we would take the decisions, but we could only succeed if we had the wholehearted backing of everyone. The response was tremendous, everyone wanted to join the Comet team. The difficulty was in picking the right people: Corby, Wilde and I interviewed every volunteer.

John Corby then told me about a young man called Jack who had just finished a 6-month jail term. Jack had previously been an outstanding employee in the inspection department before being framed by his father-in-law over the matter of crooked dealings on stolen cars in which he had unwittingly become involved; he had then been charged with dealing in stolen goods. He had now divorced his wife and wanted to come back to work at Chester, and John thought he should be given a chance. I interviewed him and was suitably impressed, so we took a chance and made him Superintendent of Comet production.

The Chester factory was quite different from Lostock; it was a vast assembly area, with only a small machine shop and tool room. The usual premium bonus system common to most DH factories was in operation, so I abandoned it and announced that we would set a monthly target for all aircraft, and when each one passed its test flight within the target we would pay a bonus to everyone, including inspectors. This was heresy, as traditionally no inspector was allowed a bonus based on output as it was considered that this would be a temptation to pass bad work. My view was that if we could not trust the integrity of our inspectors we had no chance, and Bob Wilde agreed with me.

Most of the things we did worked and the improvement of morale and output was dramatic. Everyone was full of enthusiasm for the changes and seemed to enjoy their work, and the shop stewards were very co-operative. It was the first time I ever saw operators voluntarily giving up their tea breaks and even lunch breaks to ensure that deadlines were met. We worked seven days a week – and night shifts too – and when the first three Comets were successfully test-flown we had a party with free drinks for all. John Corby pointed out that we must not forget that the others' programmes had been achieved too, so he organised a summer dance for everyone, including wives and girl friends, with a buffet and bar provided at the Company's expense. This proves the point that I have always made: treat the employees generously, trust them to do their best and they will reciprocate.

CHAPTER 34

CHESTER SHORT TIME

I managed to take a week off from Chester and went on holiday to Abersoch with Joy and the family. Going down a hill *en route* the Riley developed wheel wobble to an extent that I could hardly control the steering. All Rileys were fitted with what was called the "Enots one-shot lubrication system"; every time the driver depressed the clutch all the parts requiring lubrication received a shot of oil. The system was not delivering oil to the front steering arms, hence the trouble, but a local garage soon put it right. Rileys also had a semi-automatic Wilson gearbox; the driver selected the gear on a lever on the steering wheel and when the clutch was depressed the gear changed. It was an easy and delightful car to drive; Joy learned to drive and passed her driving test on it.

We hired a beach hut and a boat, the weather was good and we all had a grand holiday. I recharged my batteries and we returned full of excitement, looking forward to the time when we would all be able to take up residence in our grand new home in Cliveden Road. But before that could happen there was much work still to be done. The oak block floors were repaired, sanded and polished. The rooms were high-ceilinged and spacious, and when redecorated looked lovely. There was a Beeston boiler to heat the water and I had added two radiators for background heating. There were two kitchens and we redid one of them. I could not afford to do all that I would have liked, but was sure that eventually it could be a splendid family house. The factory gardeners did a good job in clearing the garden, and that autumn there was a marvellous crop of fruit.

It was not until the following March that the house was finished enough for the family was move in, and by this time we had found a buyer for 6 Sefton Road at the asking price of £2,500, a great relief. De Havilland's paid for all the removal costs, made a contribution to the cost of new carpets and curtains, and did not charge any interest on the bridging loan. In the meantime I had lived on my own for some 10 months, working long hours, plus travelling back and forward from Chester to Bolton to see the family, plus the worry of buying and selling houses, and this had tested my stamina to the maximum. Unless one has experienced this it is difficult to convey the stress involved.

The delight of all being together again in a nice comfortable house was terrific, and what made it all the more enjoyable was the satisfaction of achievement at work. Things were going very well at the factory, we had got on top of the problems, and all the targets were being met. Everyone was enthusiastic and we not only worked hard but played hard. Social life was very enjoyable and we invented a new Trophy which we called the "Chestlock Trophy"; this was presented annually for sporting events between Chester and Lostock for all kinds of sports, including indoor ones such as snooker, darts, table tennis, chess, bridge, dominoes, and crib. Friendly competition did a great deal to promote good relations between the two sites.

It is interesting to recall the kind of salaries that were being paid in those strenuous days. I still have my notebook listing these and out of 25 managers only four were earning over £1,000 per annum, the top one being on £1,450; at that time surtax started at £2,000. Just after moving into Cliveden Road I got a rise to £2,000; I was overjoyed, I thought I really had it made, I was now a surtax payer. I went out and bought Joy a synthetic fur jacket and a new pair of trousers from Austin Reed's; the trousers cost £5 and I thought that expensive.

The next problem was to find suitable schools for Gill and Alastair. There were two excellent schools in Chester, King's for boys and Queen's for girls, but there were no available places at Queen's so we had to send Gill to a private school called Merton House. Meanwhile Alastair settled in well at King's and I can remember very well going to the Sports Day. I can't remember if Alastair won anything, but I won the parents' 100 yards, and Joy and I won the three-legged race. The former was a handicap race in which the youngest parent was 'scratch' and everyone elso got a yard start depending on age; as I had just had my 40th birthday, I did have some advantage.

By the end of the summer we were really relishing life in Chester, and were beginning to settle down to a happy and relaxed way of life. However fate had another upheaval in store for us.

Five months after we had settled into Cliveden Road, I had a telephone call from Sir Ralph Sorley. He wanted to meet me but would not say what it was about. I invited him to our home but he said it was too confidential and asked me to have lunch with him in the Grosvenor Hotel the next Saturday. When he explained why he wanted to see me I could not really believe my ears, I thought I must be dreaming; he wanted me to leave Chester and go back to Lostock. He explained that things were going badly at Lostock, the Firestreak programme was miles behind and the Ministry were kicking up a fuss as these weapons were vital to the Korean War. I asked if the de Havilland Board knew about this offer, and he said that they did.

I then asked what would happen to the Comet programme. He explained that this was no longer in crisis, that everyone had been highly complimentary about the part I had played in it, and the crisis had now shifted to Firestreak; this was why he wanted me to go back to Lostock and get things sorted out there. I explained that already I had been away from my family for 10 months, we were just settling in at our new home, the children had found new schools and were making new friends, and then asked him if he thought it was fair to expose them to all the same disruption yet again.

Sir Ralph was very sympathetic, but explained that the Korean war was still raging and it was essential to have Firestreak in service as soon as possible. Lives were being lost and if de Havilland did not get back onto programme they would be in serious trouble and could suffer severe financial penalties for failing to meet the programme.

I told him that I felt it was not right to leave the decision to me; surely it was the responsibility of the de Havilland Board to decide where I was needed most, and in any case I would need to discuss it with my family. Sir Ralph then confirmed that the Board had already decided that I was most needed at Lostock, and asked me to let him know the family's views as soon as possible.

Joy was most supportive as usual and was prepared to make the move if it was going to be to my advantage. The only provisos she made was that Gill and Alastair must get back into Bolton School and that we must have a house as nice as our present one in Cliveden Road at no cost to us. When I told Sir Ralph our views he was delighted and assured me that all our requests would be granted, and that Donald McConnell would make all the arrangements. I still have Donald's hand-written notes agreeing that de Havilland would use all their influence to get Gill and Alastair back into Bolton School. All the removal and the acquisition of a house in Bolton equivalent to the one in Cliveden Road would be borne by the Company, full use of the Company's resources would be available to achieve this, and I would have the exclusive use of a company car.

When I broke the news to John Corby he was not very pleased, but he accepted the Board's decision with good grace and even organised a farewell party. I was a little embarrassed by this as when I had left Lostock only 15 months earlier I had been given a wonderful party and received handsome farewell gifts including a chiming clock from the shop stewards; this time they gave me more handsome gifts, including a beautiful Hardy spinning rod and reel.

Within a short time I was once more back at Lostock, where the family found staying in a good hotel something of a novelty and an adventure. Mind you, the first hotel chosen by the company had been the Grosvenor in Manchester Road, which had turned out to be a disaster, with peeling wallpaper, cockroaches and indifferent food; then one night when Gill found a man in her bedroom that was the last straw. We then moved to the Royal Oak in Chorley, which was much better but posed problems for Joy with two children at school in Bolton. The best part was the lovely park close by where Joy could walk, play, and relax with the children. We were then moved to another hotel in Astley Bridge, but it was unsatisfactory too. I began to suspect that certain people were a little resentful of my VIP status and were trying to be parsimonious in respect of the cost of our family accommodation. Finally I took matters into my own hands, went to see George Kay, the manager of the Packhorse Hotel, and booked accommodation for three months. The staff were very friendly and made quite a fuss of the children, especially the little porter Joe.

We had the only room with an *en suite* bathroom, and the children had two adjacent rooms; everything, including meals, was paid for by the

Company. With some sadness we put Cliveden Road up for sale, and Gill and Alastair were readmitted to Bolton School. Joy went back to Cliveden Road every weekend to do the washing and ironing, and when pressure of work allowed I went too.

When I reviewed the situation at Lostock, it was like the curate's egg, good and bad in parts. The wage code ably administered by Mac Smith was a huge success, and the manufacturing schedule was working reasonably well. However there was a conflict of interest between the conventional business of propellers and ancillaries, sub-contract work and mssile business – namely Firestreak.

Shan Wheate was full-time at Lostock and lived with his wife in a flat in Albert Road. The Ministry programme forecast a build-up to 100 Firestreak missiles per month, but Donald McConnell and Shan said that this could not be done without a new factory specially built for Firestreak production, so a lot of their time was being spent in negotiating with MOD for the acquisition of land and the erection of a purpose-built factory. No wonder the programme was seriously in arrears: there was no one driving it ahead, and there were constant squabbles with Hatfield as to who was responsible for the delays. In addition the Bridge Works at Horwich had been extensively damaged by fire, and all the repair work on propellers etc. had ceased until new premises were found at Lakefield. Also, because of a cut in the Ghost engine programme, the Engine Company was moving out of Lostock. There was just not the management strength to organise everything efficiently. A new assistant general manager had been appointed to help Donald McConnell, but he had neither sufficient experience nor drive to be successful.

My welcome back was effusive and Donald could not have been more helpful and co-operative. My appointment as deputy general manager was confirmed as from the 1st October 1955 and I would rejoin the pension scheme as from 1st January 1956. I would be entitled to a fortnight's holiday in the summer months and my salary would be £2,250 per annum. I was not very interested in the money: what motivated me was the challenge and the feeling of being wanted and being successful in fulfilling difficult assignments.

Reviewing these conditions in relation to what happened in the decade before 1997 when I first wrote this I must have been very naïve at that time. I carried the major responsibility for Comet production and for the first air-to-air guided weapon, yet I was not even a general manager, let alone a director. I was being courted by a retired Air Vice-Marshal and it never even occurred to me to play hard to get, or to ask for a substantial salary increase or promotion.

Since the Industrial Revolution, Britain's economic success and reputation had been built on a strong manufacturing base, labour-intensive and a true creator of wealth. Of course there were periods of recession, of growth and of boom, but Britain remained an industrial nation led and directed by men of integrity who invented things, developed them, manufactured them and sold them at home and abroad. We were leaders in so many activities that it is not even necessary to quote them. Men and women had the vision and the determination to pursue their ambition and attain their goal, not purely for monetary gain but for the satisfaction of achievement itself. Regrettably in the world today money and greed appear to be the dominant factors. I recalled the saying that "money is the root of all evil," and on looking in my *Chambers' Dictionary of Quotations* found that it came from the Bible, in the sixth Chapter of the first Epistle of St. Paul to Timothy (verses 9 & 10) where it says:

"For we brought nothing into this world and it is certain we can carry nothing out. And having food and raiment let us be therewith content. But they that will be rich fall into temptation and and a snare and into many foolish and hurtful lusts which drown men in destruction and perdition. Love of money is the root of all evil."

Of course it is the *love* of money and not money itself that is the problem, but that statement was written in the first century AD and what wise counsel it has proved to be ever since. The morality of business and political life has been corrupted by greed and money. Measurement of success is judged by profit, and the City analysts demand increasing profits year after year, otherwise stock market quotes steadily decline, driving directors into mergers or inadequate capital investment leading to heavy redundancies and growing unemployment. Horrible phrases like "financial engineering" and "down-sizing" are the order of the day, with the result that our manufacturing industries and our share of world markets are steadily declining. Banks, building societies, managed funds and speculation in futures & currencies do not create wealth: they only shuffle money around, and make some people very rich indeed. No credit is given for building a business, employing more people, or increasing our share of world trade. Until there is a change of heart and an understanding of real growth, this country will steadily decline, in spite of the boasts of present politicians.

I have never had a real interest in making money, or becoming seriously rich, and I can proudly boast that I have never asked for a salary increase in my whole life. The demands for rollover contracts, astronomical salaries, huge bonuses and highly profitable share options disgust me, particulary when failures are rewarded by riches never earned and never justified. Recent scandals like Barings, the copper market and disreputable dealings in money management indicate a very sick society. No wonder some MPs are tempted to be 'on the make.'

I have always believed that a factory full of work, with a skilled and happy work force, is the best recipe for success. Shortage of work, particularly for an industry with very high overheads, where the cost of research and development is very substantial, can be difficult to manage, so between the years 1949 and 1954 I had tried to fill the Lostock factory with a whole variety of sub-contract machining work. With the skills available and extensive modern machinery this was not difficult, but it caused serious arguments with the accountants who with their conventional methods of accounting claimed that it was not profitable. I fought for a more liberal approach and claimed that this work not only kept our employees busy and happy, it also made a valuable contribution to overhead recovery. I argued that this type of work did not require any research, development or design, and inspection costs were low so it should be costed at a lower overhead rate. Before going to Chester I had persuaded the accountants to adopt a lower overhead rate for sub-contract work, with the result that we obtained substantial orders from the tobacco industry, footwear machinery makers, railway workshops, pump makers, the air conditioning industry, the motor trade, mining, agriculture, machine tools, textile machinery makers, and a host of others.

When I returned I was under considerable pressure to give all this up and concentrate on our core business, namely propellers, missiles and work for the Aircraft and Engine Companies. I argued that this was unwise and that with a little reorganisation and capital investment we could meet all the programmes. We moved our assembly areas into the space vacated by the Engine Company, enlarged our machine shop and built an extension to West Block to accommodate the assembly and testing of Firestreak. The Ministry was demanding an output of 100 Firestreak missiles per month and we were miles behind. The Company was claiming that when the new factory was completed all would be well, but I could not see this happening.

To give Donald and Shan their due, they had done a great job in negotiating with the Ministry for the acquisition of the land and the allocation of money for the building and commissioning of a splendid new custom-built factory solely for Firestreak. The management effort in planning and building such a complex was substantial, and the final result was a credit to everyone involved. However in the meantime someone had to concentrate in producing some missiles. Having been brought back from Chester for this very purpose, I was in a strong position to ensure that my demands were met and my advice followed, so I concentrated on finding out why the programme was so far behind.

The Hatfield design for Firestreak was brilliant, but we were breaking new ground and frequent modifications were necessary. There was also constant bickering between Hatfield and Lostock about design changes and their effect on production, a case of "the better being the enemy of the good." As development and testing proceeded, Hatfield designers could find better ways of doing things and demanded immediate introduction of these without any thought of the effect on the programme. I suggested that a top-level design engineer from Hatfield should be sited permanently at Lostock, and that he and I would decide what modifications were mandatory, and what were desirable but not essential.

So Tim B.G. Boydell was posted to Lostock, and indeed he remained there until his untimely death in 1986. Tim was a classical scholar with an Honours degree from Cambridge; he served in the Intelligence Corps during the war and then returned to Cambridge where he took an honours degree in physics, after which he was recruited by Dr George Hough for the Firestreak programme. He was the proverbial "boffin"; many people could not understand him and as a result did not like him. But we got on well and became close friends, and he played a major part in improving relations between the North and the South.

The other problems were technical. The actuator body contained the mechanisms controlling the flight path of the missile and was very difficult to machine. The elliptical slots had to be very accurate, and using pantographs or hydro-tels did not produce a precise enough result. I had heard of a young man, Theo Williamson, who worked for Ferranti in Edinburgh and had been experimenting with a computer-controlled milling machine. So I got in touch with him, and with his knowledge and what I had acquired during my visit to Kearney & Trecker, we rebuilt a K & T vertical milling machine, fitted ball-bearing lead screws to reduce friction and fitted Theo's computer-controlled device. After a few teething troubles were overcome it worked perfectly and the problem was cured. This was the first computer-controlled machine tool to go into production anywhere in the world, and led to the development of System 24 and Flexible Manufacturing Systems.

The actuators themselves had to be made of aluminium as weight was of paramount importance. The action of the pistons inside the cylinders caused undue wear, and with all the testing that had to be done the actuators were worn out before the missiles had even gone into service. I had heard that a 'weird' Scottish inventor had developed a process to put a hard skin onto aluminium, referred to as "hard anodising." No one believed it but we made contact with the inventor, developed the process and once again it was a "first off" and a great success.

The guidance system was designed and supplied by Marconi Space and Defence Systems (MSDS) owned by GEC. Deliveries were late and the guidance system was full of 'bugs.' It was the first time that I had experienced the Weinstock principle: "The bottom line is all that matters," in other words "profit is what matters most." We had to take a very tough line to overcome that one.

As de Havillands were prime contractors for Firestreak we had overall responsibility for all contracts. When we threatened to cancel the contract with MSDS for the guidance, things improved. Flight tests were carried out at Woomera in South Australia and they were very successful. Gradually everything began to fall into place, morale improved and we started producing missiles. We increased our apprentice intake, extended the apprentice training school, engaged more labour, expanded our night shift, introduced 7-day working, and slowly but surely reduced the backlogs.

We persuaded Bolton and Horwich Councils to set aside 100 council houses so that we could recruit skilled labour from other areas with the promise of a house after a probationary period. This programme was a success and we acquired labour from Scotland & Tyneside, all highly skilled. But after about two years 80% of the work force recruited in this way had disappeared back to their own locality. Wives could not settle, missed their friends and relatives, children were unhappy and no amount of community effort solved the problem. However younger people – men and women – made friends, got married and settled into the new community. There is no doubt that relocating families into a new environment, with different cultures and dialects, is a major problem, and if a man is not happy with his domestic circumstances his working efficiency falls. Looking back over a long life with many job changes, house removals, different schools for children and foreign travel, I realise how lucky I am to have a wife and four children who were so adaptable and supportive, and who put up with so much disruptrion of family life with courage, patience and humour.

CHAPTER 35

NOT ALL FUN AND GAMES

It was now 1957 and I had been back at Lostock for nearly two years. My personal notes from the mid-fifties recall many significant events. Sir Winston Churchill resigned, Germany regained full sovereignty, and the Western European Union was formed. Anthony Eden became Prime Minister, the Conservative party was re-elected with a majority of 59, Atlee became an Earl and Gaitskell was elected leader of the Labour Party. In January 1956 Sudan became an independent state. February 1st was the coldest day since 1895, while May was the warmest month since 1922 and the driest since 1896. June brought the Suez crisis and by November the Suez Canal was blocked by 49 ships. The Hungarian uprising was brutally crushed by Soviet tanks.

In Jauuary 1957 Eden resigned and Harold McMillan became PM. In March the death penalty was restricted to those guilty of five counts of capital murder. The European Market was formed between France, Germany, Italy and the Benelux countries. By my birthday, the 8th April, the Suez canal was finally cleared and re-opened to shipping. In December the Lewisham rail crash killed 90 people including Mr Howland, the civil servant who was in charge of all our MOD projects. Calder Hall atomic power station was commissioned and the first nuclear bombs were manufactured. Lostock received a contract for a variety of precision-machined parts associated with nuclear reactors and nuclear energy. On May 14th the petrol rationing introduced in the previous December ended; during this period I had tried to set a good example by cycling to and from work every day. On June 1st the first prizes were drawn for Premium Bonds. In October the first Russian Sputnik was launched, followed later by another one with a dog on board.

During these two years life was very rewarding, and enjoyable. Donald McConnell used to say that nothing succeeds like success, and these two years were certainly successful ones for Lostock and the Company. All the contracts were back on programme, we had commissioned a new Repair Organisation at Lakefield, and the new missile factory was nearing completion. Unfortunately there was still friction between the North and South. Hatfield resented that Lostock was becoming too autonomous, and that they had less control over it. The Aircraft and Engine Companies continued to grumble that their work was not getting enough attention, but at every meeting we were able to prove that any delays in delivery were due to their own failure to deliver tools, materials and even drawings on time to meet the programme.

Sir Ralph Sorley was getting near retirement age and was not dynamic enough to knock some heads together and improve co-operation. On October 1st 1956 Shan Wheate was made Financial Director, and on 8th April 1957 a new Deputy Managing Director, Harold G. Sturgeon, was appointed. Dougie Detmarr was appointed Group Personnel Manager, and Sturgeon brought two of his colleagues with him from his previous company, Cossar Ltd. These appointments were obviously made in an endeavour to improve the problems outlined above; however they were implemented without any discussion with or reference to Lostock.

I can well remember Mr Sturgeon's first visit to Lostock. He arrived in a brand-new and very expensive Bristol saloon paid for by de Havillands. He told us how delighted he was to have joined the Group and how he had ordered two new Savile Row suits so that he would be suitably dressed for his responsibilities; he was wearing one of them that day and we duly admired it. There was no doubt that he possessed the 'gift of the gab,' and it was soon clear that another attempt was going to be made to dominate Lostock from the South, but it was a stupid decision as Lostock employed five times more people than Hatfield and provided over 80% of the turnover. Moreover our sub-contract business, contrary to the belief of the accountants, was not only profitable but made a significant contribution to overhead recovery. When Ministry contracts went down or were delayed, the sub-contract work could be increased, thus preventing major changes in the size of the work force and saving money on redundancies and recruitment.

At the first Farnborough Air Show that I attended after my return from Chester I was most enthusiastically welcomed by the Propeller Company, the Aircraft Company and the Engine Company, and congratulated on what a great job I had done at Chester and what a big contribution I could make to the new missile programmes. By the next Show the euphoria had died down a little, but I was asked by two directors if I would join them in London and help them to entertain some VIP customers. We dined in the Savoy and then they wanted to go to a night club, so we went to the Eve Club in Regent Street as I was the only one with a membership. A great time was had by all and I duly signed the bill and submitted it with my expenses in due course; it was for over £300 and was rejected, accompanied by a terse note from Shan Wheate ticking me off for extravagance. As I had already drawn the money at Lostock I sent back a terse note to Sir Ralph enclosing my cheque for the full amount, making it clear that I would not ever again entertain Company guests, and that this kind of thing was very bad for morale. Sir Ralph phoned me, very apologetic and very angry; he had torn up my cheque and assured me that such a thing would never happen again.

A little later on Harry Sturgeon told me he was buying a farm and had noticed that Lostock had on their surplus disposal list a Commer van and a diesel engine generating set. He wanted to know how he could go about buying them, so I offered him a good price and they were duly delivered. Therafter I forgot all about this transaction as I went off on another trip to America.

I had been invited over by Irl Martin of Woodward Governors, at their expense, to discuss further co-operation on the manufacture of their range of equipment at Lostock. They had expanded as far as they wished to and needed a source of manufacture of their range of products for Europe and the

Middle East. Woodward had expanded into the electronic control field and business was booming; they had already opened a dispersal factory in Colorado and now wished to establish a base in Britain or continental Europe where wage levels and costs were lower.

There had been many improvements at Rockford, but the basic principles had not changed. However I did notice that certain differences were developing between Irl and his son-in-law Billy Biddle, who thought that Irl was too much of an idealist and philanthropist. But as Billy was destined to take over changes were inevitable.

Irl was very anxious to take me to Fort Collins to show me what had been done there. Colorado University was gaining a reputation for engineering excellence, and it was easier and cheaper to recruit engineering graduates and labour. Colorado was basically an agricultural State, and with the advance of intensive farming methods there was ample labour for retraining. Irl suggested that we should go by train rather than fly, which would give us a chance to relax and talk, and the scenery would give me an insight into what American countryside was really like. The journey would take two days and one night, and he had booked six first-class sleeping berths for the party. American railways, although having the same track gauge as European railways, work to a larger loading gauge, with the result that the carriages seem much more spacious and the Pullman or Club cars are the height of luxury with lounges, bars, and restaurants. In certain areas, due to temperance laws the bars had to be closed, but we could always buy a bottle or two to see us over. Most of the train staff were black and most courteous, and gave a service every bit as good as in a first class hotel.

The next day we travelled west out of Illinois into Iowa, then across Nebraska into Colorado; Fort Collins is near the border of Colorado and Wyoming. While air travel is convenient and time-saving, you fail to see and appreciate the vast distances between the East and West coasts of the American Continent and the beauty and variety of the changing scenery. This journey was an adventure and revelation to me as the scenery was a kaleidoscope of changing landscapes; mile after mile of rolling grain fields, across the Mississippi valley, then the Missouri, the boundary between Iowa and Nebraska, and then into the cattle country. It was like watching a Western in the cinema; little townships where we stopped to pick up and let off passengers, men and women dressed in city clothes and cowboys with chaps, spurs, and cowboy hats. We took on fuel and water at staging posts, and even saw the Wells Fargo Pony Express. There was also the evocative sight of thousands of cattle being driven in clouds of dust by real cowboys. When we were not chatting, watching the scenery or sleeping we played poker, and I managed to lose over $100. On the sleeping cars, which were much more spacious and comfortable than on British Railways, there was a 24-hour service for food and drink which was excellent.

When we finally arrived at Fort Collins, I found that parts of it were real 'western'-style, with cowboys with six-shooters on the hip and saloons with hitching rails and horses. Other parts of the town were modern with high-rise buildings, and the campus of the University was huge; we spent one afternoon visiting and I was most impressed with the large playing fields, gymnasiums, swimming pools, bicycle and car parks. Living quarters for the students were extensive with air conditioning, with better facilities than back home. Irl and Bill Whitehead were very friendly with the Professors and the Administration in the Engineering faculties, who were very co-operative in the training programmes.

Woodward's new factory had been custom-built. The morale of everyone was very high, the philosophy of the "Woodward Way" was widely acclaimed and Bill Whitehead told me that output and cost per unit was better than at Rockford; it was a wonderful experience for me. Irl and Bill were keen that de Havilland should be the ideal partner for a manufacturing unit, and Bill would set up a sales and servicing establishment in Bolton or Manchester. On the train journey back we played bridge instead of poker and I recouped all my poker losses!

Finally I had a farewell dinner with Irl, Bill and their wives, but in the middle of the night woke with violent toothache. The next morning Bill took me to the company dentist and the X-ray picture showed a bad abscess. As I was flying home that day nothing more could be done except to give me an injection and painkillers. During the flight the abscess burst and by the time I arrived home I could not open my jaws. I was referred to a consultant dentist, who put me on antibiotics, but it was a week before I was able to eat and speak normally again, after which the tooth was extracted.

I was very enthusiastic about the Woodward proposal, as were all my colleagues at Lostock, but when I submitted my report to the Board at Hatfield it got a lukewarm reception; they considered that we had enough work already, but agreed to give it consideration at the next Board meeting.

At middle management level relations between Hatfield and Lostock were cordial; Lostock's Management Club and Monthly Staff Club were flourishing and we always invited our opposite numbers at Hatfield to attend the meetings and parties, with which they complied willingly. However there was no Lostock representative on the Propeller Board, and I suppose that the directors felt, quite naturally, that they should be in overall charge, and perhaps considered Donald McConnell and myself to be too independently minded.

We were regularly summoned to Hatfield, and Donald and I used to drive down in the evening in a Company Humber Hawk and stay at the Comet Hotel, where Donald's favourite supper was smoked salmon sandwiches with a bottle of white Chablis. He suffered from asthma attacks when under stress and took ephedrine for them, but the side-effects showed as anxiety attacks and insomnia, so he was not always at his best at meetings. As a result of taking yet more medication to counteract the side-effects of the ephedrine Donald tended to have great bursts of energy followed by periods of complete exhaustion. Nevertheless he was a very able man, a very kind man and a very deep thinker; I liked him and always supported him. He was fair and had strong convictions about what was right and what was wrong; for example he always preached that the shopfloor employees were the people who did the work and produced the profit and that as long as he was general manager there would never be any compulsory redundancies. He was a great socialiser, too, and attended all the functions; my only criticism of him was that he tended to become too familiar with some of his staff.

In December 1951 we had appointed a young man, David Plowes, to the personnel department to work for Herbert Mollart, the personnel manager at that time. I did not get to know David very well in these early years, but after my return from Chester the situation was rectified. He showed great initiative and was largely responsible for the continuing good labour relations, and was instrumental in offsetting some of the dominating attempts from the South. When Dougie Detmarr was appointed Group Personnel Manager, David not only had an excellent relationship with him but was able to circumvent some of the policy decisions that could have been harmful to Lostock. There was another lighter side to David; he not only wrote an annual pantomime but directed it and recruited the players. He also instigated children's Christmas parties and bonfire nights, supervised the Sports & Social Club and Open Days, and established Lostock's reputation as one of the leading Companies in community relations, fund-raising and philanthropic activities.

To return to Firestreak production, we never did reach the 100 missiles per month target planned by the Ministry, the highest we ever reached was 80. For political and financial reasons the programme was then cut to 60 per month. The new factory created at great expense was never occupied, and eventually was put up for sale, when it was purchased at a bargain price by an American company, Westinghouse Brake & Signal Company. It was later sold to a large joinery company mass-producing doors, windows and other components for the building trade. Later still it was sold on to Eaton Yale & Towne, who ran it for some years until it was badly damaged by a disastrous fire. There were many recriminations but Donald McConnell got the blame for miscalculating the requirements and being over-ambititious and 'empire-building.' This was most unfair as the estimates had originally been prepared by Hatfield, sanctioned by the directors and approved by the Ministry. Donald should have had great praise for the energetic and efficient way the factory was built and commissioned.

This setback strengthened my case for getting involved in the Woodward plan, and we started work on reviewing what would be involved. I then got reprimanded on a minor matter by the finance department at Hatfield; I was asked why the sale of a Commer van and a diesel generating set had never been paid for and why a fictitious name was on the invoice. At the time Harry

Sturgeon had asked me to invoice them to his farm manager, so it gave me a vicarious pleasure to tell them to go and ask Mr Sturgeon why the bill had not been paid. A further irritation was an edict from Hatfield that all company cars must be used for company journeys only and had to be returned to the garage every night. It was clear that someone was trying to needle us, particularly Donald who did not have any other transport.

Then one day I received an invitation to have dinner with Harry Sturgeon and two of his fellow directors at The Spinney. I paid no attention to the company edict about cars as I had been promised exclusive use of a company car, so I drove there in my Austin Westminster. We had pre-prandials and everyone was very chatty, then during dinner I was asked what I thought about Donald McConnell, to which I gave an honest answer. I was then told that they were very dissatisfied and would like to get rid of him, and that if I could produce a good reason and help them to sack him I would get his job. I was so angry that I threw down my serviette, told them what I thought of them, and walked out. I drove home so fast that I was booked for speeding, but fortunately I had had very little to drink and did not get any other booking – breathalysers were non-existent in these days.

Shortly thereafter I flew off to America to see Woodward's again; they were as keen as ever and we discussed all the possibilities. When I returned to Heathrow there was a message for me to ring Donald McConnell immediately. When I did so he sounded very upset and told me that he had been instructed to declare 750 redundancies at Lostock in three weekly stages of 250. He said he would meet me on my arrival at Ringway, and we then went to his house to discuss the matter in more detail; I told him that he must refuse to carry out such an instruction, it was nonsense and completely unjustified, especially in view of my discussions with Woodward's. I then told him about the plot at The Spinney, and that the time had come to stand up and be counted. He said that if he did not obey the instruction he would be sacked; Sir Ralph was retiring and Sturgeon was going to be Managing Director.

I persuaded Donald to phone Sturgeon and arrange a meeting. We drove down together and stayed in the Comet Hotel, but during the night Donald had a bad asthma attack, so in the morning I saw Sturgeon on my own. He then repeated his offer to give me Donald's job. I do not know how I kept my 'cool' but I argued quite logically that redundancies at that level were not only unnecessary but would do great harm to reputation and morale, and would wreck the Woodward negotiations. He told me the Board had decided against these anyhow, and with the reducing workload the redundancies were necessary. I disagreed and assured him that I could find all the work necessary to fill the factory and avoid redundancies. I told him that I felt so strongly about the situation that if he did not withdraw his instructions the first name on the redundancy list would be mine. He carried on trying to persuade me and said I could be made a director, so I told him that I had no confidence in him and that it was unlikely we could ever work in harmony. I went back to the hotel, collected Donald and drove home, very depressed.

I started to study the vacancy columns in the *Telegraph* and saw an advertisement for a managing director at Howard & Bullough in Accrington. On the Sunday we drove over with the family and had a look at the factory. It was part of the Stone-Platt empire and within driving distance of Bolton, so I applied for the job. A few weeks later I was advised that the job had been filled but they would like to interview me for a job with Platt Brothers in Oldham. There I was interviewed by George Hardman, managing director of TMM (Textile Machinery Makers) and Sir Peter Aitken, a Stone-Platt main Board director. They told me that they were looking for a young man with new technology experience to bring new ideas and modernise the company, which had become too old-fashioned and out of date. I was entertained to lunch in the directors' dining room and was subsequently offered the job of production director at double the salary I was getting at de Havilland's.

I was absolutely delighted, but said that I would have to discuss it with my family and would let them know. I thought that I was very fortunate to find a new job so quickly, and the family were pleased, so I accepted the offer. I went back to Oldham and saw Geoffrey Hawkins, the MD of Platt Bros, who told me that they had started to build a new factory, but had run out of money.

And so at the age of 42 I was launched once more on a completely new career.

CHAPTER 36

MOVING ON – AGAIN

My last few weeks at de Havilland's were a very sad time for me. I had achieved a great deal, was respected by the work force, and had made many friends, and now all my dreams of a continuing successful and long career in aviation were shattered. It grieved me to see the distress and uncertainty created while the redundancy lists were being prepared and argued over. I was sure the reasons were political and quite illogical, and my frustration was all the worse as I could do nothing to help. Changing jobs is stressful at any time, and with a family to bring up and educate, I was beset with doubts as to whether I was doing the right thing or not. Had I been too precipitate? Was I leaving an industry with a great future to join one depending on textiles, which were already in decline? Would my pension be transferrable? I also needed to bear in mind that while I could get from home to Lostock in five minutes, working in Oldham meant a journey of 45 minutes each way.

One consolation was that I owned my own house in Bolton, Balgowan, free from all debt. How wise I had been, I thought, but a shock was awaiting me. When the details of my departure were discussed I was informed that I owed the company £2,000. When I had left Chester the accountants had sent a bill to the Propeller Company for work carried out on our house in Cliveden Road. They now stated that this would have been waived if I had not been leaving. The Propeller Company had held this in suspense and had intended to waive it too as part of the deal for my transfer back to Lostock, but as I was leaving of my own accord they now wanted it paid. I did not have that kind of money, so they suggested it should be treated as a mortgage with Balgowan as security.

I refused absolutely. I phoned Stewart Kennedy, told him how angry I was and explained that the new MD was acting in a way that would be harmful to the company. Stewart invited me to stay at The Belt, his house in Gustard Wood, where I was able to pour out all my woes and explain how disgusted I felt. He said he would make some discreet enquiries, and later he advised me that for ethical and tax reasons the loan could not be written off, but it would be treated as an interest-free loan which I could pay off at £200 per annum. (I still have the original official receipt for the final £200 dated 8th December 1965.) Even then I was thoroughly miserable but business friends invited me to go fishing with them in Norway, and that helped to preserve my sanity.

After I had left de Havilland's I was of course very interested to find out what had happened. The 750 redundancies had been implemented, and at the end of July 1958 Donald McConnell was sacked. Stanley Lines was appointed works manager at Lostock; he had been a colleague of Sturgeon's and his last job had been as supervisor of the workshops at Holloway Prison. In 1959 a Conservative Government under Harold Macmillan decided to rationalise the aircraft industry and all the aircraft companies were merged into two groups,

Hawker Siddeley and British Aircraft Corporation. De Havilland's joined Hawker Siddeley, and this caused a great deal of unrest, with all top management jockeying for position.

De Havilland Propellers and the Aircraft Company were amalgamated and a new Board was formed. Harry Sturgeon became managing director of the new company and Shan Wheate became financial director. W.E. Nixon retired. Stan Lines was appointed general manager of the Northern Group and Jack Arthur became works manager at Lostock. Dougie Dettmer became general manager of Engineering, and H.L. King, another crony of Sturgeon, became production controller of the new amalgamated Company.

John Corby was so fed up that he resigned and joined the Board of J. & J. Williams, window manufacturers of Chester, whom I knew well from my SAL days because of Arcon houses (see Chapter 20). There were many other compulsory retirements.

In 1962 H.G. Sturgeon was summarily dismissed for irregularities concerning his farm and Shan Wheate became Managing Director; the same year there were the first-ever strikes at Lostock. George Anderton, who had joined Woodward Governors in 1958 to run their European operation, left and bought a brush-making business in Leigh. He did not like all the flying involved with Woodward's worldwide activities. He was a very able man and had been with de Havilland's all his working life, and had also been a good friend of mine. He came to see me at Platts and I was able to give him some sizeable orders for textile brushes. Unfortunately the business went bust, and George had a nervous breakdown.

Shan Wheate had neither the ability or experience to run the new Company and just over a year later he had to resign. He asked me if I could find him a job and I was able to prevail on my friends in Stone-Platt to find him one, so he became MD of the J. Stone & Company foundry at Deptford.

On 1st July 1963 Lostock became part of Hawker Siddeley Dynamics. Guy Gardiner became director and general manager and H.L. King became production director. MacGregor Smith got fed up and joined what had been A.V. Roe at Chadderton, which was now part of Hawker Siddeley Aviation. Strangely, although Chadderton was just down the road from Platt's, we never met. Donald McConnell went through a very bad patch in his family life with an estranged son, which caused him to have a breakdown in health.

Lostock too was suffering from shortage of work and was a very unhappy place. Many of my colleagues there were pressing me to find a job for them, but I was only able to accommodate four of them: George Watson as deputy chief inspector, Joe Gaskill in middle management, Martin Coleman (a 'whizz' with figures who introduced an effective loading system) and Eddie Markland, an expert electrician.

During these years I was thankful that I had joined Platt Brothers, but with hindsight I cannot help wondering what would have happened to me if I had remained at de Havillands in 1958.

Looking back over my working life from age 17 to 65, I changed my job 11 times. For seven years I was trying to resuscitate my father's bankrupt business. I was at Scottish Aviation from 1940 to 1949, at Lostock from 1949 to 1953, at Chester from 1953 to 1955, then back to Lostock from 1955 to 1958 when I joined Platt Brothers as Production Director (the following year I became Managing Director). In 1966 I resigned and joined Kearney & Trecker. From 1970 to 1973 I was an independent consultant, and joined Hawker Siddeley in July of that year. We were nationalised into British Aerospace in 1977 and denationalised in 1979, and I finally retired on 30th April 1980.

In retrospect, if I had to live my life over again I do not think that I would wish to change it. My conscience and strict upbringing guided me. I tried to practise what I preached and always stood up for my principles, even if it meant putting my job on the line. I always tried to help people and to my knowledge never behaved unfairly, nor did anyone harm. Perhaps I am a little envious of the astronomical salaries paid today for jobs which I did for a comparative pittance, and particularly of the "golden hellos" and the ridiculously high and unwarranted compensation paid to those who did not make the grade. However I was never motivated by money alone and never had a driving ambition to be very rich. My goals were an interesting, challenging and contented life, coupled with the happiness of a beautiful wife and lovely children. I believe I have achieved all of these.

CHAPTER 37

BRITISH GOVERNMENTS AND AVIATION – A PERSONAL VIEW

There can be no doubt that the Labour Government from 1945 to 1955 effectively destroyed the impressive lead that we enjoyed in aviation, not only in the operation of airlines but in providing the majority of civil airliners worldwide, as well as managing the busiest and largest international airport in the world.

By 1949 Geoffrey de Havilland and his team had produced the Comet, potentially a world-dominating jet airliner, and its 'offspring' the Nimrod is still first in its class after several decades of operation; indeed it is again being updated. If ever proof was needed about how bad and arrogant government, whether Conservative or Labour, can wreck a country's future, this is it. Scottish Airlines' achievements were admired throughout the world but they were sabotaged by a doctrinaire Labour government. They could have achieved in the fifties what British Airways and Virgin did in the late eighties & nineties. It took a Maggie Thatcher to give entrepreneurs their head.

The Government would not support Frank Whittle's world-beating jet engine. The Comet 1 was developed by the private capital of de Havilland's, who were so strapped for cash that they could afford to build only one test fuselage on which they had to do all the reversal testing, pressure testing and stress testing. At the time, relatively little was known about metal fatigue, although Nevil Shute's now-famous novel *No Highway* had been published in 1948. If de Havilland's had been able to afford to carry out the various tests on three separate fuselages, they would not have been misled on the calculations on the safe flying life of the Comet, and the two crashes in Italy probably would never have happened.

As a result of these crashes the authorities saw fit to ground the Comet fleet indefinitely. What was even worse, all the research was made available to the Americans (and it was not the first time this had happened – witness the earlier cancellation of the M-52 supersonic project); consequently we never competed successfully with them until the emergence of the Airbus. When the Americans suffered their share of disasters on Lockheed Electras, Boeing 747s, 737s and 727s, with significant loss of life, these aircraft were never grounded.

When a choice was being made for early warning aircraft systems, the British Nimrod had the edge on the Boeing AWACS. The contract for the airborne radar systems was given to MSDS (Marconi Space & Defence Systems), a GEC company, but there was so much squabbling between MOD and GEC, both over price and a confused specification, that the eventual contract went to Boeing. This scandal was adequately reported in the Press at the time.

Then we must not forget the cancellation of the TSR.2 aircraft, which gave the lead to the American F-111s. Another achievement, the very first vertical take-off device, called the "Flying Bedstead," was invented and developed by Rolls Royce in conjunction with the Hawker Group, and this led to the ubiquitous Harrier, but the technology of that too was passed over to the Americans. Then there was the Westland scandal, which led to the resignation of Heseltine and Leon Britton.

In the mid-1970s I was a witness to the Parliamentary Select Committee examining the relationship of the MOD Procurement Establishment with the Services and the Defence Industry. We made very constructive criticism of the relationship and offered sound and logical advice, but nothing happened. Even Lord Rainer of M & S fame, when he was appointed by Margaret Thatcher to streamline the system, got nowhere.

In spite of claims that we have the best parliamentary system of government in the world, I have over the years become more and more disillusioned with it. I am certain that we are getting the wrong kind of people as MPs. We need a preponderance of people who have had successful careers in their own jobs, who are sufficiently financially independent not to be influenced by money or the craving for power, who have the experience to make objective judgements, and who will remember that they were elected to serve the people, not for their own gratification. Instead we are getting career politicians with the 'gift of the gab,' who have made a reputation in their University Unions and who go straight from University to politics. Examine the Cabinet of any Government over the past 50 years, and one will find that men already successful in the cold hard world are few and far between.

Even the Conservative Governments which followed Labour from 1955 to 1964 failed to appreciate the harm that had been done, and did nothing to reverse the trend. BOAC and BEA were never major players in world airlines, and never made the profits they could – and should – have made. Even the amalgamation of them both under the Chairmanship of David Nicolson was not a success, and it was only after British Airways was privatised under the Chairmanship of John King that we started to regain a dominant position, finally showing that we could be world leaders.

When I first wrote this in 1997 the relationship between BA and American Airlines was being frustrated by bureaucracy and uncertainty, and the Office of Fair Trading was dragging its feet about whether or not to refer the matter to the Merger & Monopolies Commission, a costly and time-wasting business. Whether this merger would provide a better service and more competition was debatable, but what was never in doubt was that Government interference, vacillation and attempts to regulate and control has been harmful throughout the last 50 years. Many famous names in the USA have vanished – notably Pan American and Braniff, but others too – and in Europe Air France, KLM, and Alitalia depend on government subsidies, while others such as Swissair, SAS, and Lufthansa have been struggling to make a profit. Now, at the end of 2001, everything has changed yet again following the September 11th terrorist attacks in New York and Washington; some of these (and other) long-famous airline names have sadly ceased to trade.

In aircraft manufacture there has been a dramatic change also. In America McDonald Douglas has merged with Boeing and in Europe there is a three-country partnership in Airbus Industries – now trying to become a public corporation – but it has already proved very competitive with the American giants.

British Aerospace under Sir Richard Evans has been hailed by the financial gurus as successful and, judged on share price alone, this is true. However the savage reduction in skilled manpower and drastic factory closures has done great harm to the country long-term, and has destroyed skills both in design and manufacture which will be hard to replace. Great names like Avro, Blackburn, de Havilland, English Electric, Handley Page, Hawker, English Electric, Saunders-Roe, Shorts and Vickers Supermarine have all disappeared for ever. Some reductions and amalgamations were essential, but destruction due to bad government and lack of entrepreneurial and dedicated management skills resulted in a failure to exploit the great technical advances developed during wartime.

These changes do not apply solely to the aircraft industry. There has been a steady decline throughout manufacturing industry over the past 50 years. We are no longer leaders in the following engineering disciplines: machine tools, textiles, railways, automobiles, motor- & pedal-cycles, agriculture, mining, marine & shipbuilding, hydraulics & air compressors, and computers. All of these are labour-intensive, whereas the professions, the distributive network and retail outlets are not. It is not surprising therefore that unemployment has soared. The Major government boasted loudly that we had the lowest unemployment in Europe, and this may have been so, but it gave a wrong impression. The true comparison should be with the 1960s and 1970s, which show a substantial decline.

When I retired in 1980 the number of engineers working in companies belonging to the North-West Engineering Employers' Association was 137,000; in 1997 there were only 20,000. In that year the public sector borrowing rate was £29.9 billion; interest on that was at least £2.39 billion per annum, or £459 million every single week.

The trend still continues. Promised cuts in Government spending have not materialised and forecasts for Tax Revenues are wildly out. Grave doubts are being expressed about ability to fund pension schemes and to take care of the aged and the sick.

What has caused this decline? Firstly, the Governments are culpable. Since 1945 we have had 17 years of Labour and 35 years of Conservative rule. Neither party has made any significant difference in halting the decline. History will probably judge Churchill and Thatcher as the best Prime Ministers of the 20th Century and Heath and Major as the worst. Without

Churchill and Roosevelt we would have lost the war. Without Thatcher we would have lost the Falklands with all their potential for fishing wealth and now the prospects of oil production. Without Thatcher and Reagan we would not have had the resolve, nor the offensive power, to prevent Saddam Hussein conquering the whole of the Gulf States.

CHAPTER 38

THE HONOURS SYSTEM

It is still highly debatable whether the Honours system is a fair one, and if it does any good. There is certainly a case to be made for revising the procedure as to how the awards are given, but on balance it would be tragic if Honours awards disappeared. There can be no doubt that an award gives tremendous satisfaction and pride to the recipients and their families and friends. There will always be contention about who got what, and there will always be examples of some people getting more than they deserve and others less. As I said in chapter 20 John Major tried to make the system more democratic, but his efforts did more harm than good. It is my view that the British Empire Medal should be brought back. John Major's amendment, enabling any group of people to recommend deserving cases for an award, was a good one, and many people who otherwise would have been excluded received awards. It has always been true that Honours could be bought, particularly in the higher echelons of the Order of Chivalry, by giving large donations to the political party in power at the time, and this discredited the system. It is custom and practise for large organisations to be given the right to nominate people for awards. For example the Machine Tool Trades' Association could nominate, one KBE, one CBE, one OBE, two MBEs & two BEMs for both the New Year and Birthday Honours list.

The number of award holders at each level is laid down in the Charter of The Most Excellent Order of the British Empire, both Civil and Military divisions, and if these are full no awards can be made. Of course with people dying and others being promoted to higher levels, vacancies always occur. When this happens the medal has to be returned to the Central Chancery of the Orders of Knighthood at St. James's Palace. They are then refurbished where necessary and reissued. This often leads to anomalies in the system; if one level is full and the one above or below has vacancies, the award can get upgraded or downgraded. So someone recommended for an MBE could get an OBE and *vice versa*. This actually happened in Bolton; a respected engineer was recommended for an MBE and he was awarded an OBE. His wife, an ex-mayor and long-serving councillor was recommended for a CBE and finished up with an MBE. Another councillor was put forward for an OBE and got a CBE, in spite of the fact that he was a less deserving case than the ex-mayor. Another anomaly is that when recommendees are put forward the Chairman of the group has to approve the submission. When the submission is reviewed by the Honours office, before it is confirmed, the boss of the individual concerned will be asked for comments and approval or otherwise. This can lead to prejudice or favouritism.

Long after I had left Kearney & Trecker I discovered that the MTTA had unanimously recommended me for a KBE. This was because of all the publicity that I had received over Hollingbury plus the fact that we had received outstanding praise for winning the Queen's Award for Export, and I had been appointed to the Government's Expert Committee. My Chairman thought that if a KBE was going he was the one who should get it, although he had contributed virtually nothing to the wellbeing of K & T. The KBE was awarded to Dick Young, the Chairman of Alfred Herbert, the largest and oldest machine tool company in the country. Shortly thereafter Alfred Herbert went into liquidation.

Yet another criticism of the system is an Honour going to the job and not to the person in it. For example, the President of the Engineering Employers' Association nearly always finishes up with a Knighthood, irrespective of how well or how badly he did the job. In another example, the Director of the Association in Bolton received an MBE, and the Director in Manchester received an OBE. There was little doubt that in terms of ability and efficiency these awards should have been reversed, but the award went with the job, not to the incumbent. This practice is particularly prevalent in the Civil Service.

When British Aerospace was formed after nationalisation, I made a number of recommendations for awards. None of these were granted and it eventually dawned on me that awards were going to the BAC part of BAe, and not to the Hawker Siddeley part. Shortly before my retirement I was told by Drunkie Lewin, in confidence, that he had recommended me for a CBE. On 14th May 1979 I received a letter from 10 Downing Street. It said: "The Prime Minister has asked me to inform you, in strict confidence, that she has it in mind to submit your name to the Queen with a recommendation that her Majesty may be graciously pleased to approve that you be appointed an Officer of the Order of the British Empire (OBE). Before doing so, the Prime Minister would be glad to be assured that this would be agreeable to you."

My feelings were mixed; I had missed a KBE and now I had missed a CBE – I felt like rejecting the offer. But after serious thought I decided it would be churlish to turn it down; it would be unfair to my colleagues, and might affect other awards to Lostock in the future.

The only award that had ever been made to Lostock was in 1952 when an MBE was awarded to Herbert Morton, head of the maintenance department, but this was more to do with his connection with the Ford Foundation than his work at de Havilland's. I managed to get a BEM for Norman Vickers in 1956; Norman was Shop Steward Convenor for many years. He was a man of great integrity, always objective and fair; he was a good mixer and his wife was a great help to him in all the social activities. In 1976 I was able to get a BEM for Ted Llewellyn who was foreman of labourers. Ted was ex-army and was heavyweight boxing champion of the British Army for several years. He had a great personality, but regrettably died of cancer shortly after the award. Both the BEMs were presented at Lostock by the Lord Lieutenant of the County, with great pomp and ceremony, followed by suitable celebrations. The official presentations were made in the factory, and all the family, friends and colleagues of the recipients were able to attend and join in the celebrations. This was even better than a trip to the Palace were guests were limited to three. Whoever advised John Major to scrap the BEM did a great disservice to the Most Excellent Order of the British Empire, and disclosed a complete misunderstanding of what democracy is all about. Did no one understand that a labourer or toilet attendant was just as proud of his BEM as a tycoon would be of his Knighthood or Peerage? The change has denigrated the status of the MBE, and has denied a BEM to those who otherwise might have qualified.

One must query the wisdom of having to return medals when promotion to a higher grade occurs. It is not permissable to use more than the letters of one rank after one's name. So if someone receives a MBE followed by an OBE followed by a CBE, he or she is only allowed to use the latter, CBE. No one knows therefore that someone with a long dedicated career has been honoured three times. This seems to me to be blatantly unfair, especially when one is attending a function where miniature decorations are worn, and one minature medal is all that is allowed and not three; that is undemocratic. Surely someone who has been honoured three times deserves more recognition than someone who has only been honoured once, and should be able to show it.

Nevertheless, and in spite of my criticisms, no one, however blasé, can deny that getting an honour is a great thrill. First there is the confidential letter containing the recommendation, then there is the publication in the Press, then the invitation to the Investiture at the Palace, then the excitement of being marshalled in the ante-rooms and being briefed in the correct procedure, then having the medal pinned on by the Sovereign, and finally the photographs in the palace forecourt. Marshalling in the ante-rooms is done alphabetically and not by rank, so MBEs might be flanked by someone getting a knighthood or a peerage. The waiting time can be as long as 1½ hours, so the conversations with one's neighbours can be quite fascinating.

When one receives a letter from the Secretary of the Central Chancery of the Orders of Knighthood, it gives advice about dress, about procedures, date and time of the investiture, and strictly limits tickets for guests to a spouse and two children. It states that under no circumstances will a fourth ticket be issued. It also includes details of expenses that can be claimed for travelling to the Investiture. These must be claimed from the sponsoring authority, in my case the MOD. In 1979 I could claim a maximum of £14.80 for myself and three guests, plus taxi fares from hotel to the Palace; I wonder what the rates are now!

Finally, the most thrilling thing of all about receiving an award is the mass of congratulations, by telephone, telex and letter – I received 23 telexes and 118 letters. Most of the letters were hand-written and were very moving; they came from Air Chief Marshals, Admirals, Cabinet Ministers past and present, from relatives and friends, from people from all walks of life, and from those who had known me in the past. I received one from my old chauffeur Tom

Watson, and some from Scottish Aviation, Platt Brothers, Kearney and Trecker, from my old school friends and even one from my English teacher. Although it took some time I took a pride in replying to each and every one, all in my own fair hand.

After I retired I watched carefully all the Honours Lists to see how many of my recommendations had been accepted. I was particularly disappointed that one man who I considered to be worthy of an OBE had been passed over time after time. His name was Eric Farnworth and he was one of the most outstanding executives at Lostock, hardworking, dedicated and experienced. I logged the awards going to the BAC part of BAe and the HSD part, and found that they were all going to the former. I suppose that this was natural as the Chairman of BAe Dynamics was ex-BAC and he would favour the people he would know best and who had worked for him for many years. I was particularly annoyed when I found that he was the one who had reduced Drunkie Lewin's recommendation of a CBE for me to an OBE and had given the CBE to the production director ex-BAC of Stevenage, who was junior and much less experienced than I was. Another weakness in the system. So I wrote to the Chancery Office and suggested that they should review the awards to Lostock. They duly took note and assured me that Eric Farnworth would be favourably considered in the next Honours List. He did receive his award, which was followed later with a further two MBEs and a BEM to Lostock. This goes to show that the Chancery strive to be fair but can only act on information given to them.

CHAPTER 39

THE 1994 CHINOOK HELICOPTER CRASH

The reason why I have been so interested in the crash of Chinook ZD576 relates to a lengthy conversation that I had in Buckingham Palace in 1979 when I was being honoured with an OBE.

My neighbour was receiving an Honour for bravery on undercover work in Ireland. He spoke quite openly about the problems in Ireland and was very frustrated with the lack of political will. He claimed that all the violence was being orchestrated by a small minority of vicious ruthless fanatics. Some were motivated by the folklore of the past, from the Battle of the Boyne to the Black & Tans and the hatred of British rule. However the majority were violent hard men, who were exploiting the 'Time of the Troubles' for their own greedy ends by protection rackets, robberies, prostitution and drugs. The problem was no longer a religious one or a political one; it was a problem of gangsterism and terrorism; thy claimed that they were at war with the British. He could not understand why the Irish and British Governments could not accept this. He said we know the leaders who are behind all the violence, and if we were allowed to arrest them and put them away for life, or better still eliminate them, the problems could be over in six months. By far the great majority of people in Eire and Ulster wish to live together in harmony and peace. However successive Eire Governments were not prepared to give up their *cause célèbre* of a United Ireland. This myth is exacerbated by many Irish Americans, brainwashed by the romantic stories related by their ancestors of the persecution of the Catholics by the Protestants. The most ridiculous part of this tragic and ridiculous situation is that the Irish Government do not want a United Ireland – it would cost too much. The terrorists do not want peace as this would reduce their affluent life style. British Governments have failed to accept this and naïvely look for a political solution, which seems impossible as recent events have shown. The so called 'peace initiative' is a mockery and only compounds the real issue.

Tragically this intelligence officer with whom I had discussed all of this was one of the high-ranking staff killed in the crash of the Chinook helicopter ZD576 on the Mull of Kintyre in 1994.

The crew belonged to the Special Air Service and were flying from Aldergrove to an unknown destination in Scotland. The passengers were 19 of the most important and highly experienced intelligence officers in Northern Ireland. Many of them had already been decorated for bravery in undercover work or other secret operations. Of course sabotage was suspected, and many thought that the IRA had pulled off one of their most devastating attacks of all time.

The Inquiry took two forms. One was a Fatal Accident Inquiry by a very esteemed Scottish Sheriff under the laws of Scotland – which are different to those in England – and the other was conducted by the Accident Investigation

Branch of the RAF. No evidence ever emerged from either Inquiry of an IRA connection.

The RAF Inquiry found that the crash had been caused by pilot error and that both pilot and navigator had been guilty of gross negligence. However, the Sheriff's Inquiry, which had been just as thorough, found no evidence whatsoever to establish that the crew had not been carrying out their duties to the high standards of the Special Air Service, nor was there any evidence of malfunction of the helicopter or any of its systems. Sir Steven Young, the Sheriff, concluded that on the evidence submitted it was impossible for anyone to establish the cause of the crash. In due course compensation was paid to the families of the passengers on board, but because of the findings of the RAF enquiry no compensation was paid to the flying crew. This caused the families to embark on their own Inquiry.

John Cook, father of one of the pilots, had had a distinguished career as a pilot. He had been a flying instructor, a pilot with British Airways on Boeing 747s and Concordes, and finally a training instructor on simulators; he knew what he was talking about. His investigations exposed some disturbing evidence. The Mark 2 Chinook had shown so many malfunctions when being evaluated by test pilots at Boscombe Down that they had refused to fly it until the cause of the errors had been established and corrected. The faults included unexplained and sudden engine shut-downs, unreliability of the navigational equipment, and unreliability of the control mechanisms.

Interviews with some of the other Special Air Service pilots disclosed some unease on their part that they were being asked to fly operational missions on an aircraft that was still not cleared by the test facility at Boscombe Down. No 'black boxes' or voice recorders were fitted so there was no technical evidence to justify the RAF Inquiry's decision.

Nearly eight years after this tragic event the recent House of Lords Inquiry has ruled that there was no evidence whatsoever to justify the pilot and co-pilot being charged with gross negligence, and doubts were cast as to the interpretation of the evidence by the two very senior RAF officers who made what was an outrageous allegation against the pilots, which caused their parents, relations and colleagues such pain and anger.

But even now the MOD and RAF are refusing to accept this verdict. In my view there must be a very sinister reason for this: either, those in high places who organised this flight, knowing the hazards on this helicopter and this journey, are being protected for political reasons, and for charges of criminal negligence and perhaps substantial damages or, even worse, the IRA did have an influence somewhere and the powers-that-be are afraid that their absolute incompetence is going to be exposed.

It is extraordinary that the obvious questions have not been asked, or if they have been asked they have not been answered. Who planned the operation and who authorised it? Why were so many top-level officers, party to so much secret and sensitive information on terrorists, allowed to travel on one aircraft – especially when the weather was doubtful, – and on an aircraft that had not been cleared and had a number of known deficiencies? Surely those in power who authorised the mission are far more guilty than the pilots. They have never been named, they have not been charged with criminal negligence, the RAF 'top brass' have refused even to discuss the evidence, and once more there has been a disgraceful political whitewash and cover-up. Add to this the revelation that the same politicians were caught out when they denied having secret meetings with the IRA, which were later admitted. Talk about pragmatism, or deceit, or the end justifying the means: no wonder peace negotiations have foundered.

But it's time for me to finish! Although, due to my life's varied experiences, I am bound to retain strong personal opinions on many matters, I don't feel it appropriate to continue airing them here; after all, my prime intention has been to put on permanent record my reminiscences about the wonderful years I spent as an engineer in the aviation industry – as just one of the pioneers.